Computerized Document Imaging Systems: Technology and Applications

For a complete listing of the *Artech House Telecommunciations* Library,
turn to the back of this book.

Computerized Document Imaging Systems: Technology and Applications

Nathan J. Muller

Illustrations by Linda Lee Tyke

Artech House
Boston • London

Library of Congress Cataloging-in-Publication Data

Muller, Nathan J.
Computerized document imaging systems: technology and applications / Nathan Muller
Includes bibliographical references and index.
ISBN 0-89006-661-2
1. Business records—Management—Data processing. 2. Imaging systems. 3. Documents in optical storage. 4. Information storage and retrieval systems—Business. I. Title.

HF5736.M84   1993   92-37800
651.5'0285—dc20   CIP

British Library Cataloguing in Publication Data

Muller, Nathan J.
Computerized Document Imaging Systems: Technology and Applications
I. Title
006.4

ISBN 0-89006-661-2

© 1993 ARTECH HOUSE, INC.
685 Canton Street
Norwood, MA 02062

International Standard Book Number: 0-89006-661-2
Library of Congress Catalog Card Number: HF5736.M84   1993

10 9 8 7 6 5 4 3 2 1

To my son, Matthew

Contents

Introduction

Corporate America's huge investment in personal computers has done little to ameliorate white-collar productivity, except to generate more paper. Yet there is still hope for improvement. Because of advances in technology and the consequent lower cost inherent in mass production, more companies are willing to consider computerized document imaging systems for improving business processes and workflow dynamics.

Companies of many types and sizes are reaping efficiency improvements and productivity increases through implementations of document imaging systems that simplify and reduce access time and enhance document integrity. Users can retrieve documents much faster from electronic systems than is possible with traditional, paper-based methods. Also, access to documents can be effected by a variety of methods involving content-based retrieval techniques. Document imaging systems can minimize paper use and ultimately reduce the amount of space required for storage.

Contributing to the growing popularity of document imaging systems are decreased hardware costs and the standardization of interfaces between major components. These advances have resulted in a move away from proprietary hardware and toward general-purpose hardware. Standards enable users to run image applications on nondedicated systems and across different hosts and networks. *Application programming interfaces* (APIs) and other development tools permit existing programs to be image-enabled.

Some vendors have introduced imaging systems that allow users to build applications that run on mainframes, microcomputers, and *local-area networks* (LANs). Other vendors offer script- and object-oriented languages that facilitate the building of workflow applications that work under *Microsoft disk operating system* (MS-DOS) and *Microsoft Windows* (MS-Windows).

Benefits of Imaging

Modern imaging technology allows a document to be captured digitally via scanning, converted into a bit-mapped image, indexed, compressed, and stored in a database. The image can then be retrieved and distributed for processing.

Workflow software, meanwhile, has advanced to deliver a multitude of benefits that can result in lower operating costs, less exposure to litigation, and higher revenue potential for many businesses.

The first benefit is better document access. Because documents are stored electronically, and retrieval is accomplished via key field values, documents can be retrieved very quickly. Documents stored on line on optical or magnetic disk can be retrieved virtually instantaneously, and those on jukeboxes (which are sometimes described as "near on line") can be retrieved in under a minute. This contrasts with waiting up to hours to retrieve information from a file cabinet, or up to days to retrieve information that has been archived in a warehouse.

Furthermore, with content-based retrieval a file can be accessed in different ways, such as by case number, date, or type. Documents can be stored as both text and image and retrieved based on any word or combination of words. And, because the file is like any other computer record, it can be accessed concurrently by multiple workstation operators.

A second major benefit of computerized document imaging systems is vastly improved document integrity. Because files are stored electronically, they are less likely to get lost or physically damaged. Relational database features reconcile document changes and carry them forward to other databases. Additionally, it is easy to create backups and store them off-site for added security.

Reduction in the amount of paper used is a third major benefit. Fewer paper copies are needed because the document can be stored electronically. The physical space for paper is also greatly reduced–a single 5.25-in optical disk (approximately 600 MB) holds a quantity of images equivalent to all the papers stored in a four-drawer file cabinet.

It is not uncommon for companies to cost-justify imaging technology based on a short payback period. Tangible savings from eliminating microfilm, reducing the head count of clerical staff, and saving storage space can result in payback periods of 18 months or less. When intangibles such as better response, improved security, and fewer lost documents are added in, the payback period can be under one year.

Workflow Automation and Management

The biggest payoff comes from using images to automate and manage workflow. Workflow processing actively routes documents through a system, using rules that reflect the decision criteria that is used to process the documents. Instead of just dumping all information into an "in-basket," logical queues of documents are established that enable workstation operators to obtain the next available document for processing. This results in streamlined processing of documents, speedier distribution that requires fewer people, and more productivity from the people who must process the information.

For example, incoming documents are scanned into the system, and then they are indexed by the claim number, name, form type, and scan date. All documents for the same case can be grouped in an electronic file folder. When a file folder is opened, the whole folder or one or more individual documents are routed immediately to the appropriate queue. Other information might reside in a mainframe database and can be integrated into the document via terminal emulation. In fact, multiple mainframe sessions can be established, each displayed in a separate window on the image workstation.

When a document processing step is completed, the file is placed in the appropriate logical queue, to be forwarded to the next processing step. No physical transfer need take place. If further work is needed, the document can be sent back to the person who previously handled it, or can be held in suspense until the additional information is obtained.

With fewer people required to process documents, compared to a paper-based system, an organization can be more responsive to the needs of its customers or clients. In the past, important documents might have taken days to get from the mailroom to the right person's desk. That wait has been replaced by the capability to transfer document images instantaneously.

Another benefit of imaging systems is the ability to manage the flow of work through the office. Supervisors can easily monitor the status of documents and files to ensure that high-priority cases are handled expeditiously. The results are more productive workers and happier clients.

Some industry observers view this new way of document handling as signaling a paradigm shift from data management to work management. According to this view, imaging systems are changing not only the kind of information that moves within organizations, but how it moves as well.

Workflow systems are particularly successful when designed to allow the process to be altered to match the technology. This radical change in information systems philosophy is called *business process redesign,* or *business re-engineering.* Instead of simply computerizing an existing manual system, a business must determine the goal of the manual process. Then the business must look for a way to achieve that goal in an efficient, cost-effective manner, even if it requires altering the current business practice.

Projects in which business processes have been altered to take advantage of new technologies often result in the biggest productivity increases. However, caution should be taken to prevent sudden and sweeping changes. After all, when people perceive a threat to job security, they might rebel against change and jeopardize success, either through inaction or deliberate means.

In fact, the organizational problems are often more difficult to solve than the technical ones. For example, a large insurance company wanted to implement an imaging system in its field offices, but was concerned that the staff would feel threatened and resist contributing to the design. The company solved this problem by selecting one field office for a pilot and guaranteeing job security regardless of the outcome of the new system. This not only alleviated the immediate problem of staff concerns, the staff's increased participation also ensured the long-term success of the project.

Integration Issues

Any image system implementation project requires that images be integrated with existing applications and with record-oriented data that might already exist in a corporate database.

Accordingly, an important factor in the purchasing decision is the ability of the product to integrate with existing equipment and software. The strong requirement for integration is also one of the major forces pushing vendors toward "open systems" built on industry-standard platforms.

At the applications level, integration is achieved by setting up image windows and database windows on the same screen. Data can then be transferred from the database window to the image window. This type of data transfer can be done in a variety of ways, including through the use of MS-Windows' linkage mechanism, *dynamic data exchange* (DDE).

A much better approach than using DDE is to use cooperative processing to build applications that span microcomputers, minicomputers, and mainframes. Portions of an application can run on any machine in a network, and data from a variety of databases can be linked with images. To provide easier integration of images with existing applications, APIs are used, allowing images to be accessed from standard programming languages.

Another reason for integration is that users do not want to bring in a new *database management system* (DBMS) just to support the imaging system. Not only does this increase the cost of the imaging system, it also makes support of the system more difficult. The solution that many vendors have chosen is to allow their image filing and retrieval systems to work with a variety of *relational database management systems* (RDBMSs), including Microsoft/Sybase SQL Server and Oracle, from Oracle Corp.

One possible result of the need for integration and the push to standard systems might be the absorption of image management into the standard data processing mix. While the interfaces are now mostly nonstandard, that is changing. As systems builders learn the new design techniques necessary to succeed with imaging applications, those techniques will become part of any designer's skill repertoire.

Technical Issues

Implementing an imaging system is a difficult technical task. The problem with images stems from the size of the bit map. For example, a scanned 8.5-in by 11-in text document can produce a file size of over 1 MB. Even with compression, the file is still between 50 KB and 100 KB. For color documents, these storage requirements may be 10 or 20 times larger.

This large size affects every aspect of image manipulation. Primarily, the large size makes file compression a requirement. Compression occurs after the image is scanned, and decompression occurs when it is displayed or printed. Until recently, compression and decompression were done in hardware, because of the amount of computation required. Add-on boards were required for adequate performance. But these boards added significantly to the cost of each display station. The trend today is toward software-based compression, which on a fast 80386 or 80486 *personal computer* (PC) provides a comparable level of performance–and at far lower cost.

Integration with DBMSs is also a problem. Even when the DBMS supports a *binary large object* (BLOB) data type, in which image data can be stored, most DBMSs do not do all that is necessary to support images. For example, the DBMS must permit the image to be physically stored separately from the rest of the record, so that it can be put on optical media, which provides more long-term storage capacity. Furthermore, when a record is retrieved, the image buffers need to be separate from the record buffers, otherwise the size of the image will quickly fill the allocated space. Some DBMS vendors are adding these and other capabilities to facilitate the treating of images as just another data type.

Another potential problem area is networking. A large imaging application might require shipping many compressed images of 100 KB or more across the network. While many LANs can be configured to accommodate imaging applications, sending images over the slower *wide-area network* (WAN) results in unacceptable performance, in which case a wide-bandwidth solution is required. Such solutions include private T1 lines operating at 1.536 Mbps or emerging public network offerings, such as frame relay or *switched multimegabit data services* (SMDS).

This book covers these and other important issues related to the effective design and implementation of computerized document imaging systems. The book progresses from basic concepts to applications, to vendor implementations, to planning. As such, it is of value to those who need a central source of introductory information, as well as to those who are well along in planning or implementing document imaging systems and can use further input into their decision-making processes. The book is written with a minimum of technical jargon, yet the subject matter is covered in sufficient detail to appeal to those who are more technically oriented.

Although microfilm and microfiche are still important imaging technologies, the projected market growth for these systems is only 5% per year. There are also specialized imaging systems for medical applications, such as *magnetic resonance imaging* (MRI) and *computerized tomography* (CT). There are highly sophisticated imaging systems used in oil and mineral exploration and environmental applications. Likewise, there are many experimental imaging technologies, such as virtual reality and three-dimensional holography. These specialized topics are beyond the scope of this book, especially since there are many fine books already available that very capably treat these subjects. Accordingly, the focus of this book is the computerized document imaging systems used in today's office environment.

This book is organized into six parts: basic principles, imaging system platforms, vendor implementations, wide-area networking, related integration areas, and planning and services.

Part I describes the basic principles—introducing the reader to concepts, information management issues, and applications—and lays the foundation for more detailed discussions of document imaging.

Chapter 1 provides an overview of document imaging concepts, introducing the reader to the basic categories of office document imaging systems and the various discrete processes that comprise the imaging system function. These processes include scanning and indexing, storage and retrieval, compression, and workflow and office automation. Also covered in this chapter are overviews of imaging system components, complementary technologies, and networking requirements. The chapter ends with a discussion of the impact of open systems on imaging and some of the considerations that go into needs assessment.

Chapter 2 provides a general discussion of information management. With this background, the reader will have a better understanding of how image documents are organized for storage, search, and retrieval. Among the key concepts covered in this chapter are Boolean searches, *structured query language* (SQL), hypertext, and various document architectures.

Chapter 3 provides in-depth descriptions of selected office applications of document imaging, including processing technical documentation, credit card transactions, accounts payable transactions, insurance claims, and loan origination documents. Other applications are briefly mentioned as well. The intent of this chapter is to highlight some practical applications of document imaging and to stimulate readers to imagine how document imaging might be applied to their organizations to streamline workflows, alleviate paper logjams, and increase office productivity.

Part II describes the major platforms on which document imaging systems are built: microcomputers (desktops), LANs (departmental systems), and mainframes (enterprisewide systems).

Chapter 4 gives an overview of a category of document imaging products that are commonly referred to as *desktop imaging systems*. This type of imaging system is aimed at small businesses or work groups within the departments of large organizations. The chapter describes a range of affordable technologies and system components that come together in the low-volume office environment.

Chapter 5 describes LAN-based imaging systems and some of the considerations that make for successful implementation. This chapter explains some of the popular LAN approaches, along with the associated advantages and disadvantages. Since the choice of a LAN can have a bearing on imaging system performance, this chapter includes a discussion of the various LAN topologies. A synopsis of the popular LAN types is also provided, including Ethernet, token ring, StarLAN, ARCnet and FDDI. In addition, the roles of hubs and servers on the LAN are described.

Chapter 6 describes mainframe-based imaging. Despite the much publicized migration of mainframe applications to the distributed computing environment characterized by LANs, many companies still have a large investment in mainframe computers and are seeking to leverage that investment by adding applications such as imaging. This chapter explores the role of the mainframe within the context of document imaging applications and highlights the associated system components. For the most part, the types of system components used in the mainframe environment are the same as those used in desktop and LAN-based imaging systems; they differ only in their capacity to support a high volume of transactions. Of course, there are equipment types, such as *front-end processors* (FEPs), communications controllers, and certain types of storage facilities, that are unique to the mainframe environment. These too are covered.

Part III is a series of chapters that focus on the document imaging products of specific vendors. The selection of vendors was dictated by the willingness of the various companies to provide technical documentation and other proprietary information that adequately described the operation of their systems. Accordingly, the cooperation of IBM Corp., Unisys Corp., Hewlett-Packard Co., *Digital Equipment Corp.* (DEC), and FileNet Corp. was instrumental in the development of the core content of this book. If only one of these vendors declined to participate, I would have considered this book seriously deficient. So I am very appreciative of their assistance.

Chapter 7 describes IBM's ImagePlus system. Although IBM offers a version of ImagePlus for all three processing platforms—mainframe, midrange, and microcomputer—this chapter focuses on the SAA ImagePlus MVS/ESA system, which supports high-volume operational and production applications.

Chapter 8 discusses Unisys' InfoImage system, highlighting the major hardware and software components and describing how the components work together to provide customers with a comprehensive imaging solution.

Chapter 9 describes Hewlett-Packard's *Advanced Image Management System* (AIMS). In addition to providing information on basic system operation, this chapter highlights the software modules that are used to support specific imaging system functions, as well as the various tools that are available for applications integration.

Chapter 10 describes DECimage EXpress, including its development history, functionality, and applications-development environment. Options that can be added to DECimage EXpress are discussed, as well as third-party offerings that are based on DECimage EXpress and can be brought into DECimage EXpress to expand its functionality or provide links into DECimage EXpress.

Chapter 11 describes the document image products of FileNet Corp., specifically, its WorkFlo Business System and FolderView offerings. This chapter also provides information on how applications are developed using object-oriented and script-oriented programming methods.

Part IV is concerned with wide-area networking. Its single chapter, Chapter 12, provides a survey of transmission facilities and services that are available for users of public or private networks. Each type of facility and service is reviewed according to its ability to support the transmission of document images. The facilities described include analog leased lines, T1 and Fractional T1, and T3 and Fractional T3. The services described include dial-up, packet-switched, *digital data services* (DDS), the *integrated services digital network* (ISDN), frame relay, and *switched multimegabit data services* (SMDS). Also covered in this chapter is *inverse multiplexing*, which is an economical way of supporting image applications by locally assembling bandwidth increments of 56/64 Kbps into higher-speed digital pipes, rather than paying high monthly local-access fees for dedicated T1 lines.

Part V contains two chapters on topics that, increasingly, will have a relationship with document imaging: videoconferencing and the emerging set of technologies that comprise multimedia.

Chapter 13 provides an introduction to videoconferencing and, along the way, describes how document imaging can be integrated into conferencing sessions.

Chapter 14 describes multimedia technologies and applications, as well as how document imaging can be integrated into multimedia presentations.

Part VI addresses the formative stages of document imaging system implementation.

Chapter 15 deals with a variety of issues that must be addressed to ensure the successful planning, acceptance, and implementation of a document imaging system. These issues include personnel, political, and technical concerns, as well as support requirements.

Chapter 16 focuses on the professional services that vendors offer to help customers assess the need for document imaging systems. The chapter evaluates the potential performance of these companies and the potential return on investment for the services. The chapter focuses on the professional services offered by Unisys Corp., although most of the large imaging system vendors also offer similar types of services. Unisys was selected as the illustration because it was the most willing of any other vendor to discuss this type of service in great detail.

The information contained in this book, especially as it relates to specific vendors and products, is believed to be accurate at the time it was written and is, of course, subject to change with continued advancements in technology and shifts in market forces. The mention of specific products and vendors is for illustration purposes only and does not constitute or imply an endorsement of any kind by the author or the publisher.

Nathan J. Muller

PART I
BASIC PRINCIPLES

Chapter 1

Document Imaging Concepts

1.1 INTRODUCTION

In the United States alone, 95% of the more than three trillion documents currently stored in corporate offices still exist in paper form, with the number growing by one billion pages daily. The cost of storing these documents is quite substantial. A typical office in a Manhattan building, for example, contains ten file cabinets, each capable of holding 10,000 pieces of paper, for a total of 100,000 pieces of paper. At $70 a square foot, this translates into $14,000 a year in rent, or $0.14 a page. Assuming that each piece of paper will be copied at least once during the year adds another $0.03 per page, or $3,000 a year. A filing clerk to maintain the files and make the copies adds $25,000 per year in salary and benefits. The total cost associated with storing information in only ten filing cabinets reaches $42,000 a year or $2.38 per page.

There are other expenses associated with keeping paper documents that drive the cost of doing business even higher. Not only is a lot of paper wasted, it is also lost. Various estimates put the average cost of tracking down a lost or misfiled document at $120. The average executive spends one month per year waiting for the documents he or she needs. And then there is the cost of mailing documents, many of them by expensive overnight services. Implementing security procedures for sensitive documents also adds to the cost of maintaining paper documents.

Dealing with paper documents has been a lingering problem for most businesses. The first document imaging systems were based on microfilm, which came into widespread use in the late 1960s. Microfilm offered numerous benefits over paper filing systems, including easier and faster access to documents, improved file integrity, better security, longer document life, and cost savings based on space savings and productivity gains. But, while microfilm offered incremental improvements, it fell short of providing the means to efficiently process and retrieve documents, especially as advances in computer technology during the 1970s and 1980s greatly increased the output of paper. In addition, microfilm did not solve the persistent problem of documents lost because of data entry errors. Document losses of 30% were not uncommon.

Moreover, microfilm required that documents be sent off-site to be filmed, a process that typically took two weeks, during which time companies were left without access to their files. Retrieval was a mechanical task that was often as time-consuming as rummaging through documents stored in file cabinets.

According to a 1991 report by the *Association for Information and Image Management* (AIIM), although microfilm still accounts for about half the image management market, it is under intense competitive pressure from optical disk technology. Consequently, the market growth for microfilm has all but stopped, at a time when the market for optical disks is taking off. AIIM predicts that microfilm will grow at an annual rate of only 5% from now until 1995, compared with a 47% growth rate for electronic image management using optical disks.

Microfilm system vendors like Eastman Kodak, Bell & Howell, and 3M sensed a limited future for their products, correctly assessing that most companies would bypass microfilm and store their records on a more compact, readily accessible online medium, such as optical disk. From this defensive posture, these vendors began investing substantial research and development resources in digital imaging systems—systems that would largely mimic their existing products but replace microfilm and microfiche with optical disk technology.

Of note is the new strategy of some vendors of providing customers with the means to facilitate the migration from microfilm to electronic document storage. Kodak's Imagelink Scanner/Microimager 990S, for example, can capture as many as 120 documents per minute onto microfilm and electronic media simultaneously in one scanning pass. Bell & Howell's Filmer/Scanner is both a high-speed document scanner and microfilm camera that creates both an electronic and microfilm image of a document in one pass.

With optical disk technology, document imaging systems move businesses and government agencies closer to the paperless office by providing the means to digitally store paper documents in massive image databases that can be accessed in real time. Storing documents in digital form can solve many of the problems commonly experienced with paper files, such as misfilings that cause confusion and waste time, outdated documents that are mixed in with current documents, and paper that becomes damaged with age.

Having information stored in digital form can eliminate extensive, exhaustive searches for documents and files that tend to "disappear" in traditional storage facilities. Access to an image document can be effected by a variety of methods using content- and concept-based retrieval methods. Documents in either electronic or microfilm form can even be indexed in multiple ways that allow them to be retrieved in accordance with each user's informational needs.

With imaging systems in place, companies can realize other benefits that come with streamlining business operations. In the process of redesigning workflow to accommodate imaging systems, it is not uncommon for companies to find that they can combine several departments into one. For example, firms that previously employed separate work groups to process and store orders, invoices, and canceled checks are finding that the introduction of imaging systems enables all the documents to be stored on the same system. The queuing capabilities of the imaging system direct and monitor the flow of image files from station to station on the network. Because the documents can be accessed from any workstation simply by cross-training employees to handle multiple job functions, several operations can easily be merged. This, in turn, means that fewer people are needed to handle the same functions. In the bargain, overtime pay can become a relic of the past.

This brings up another benefit of imaging systems: they can solve the familiar problem of multiple access. In a paper-filing system, only one person can access a document at a time. If that person brings that document back to his or her desk or—worse—takes it home, others are denied access until it is returned and properly filed. Prioritization schemes that attempt to determine who gets documents and when almost never work, causing frustration among staff members whose work is delayed. With imaging systems, documents can be called up simultaneously by multiple users. Some imaging systems even allow the documents to be updated by different users, whereupon the updated document is filed in the order of the last update first. That way, a complete history of a document can be maintained.

When imaging applications are supported by private networks or public network services, the benefits are even more pronounced. According to the Yankee Group, a market research company in Boston, network support of imaging applications can reduce staff needs by as much as 33% and can free up floor space by as much as 80%.

1.2 OFFICE DOCUMENT IMAGING SYSTEMS

There are four categories of office document imaging systems, each based on document size and other information-related factors. The size of the document is important because it impacts the type of input and output peripherals required, including the type of workstations needed, as well as basic architectural considerations.

1.2.1 General Business Systems

General business systems vary depending on whether they are oriented toward transaction processing or a central repository function. In a transaction processing environment, image management systems improve the economics of managing the active life cycle of the document. This type of system is used to automate workflow. In a central repository, the objective is to store vast quantities of images over a prolonged period of time. This type of system is used to archive documents after they reach a certain age, perhaps in compliance with various legal and regulatory requirements.

1.2.2 Image Processing Systems

Item processing is a special form of imaging in which small documents, such as checks and credit card receipts, are scanned in high volumes. Banks and other financial services firms scan millions of such documents daily. In 1990, the U.S. banking industry alone processed 50 billion checks at an average cost of only $0.05. The image management systems in use today improve processing throughput by as much as 40% over previous generation systems and 80% over manual methods.

1.2.3 Engineering Drawing Systems

Engineering drawings typically depict complex, two-dimensional product specifications or design plans. Some of these drawings are 100 feet or more in length, depending on the level of detail required. They require the use of special-width scanners and plotters, in addition to specialized drawing software. Although many engineering firms employ *computer-aided design* (CAD) and *computer-aided manufacturing* (CAM) systems to create and manipulate drawings, these systems are not able to convert the massive base of paper drawings that have already been accumulated throughout the organization. An image system can bridge the two environments by electronically converting the paper drawings and storing them in image databases for easy access.

1.2.4 Mapping Systems

Mapping systems are typically used to manage land use by government agencies. They can be used to assess property taxes because of their ability to depict the amount of available land, the number of buildings on the land, and the number of new buildings the land will allow. Mapping systems can also depict any number of other features about the land, including the location of gas and water mains, underground wiring and pipelines, dump sites, and watershed and wildlife areas—anything that might be impacted by construction. These mapping systems rely extensively on color and graphics capabilities, as well as compatibility with the dissimilar systems used by other government agencies. Many of these maps are in paper form and could benefit from image management systems. When the maps are stored as images, they are often referred to as *geobases*.

There are a number of other types of imaging systems, such as medical imaging systems, holographic imaging, fractal imaging, and virtual reality. These specialized concepts are beyond the scope of this book, but are summarized in Appendix A.

1.3 IMAGING FUNCTIONS

The functions provided by document imaging systems differ according to vendor. There are several pivotal functions performed by imaging systems that have broad significance for potential users in any industry. These functions include:

- Scanning and indexing—scanning transforms paper documents into digital form for storage on magnetic or optical media and indexing documents allows for easy identification;
- Storage and retrieval, which are the basic functions of any imaging system;
- Compression, which applies an encoding algorithm to images for minimizing storage requirements;

- Workflow automation, which enhances basic imaging systems by facilitating control over various work processes;
- Office automation, which integrates imaging into a much broader information processing context.

1.3.1 Scanning and Indexing

Scanning is the process of reading paper documents into digital form. *Image scanning* produces a digital replica of the document, which can be displayed on a computer screen. This type of scanning reproduces corporate logos, drawings, photographs, and signatures with a high degree of accuracy. Editing tools allow the scanned items to be appropriately sized and cropped. Another type of scanning is *optical character recognition* (OCR), which is used to read machine-printed text and store it in word processor or *American National Standard Code for Information Interchange* (ASCII) format. Once in digital form, the text can be indexed, edited, written to floppy disk, or transmitted over the network.

1.3.2 Storage and Retrieval

Images are usually stored on high-capacity optical disks. The storage capacity of the common *compact disk read-only memory* (CD-ROM), is equivalent to approximately 700 conventional floppy disks. Improvements in lasers will double capacity in the next few years. *Write-once read-many* (WORM) optical disks and *compact disk recordable* (CD-R) optical disks provide more archiving flexibility and are becoming more affordable. Access time is also improving. Whereas 340 ms is typical for CD-ROMs, the access time for rewritable optical disks is about 80 ms. In a few years, 40-ms access time will be the norm. Another advantage of optical disks is the ease with which they can be integrated into a network via servers.

Retrieval is a basic function provided by all document imaging systems, differing in the speed of image retrieval and the amount of flexibility afforded to the user. Some systems allow the user to change fields and set up unique processes for accessing images. Others set up these processes in advance, making subsequent alteration difficult. Some vendors are oriented more to storage than retrieval, reflecting their backgrounds in paper and film records. These types of vendors typically serve customers with acute record management needs.

Several document retrieval approaches are available, including index and full text. With text-based retrieval, the user can access images using any word, rather than having to choose from a limited selection of key words in an index. With the index approach, the user enters a key word and is presented with a list of image files that contain that word. The user may have to call up several image documents before finding the item of interest. The benefits of the full-text approach are obvious: users can locate image documents based on their precise informational needs and inquiry preferences. Some imaging systems support both document retrieval methods and allow a fair degree of user customization.

1.3.3 Compression

Compression algorithms have become highly sophisticated, allowing image files to be shrunk by a ratio of at least 2 to 1 and as high as 100 to 1 without any loss of image quality. There are compression techniques that offer compression ratios up to 250 to 1, but with a slight loss of image quality.

Compression algorithms work by removing extraneous or repetitive data from an image. This permits more efficient storage, as well as faster transmission over *local-area networks* (LANs) and *wide-area networks* (WANs). When the document is retrieved from storage, it is decompressed within seconds so it can be viewed on a computer screen.

1.3.4 Workflow Automation

Beyond storing and retrieving images, workflow software automates the flow of documents from one processing step to another, eliminating many intervening processing stages and streamlining others. Workflow automation can be compared to an assembly line—workers in various departments or work groups collect information from many different sources and in many different formats and append the information to a core document until eventually a finished product is produced. A core document can, for example, be a purchase order from a customer that arrives by mail in paper form. In the mail room, the document is scanned into digital form and stored in a database for access by a customer service representative. The service representative files the purchase order in the customer's electronic file folder, which is ready for access by several other department workstations in sequence. The process ends when the order is shipped and an invoice sent via mail or *electronic data interchange* (EDI). The whole process is accomplished within a few hours rather than days or weeks, as in paper-based systems.

1.3.5 Office Automation

Rather than view document imaging as a separate application, businesses are coming to understand how imaging can be an extension of office automation. This entails treating images as just another type of data that can be combined with text, tables, graphics, and even voice and video. While integrating document imaging into the broader context of office automation is complicated, it offers significant efficiencies. Among other things, such integration can eliminate the need for redundant information system components—one set for images and another for other kinds of data. Although full integration of imaging and office automation is not yet common, it is expected to become widespread by the turn of the century.

1.4 IMAGING SYSTEM COMPONENTS

A complete imaging system typically includes the following components:

- Workstations with high-resolution displays;
- Scanners and OCR software, for digitizing hard-copy information;
- Software designed to manage document retrieval, workflow automation, and communications functions;
- Output devices, such as printers and plotters;
- Storage media—most notably the optical disks.

These imaging system components are illustrated in Figure 1.1.

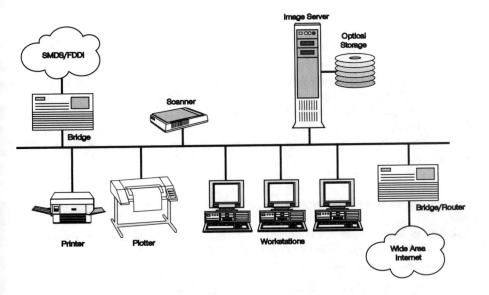

Figure 1.1 Document imaging system components.

Document imaging systems are available for microcomputer, minicomputer, and mainframe platforms. Moreover, imaging products address a broad range of user configurations, from single users, to work groups large and small, to enterprisewide operations. Prices are as diverse as the configurations themselves, ranging from only a few thousand dollars for a stand-alone desktop system to $2 million or more for enterprisewide systems.

1.5 MARKET PLAYERS

The involvement of the major computer manufacturers is speeding market acceptance of document imaging. IBM, DEC, Unisys, Wang Laboratories, and Hewlett-Packard are among the traditional computer giants that offer advanced document imaging systems and planning services. Some, like Unisys, even offer their customers comprehensive educational programs that provide a management-level overview of the key issues, component technologies, applications, functionality, and motivations involved in imaging.

Among the newer (post-1985) entrants into the imaging system market is FileNet Corp., which is posing a serious challenge to the larger computer manufacturers. FileNet offers an array of high-end imaging systems and sophisticated workflow software. According to industry analysts, FileNet has more installations (but less revenue) than IBM.

While entire imaging systems that can support complex workflow applications and large numbers of users are available from big and small vendors alike, there are many more smaller firms that provide the discrete components of imaging systems, such as workstations, CD-ROM units and optical jukeboxes, scanners, software, and network facilities. These components can be put together by systems integrators to meet specific user requirements. The systems integrator is especially useful when there is the need to customize hardware and software interfaces to make components from different manufacturers work together in seamless fashion.

And, because the *regional Bell holding companies* (RBHCs) are free to enter the market for information services, analysts expect that these companies will eventually offer document imaging services to their business customers on a service bureau basis. This is a logical extension of the voice mail, electronic mail, and facsimile service bureaus that long-distance carriers, local telephone companies, and *value-added network* (VAN) providers now operate.

1.6 COMPLEMENTARY TECHNOLOGIES

A document imaging system can coexist with and complement other related technologies, such as EDI, multimedia, videoconferencing, and facsimile, further extending its benefits throughout the organization.

1.6.1 Electronic Data Interchange

EDI entails the transmission of machine-readable information between business partners' computers in a mutually agreed upon format. For example, instead of processing a purchase order with multiple paper forms and mailing it to the supplier, the data is passed through an application link, where software maps the data into the standard machine-readable data format. That data is then transmitted to the supplier's computer, where it is passed to an application link that maps the data into the internal format expected by the supplier's order entry system.

This interchange of data offers numerous benefits to users, including streamlined dataflow, which makes it easier to develop and maintain complete audit trails for all transactions. Having all of this information on line also provides the means to track vendor performance, perform cost-benefit analyses, improve project management, and enhance overall financial control.

EDI works well in established customer and supplier relationships in which both parties have approximately the same level of automation and adhere to agreed-upon procedures for transaction processing. The problem with EDI is that the great majority of job functions either cannot benefit from this type of communication or require more advanced capabilities than EDI can provide. In these situations, document imaging systems are more appropriate. This is not to say that there is no point of convergence between document imaging and EDI. In fact, documents in image form can complement the documents sent via EDI. For example, although EDI is routinely used to deliver a purchase order for a part, it typically does not include a diagram of the part. Imaging can change that, allowing users to incorporate graphical information into the EDI document.

EDI is most often used in parallel with a document imaging system to process and manage invoices electronically. EDI facilitates the electronic exchange of documents between trading partners, and the imaging system's workflow software creates the link to accounting and imaging applications. In this way, the actions of coding an invoice, which is now an image, and updating the accounting package with the data can be combined into a single step. Some companies that use this approach have reported productivity gains of up to 25% and paper reductions of up to 40%.

1.6.2 Multimedia

The term *multimedia* generally refers to the integration of text, image, audio, and video within a single application program or online session. This integration of formerly separate applications has already found practical uses in education and business. In a training application program, for example, a CD-ROM contains all the information necessary to teach an installer how to set up and operate a new product for a customer. Through a combination of text, audio, image, and full-motion video, the installer can read the relevant technical documentation, view a demonstration of the setup procedures, and listen to a warning about possible electrical hazards—all accessed from the same program. When the installer completes a module of instruction, a built-in test facility can determine the installer's level of proficiency and provide suggestions for review.

Although there is a convergence between document imaging and multimedia—even multimedia that relies extensively on imaged documents—each is appropriate for specific applications. Multimedia is ideally suited for training and education, while document imaging is appropriate for document storage and retrieval, as well as for automating workflow in transaction processing environments.

1.6.3 Videoconferencing

When imaging is coupled with videoconferencing, documents can be viewed by all participants. *Videoconferencing* is the capability to broadcast audio and full-motion, slow-scan, and freeze-frame images over a closed circuit to one or more locations. Image, text, and graphics from a variety of sources can even be combined over a single video circuit, eliminating the need (and cost) of additional communications links to handle each traffic type separately. With a split-screen capability, an imaged document can be displayed on one side of the screen (or window), while the participants continue their discussion on the other side of the screen. Participants who want a copy of the displayed document can request a fax or use screen-capture software to capture the image directly into their computers.

1.6.4 Facsimile

In a typical application of facsimile, a computer-generated text document is delivered electronically for output on paper. When imaging is added, graphics can be integrated with text for transmission. An incoming fax can be delivered directly into a document imaging system, skipping the paper process. More elaborate imaging systems allow documents to be faxed, or form letters printed, from within the imaging application itself.

1.7 NETWORK REQUIREMENTS

Networked imaging systems are capable of more advanced applications than stand-alone systems. Stand-alone systems are little more than electronic file cabinets, whereas networked systems allow multiple access and facilitate information flow throughout the organization.

In the workflow environment, managers can distribute work among their staff. In turn, staff members use the network to access the information they need to fulfill their functions. In the end, a complete information package is produced. In the case of a home loan mortgage, a bank's imaging system can facilitate the title search, locate the property appraisal, find a photo of the house, call up the applicant's credit report, and process the loan application. This process, which once took many days or weeks to complete, can now be done in a matter of hours.

To fully realize the efficiencies and economies of imaging systems would require that documents be accessible not only to local users over the LAN, but also to remote users over the WAN. Imaging requires higher transmission speed and throughput, consistent data access, high-speed workstation interfaces, and interoperable communications protocols.

Most companies are still making the transition from mainframe-centered networks to local-area networks. In the former, access to host resources is typically provided through low- to medium-speed (4.8 Kbps to 56 Kbps) lines. Because imaging systems can impose a tremendous burden on existing networks by the sheer size of their files, such companies are finding it necessary to redesign their networks to handle the increased load. While a single-page text file might consist of 3 KB and a technical drawing one or more megabytes, the scanning process can easily double or triple the file size.

With many users simultaneously exchanging image documents, even 10-Mbps Ethernet and 16-Mbps token-ring LANs can quickly become overloaded. For Ethernet, associated network management overhead, access contention, and the possibility of collisions can reduce data throughput by more than 50% under heavy loads. A scanned paper document of 50 to 100 KB, for example, can take one second to transmit over a fully loaded Ethernet, while medical images or photographs of 2 to 5 MB can take 45 sec or more to transmit. Token-ring networks offer a substantial increase in speed at 16 Mbps, but actual network throughput is often substantially lower because of network overhead.

Although the situation can be improved somewhat by using compression and de-compression algorithms and by making the packet sizes as large as possible via the network drivers, a thorough review of the network topology might be required. The new topology would be determined by such factors as the frequency of image transfers and the size of the files. Other factors that bear consideration in the network modeling phase include average and peak input and retrieval volumes, average and maximum numbers of "pages," the retention period, the annual growth rate of electronic files, the number of shifts per day, and the number of individuals and productive hours per shift.

For imaging applications in the campus environment, LANs based on the 100-Mbps *fiber distributed data interface* (FDDI) standard can be used, especially for bandwidth-intensive medical imaging applications. Bridges and routers are available that connect Ethernet and token-ring LANs to FDDI backbones. Bridges more than routers, however, introduce an element of network filtering and forwarding delay that must be considered when planning such internets.

To support volume image traffic over a wide area, along with other voice and data applications, the backbone portion of the enterprise network requires at least T3 facilities, which provide a throughput rate of 44.736 Mbps over fiber-optic lines. But T3 equipment is proprietary and requires that the same type of equipment be used from end to end, even through the various carrier-serving offices that support the link. In essence, T3 is a custom service that entails high installation costs and recurring monthly costs.

The new carrier-provided metropolitan-area network services, such as *switched multimegabit data service* (SMDS) provide an alternative to expensive, private T3 fiber facilities and offer T3 as well as T1 transmission speeds. SMDS is a fast packet service that is optimized for high-speed data and image traffic. SMDS can even be used in conjunction with FDDI, extending the geographical range of the FDDI backbone across a metropolitan area.

Some local-exchange and alternative-access carriers offer higher-speed fiber services based on *synchronous optical network* (SONET) standards. Under SONET, these networks provide transmission speeds of 155 Mbps and 622 Mbps, with upgrades to gigabyte speeds planned for the future.

Other options for long-distance image transmission include universally available circuit-switched digital services, such as T1. For limited image traffic, there are also Fractional T1 circuits (64 Kbps to 768 Kbps) and switched 56-Kbps digital services. Newer offerings, such as AT&T's 384-Kbps and 1.536-Mbps switched digital services, can also be used to support certain types of image applications.

Integrated services digital network (ISDN) can also support image traffic. It offers some very tangible benefits, including faster call setup and network response times, bandwidth control, reconfiguration flexibility, and restoral options. Another benefit of ISDN is that the user pays only for the bandwidth used. If the organization's image traffic is infrequent and of low volume, ISDN bandwidth can be dialed up when needed. The user is billed for the amount of bandwidth used (up to 1.536 Mbps), based on time and distance, just like an ordinary phone call.

Satellite services can also be used for image transmission between international locations. For example, images stored on optical disks in the United States can be retrieved by corporate sites in Europe or the Pacific Rim.

Whatever transmission facilities or services are used, provisions must be made to keep the wide-area links up and running. After all, companies are conveying business-critical documents, which means that imaging systems, as well as the networks they run on, must be robust in terms of reliability and availability. This means having redundant subsystems in place, spare bandwidth capacity available, and management tools accessible that can identify and isolate problems before they degrade overall system or network performance.

1.8 SELECTION CRITERIA

Selecting a document imaging system requires balancing the features and functionality with such information systems criteria as compatibility, architecture, and growth potential. Buyers need to find a system that will accommodate both initial and future applications.

Buyers should not limit their investigation of imaging systems and components to only the advertised capabilities, however. Of equal importance is the vendor's financial stability and ability to service and support the system at all locations. A careful evaluation will determine the vendor's ability to support products and systems well into the future.

During the evaluation process, it is important to look for a vendor who is willing to get involved with the end users of the imaging system, perhaps in a pilot project. This is an opportunity to take advantage of the vendor's expertise in on-the-job training, as well as an opportunity to spread the benefits of imaging throughout the rest of the organization and win over some skeptics in the process.

Other challenges await *information systems* (IS) and LAN managers planning image information systems, such as deciding whether a client/server or a host-based system is best and choosing the right peripherals.

1.9 IMPACT OF OPEN SYSTEMS

Open systems is a key issue in the imaging industry. Open systems offer a number of advantages, including transportability of applications across hardware platforms, flexibility in hardware selection, reduced training and support costs, and interconnectivity with external constituents, such as customers and trading partners.

Open systems interfaces begin with an operating system interface and extend to interfaces for graphics services, programming tools, languages, utilities, libraries, windowing and user interfaces, data and file management, and network facilities and services. Strict adherence to these interfaces allows different applications to communicate and exchange data across different devices, operating systems, and networks.

Several organizations are defining interface specifications and open system architectures, while vendors are attempting to develop products that adhere to preliminary specifications or that can be easily upgraded to the final specifications once they become accepted as standards. The characteristics of an open image system include:

- The availability of images in standard formats;
- The ability to exchange index data and images with other systems;
- Workstations that use standard user interfaces and run standard application software;
- The attachment of peripherals through standard interfaces.

Lack of standards in key areas of document imaging could impede its acceptance among companies that are concerned about such matters as premature system obsolescence and the offered system's compatibility with other vendors' products. Ultimately, users will drive the movement toward standards by choosing systems that offer the broadest range of compatibility. Users should try to select the most open imaging system possible, to support mission-critical applications, and should avoid wholly proprietary systems unless the offered features are technically essential. Since manufacturers have an interest in creating an environment that will promote rapid market growth—so they can recoup their research and development investments as quickly as possible—this point is not likely to escape their notice.

On the bright side, standards for open image systems already exist in many areas, including communications and networking, peripheral interfaces, user interfaces, workstation operating systems, database management system access, image format, and image compression.

Although open systems offer the highest degree of flexibility and investment protection, insisting on standards—while competitors are not—can result in a competitive disadvantage. This is because competitors will be in a position to reap the rewards of their imaging systems sooner, resulting in a lower cost of doing business. With the resulting savings passed on to their customers, they are in a better position to enlarge market share.

The standards process is unavoidably slow, since many diverse opinions must be considered and reconciled into a set of specifications that will be broadly accepted. Companies do not always have the luxury of waiting for standards before deciding which technologies to deploy. After all, they must be competitive in the world today to ensure their survival in the future.

1.10 DETERMINING NEEDS

If an organization's work environment is characterized by one or more of the following circumstances, it may be a prime candidate for a document imaging system:

- High volume of paper documents;
- High frequency of document retrieval;
- Complex, procedural orientation;

- Large clerical staff;
- Long document processing periods before data is finally made available to users;
- Corporate-level interest in improving customer service.

Implementing an enterprisewide document imaging system is not an easy task. Once the need for a system is determined, interdepartmental cooperation and coordination is essential to implementation success.

Successful implementation often involves breaking apart established business processes and recombining them in new and streamlined ways. The fact that many businesses do not adopt document imaging systems after extensive workflow studies and planning sessions is attributable more to the failure to resolve managerial issues than failure to overcome technical and logistical obstacles. This is understandable, since it is inevitable that the imaging system will have to be merged with existing information systems to provide enterprisewide benefits. This will necessarily have implications that cross departmental boundaries. Sometimes the prevailing belief among corporate managers is that their business processes have evolved a certain way for good reasons, and should not be changed—at least not yet.

It is likely that imaging will result in the elimination of some clerical jobs, especially if these jobs grew out of the need to administer paper records. However, staff elimination should not enter into the decision to move to a document imaging system. Many times, the clerical jobs can be redefined, allowing individuals to expand their responsibilities or, with some retraining, move into entirely new areas. In fact, adopting a document imaging system virtually ensures that few, if any, new paper-intensive administrative jobs ever have to be added to the corporate payroll.

At the same time, it must be emphasized that the introduction of imaging will bring with it new tasks and responsibilities. There may be the need to add staff to handle document entry and conversion, database indexing, system training, and on-site support. Clerical staff who are no longer needed to administer paper files can be retrained to fill some of these new slots.

Of course, imaging will force the restructuring of work within most organizations, resulting in changes in workflow, job content, and work habits in general. Imaging might even dictate the consolidation of work groups or whole departments to achieve optimal work performance. It will certainly eliminate redundant operations and result in less duplication of files. Speedy access to comprehensive databases promises improvements in staff productivity and customer service, making the effort at restructuring internal workflow entirely worthwhile.

1.11 CONCLUSION

Although imaging is still a rapidly evolving technology, it is already becoming indispensable at many companies where paper storage has reached critical mass. Imaging promises to impact businesses in a number of ways, not only reducing paper load but also paperwork. In the process, business operations will become streamlined, resulting in new efficiencies and economies that will impact competitive position.

With the price-to-performance ratio continually improving on all components of document imaging systems—particularly for scanners, optical storage systems and applications software—imaging will not only become more attractive to more companies, it will stretch to embrace more territory, both in terms of actual distance covered and areas of use. As imaging increases in importance, there will be new opportunities to enrich current image applications and spur the creation of new ones.

Imaging systems also offer opportunities for entirely new product and service offerings. Businesses have barely begun to discover the myriad competitive opportunities image systems can present. Technological advances, primarily in mass storage, graphic display, and networking, have already cleared the way for full-fledged electronic image processing. No longer must daily mail delivery be a traumatic experience for today's information-dependent office.

Chapter 2

Information Management

2.1 INTRODUCTION

The so-called "paperless office" demands new ways of building documents, sorting through databases, and accessing information with more precision. With massive amounts of information already in electronic form, the foundation has been laid for better ways of organizing text, graphics, and images—and even combining these traditionally separate data types into complex documents.

Another challenge is finding an effective search and retrieval mechanism so specific information can be extracted from voluminous databases. After users download information to their workstations from the main database, they can further manipulate the information according to their own application needs, or transfer it via local- and wide-area networks for further processing.

The emergence of document imaging systems is bringing about a more document-centric approach to handling data. In this approach, the data is treated as objects and the document at hand is the context within which people work. This, in turn, greatly changes the way computers are used.

This chapter explores some of the latest techniques for managing information and some of the ways vendors are attempting to expand the scope of their products to address document access, integration, and imaging.

2.2 TEXT SEARCH AND RETRIEVAL

As the amount of information stored in databases grows, there is the need for tools that allow users to quickly find and retrieve files without having to use hit-or-miss tactics or scroll through screens of data to find exactly what they need. Text-retrieval systems have been in use since the early 1970s, when IBM first introduced its Stairs mainframe-based system. Over the years, text search and retrieval programs (Table 2.1) have progressed from simple key-word search routines and full text retrieval, to the use of Boolean algorithms, to structured query language, to automatic clustering by topic and, finally, to concept-based retrieval.

Table 2.1
Common Features of Search and Retrieval Programs

Annotation support	Append "sticky notes" anywhere in a document.
Automatic document format detection	Determine the format of documents in the database.
Boolean search	Narrow search routines, using one or more operators (i.e., AND, OR, NOT).
Browse	Explore the directory structure, including all subdirectories and files, for purposes of planning a search strategy.
Concept search	Name a search statement for repeated use, thus ensuring that the same search is made each time.
Conflation	Search regardless of word tense.
Data compression support	Index and search compressed files.
Dynamic hypertext	Highlight words or phrases within a browsed document and locate all other documents containing those words or phrases.
Edit options	After a search is complete, physically manage text using such comments as cut, copy, paste, clear, print, and append.
Find options	After a search is complete, call for the next hit, previous hit, next file, or previous file with a single keystroke.
Graphic links	Link graphic images throughout a document.
Saved query library	Maintain a library of saved queries to run again.
Saved recall	Save command-based query recall history to disk between sessions.
Spreadsheet interface	Search and index text portions of spreadsheets.
Terminal stay resident	Call up the search program from within another application, using a keystroke combination.
Thesaurus	Locate synonyms for a term in the search statement, thereby extending its power and versatility.
Truncation	Use wild card symbols to search for prefix, root, suffix, and variations of the same word.

2.2.1 Key-Word Indexing

The simplest information management technique is referred to as *key-word indexing*. Under this scheme, one person is responsible for allocating relevant topics under which information is indexed, using a master list of accepted topics. There are several problems with this approach. Many times topics do not fit into the master list of accepted topics and an arbitrary decision must be made on how to file the information. This makes it difficult for other users to find what they need, since they are probably not familiar with the rationale for another person's filing system.

Another problem with the key-word approach to indexing is that any change in the master list requires a review of all existing files to see if they should be changed to reflect additional or revised topic entries. As the database grows, this eventually becomes a mammoth and self-defeating undertaking.

2.2.2 Full Text Retrieval

An improvement to the key-word indexing method is *full text retrieval*. With this method, there is no need to predict which topics will be of interest weeks, months, or years from now. Full text retrieval employs a front-end program applied to a database that indexes every word in each document, unless explicitly told not to. From this comprehensive index, the front-end program retrieves all relevant documents that pertain to the user's query instructions.

The query instructions can be simple or complex, depending on the informational needs of the user. For example, the key word "budget" might call up a list of thousands of documents and be of no use at all in finding the right information. To narrow down the search, the user might enter the key words "budget," "marketing," and "1993." The search can be narrowed down further using the Boolean search methodology.

2.2.3 Boolean Search

A search algorithm based on Boolean query logic, which makes use of such operators as AND, OR, and NOT, can narrow considerably the number of documents retrieved. Other types of operators, nonstandard among vendors, indicate proximity. All of these operators can be combined in a single search query to precisely define the information to be retrieved.

The AND operator is placed between two key words or phrases, and tells the system to search for all documents that contain both the first word or phrase and the second. Documents that contain only one of the two terms will not be retrieved. To be retrieved, the document must contain both terms, regardless of where or in what order they appear.

The OR operator is placed between two key words or phrases. The system locates all documents that contain either one term or the other, or both.

The NOT operator is also placed between two terms. The system selects all documents that contain the first term, but not the second. Unlike for the AND and OR operators, the order of term placement for the NOT operator does make a difference. For example, the query "manager NOT bonus" will clearly yield a different answer than "bonus NOT manager."

There are several variations of the proximity operator. One operator, which indicates nearby, can be marked with a double slash (//) or any other vendor-selected symbol. This operator can be used to locate documents that contain two or more terms that appear together in the same paragraph in any order, or within a defined number of lines. For example, when locating terms that appear together within ten lines of each other, the proximity operator might be entered as /10/. Another variation of the proximity operator locates terms that appear together within a specified number of paragraphs.

2.2.4 Automatic Clustering by Topic

Most text retrieval products require the user to define the topics to be located within a database. A significant new approach to computerized document analysis and text retrieval is provided by PAR Technology Corporation's ActiveWatch. This "smart" document retrieval program searches the database, identifies the subjects contained in each document, and clusters the documents by topic, without further user input.

Because users of most retrieval systems obtain only the documents that match their specific inquiry, they have no visibility into other related information in the database that does not precisely match the profile of their query. PAR's ActiveWatch provides access to a larger pool of information than the user would otherwise have been able to review. This capability of revealing hidden topics can help users avoid mistakes and complete more thorough research.

2.2.5 Concept-Based Retrieval

Another advanced text retrieval product employs *concept-based retrieval*, a search method introduced by Verity, Inc. The product, Topic, lets users search for ideas or concepts in documents. This is very different from key-word searching, in which users know precisely what they are looking for.

Using a knowledge-based approach to accessing structured and unstructured data from both internal and external sources, Topic provides an intelligent front end to enterprise databases, permitting rapid retrieval of information by searching for concepts. Topic searches for information that might be of assistance, but that users can't know the exact parameters of until after they have retrieved it.

If a user at a pharmaceuticals company wants information on the latest virus research, for example, the retrieved documents might not include such phrases as "vaccine," "patent," "grant," "joint venture," or "Food and Drug Administration"—all of which might have a direct bearing on how the retrieved information is used or acted upon. A typical key-word or Boolean search might not find the right articles because the user would not necessarily search for the exact words used in other important documents. Alternatively, if these phrases were added to the search, the user might be inundated with extraneous information unrelated to virus research. Using Topic, the user will get only the information related to all of the phrases and key words associated with a particular query.

A utility called Topic-By-Example allows users to find one appropriate article and have the search engine find others like it. Ultimately, the product will also be able to link to other relevant "document" formats, such as voice and video.

Verity's Topic is packaged with several database products, including Lotus Development Corporation's Notes (Release 3.0) database. Notes is an open work group computing environment that facilitates information flow across geographical locations, incompatible technologies, and organizational boundaries, enabling people to work together more effectively. Verity's end user interface gives Notes users expanded searching abilities, such as the ability to search not only data stored in Notes, but also external data that is in a variety of formats. Notes also allows users to perform selective filtering of on-line news sources.

Previous versions of Notes allowed users to regroup documents based on criteria, such as author and subject, or to retrieve files that contained a particular word or number. But Notes had no provision for retrieving documents based on more than one criterion, nor could it highlight exactly where in a document the particular word or number appeared.

Verity's front end enables Notes users to retrieve documents based on any single word or number, and to perform Boolean searches. Based on the search criteria, Notes 3.0 provides a list of relevant documents, beginning with the closest match. When the user opens the documents, matched words and numbers are highlighted throughout the text.

Version 3.1 of Topic adds a *structured query language* (SQL) gateway, which translates Topic queries into SQL statements to allow searches of SQL databases.

2.3 STRUCTURED QUERY LANGUAGE

In the distributed-computing environment characterized by local- and wide-area networks, users access information resources stored on host computers or servers. This arrangement is often called client/server computing (Figure 2.1). The client/server concept is a method for splitting up the workload demands placed on computers by application systems. The client is the user's machine, the one requesting the information. The server is either the machine that stores the files or the machine that assists in delivering files to the clients. Information sharing is carried out with the aid of a database specification and access language, Or SQL.

Although SQL works in a centralized mainframe environment as well as on local workstation databases, it is also well suited for the client/server environment. In this case, the front end part of the program executes on the user's workstation (client), drawing upon its *random access memory* (RAM) and *central processing unit* (CPU).

As a standard relational-database access language, SQL offers a number of benefits. Briefly, it facilitates data extraction from client stations, regardless of where the required data is located on the network, the database or operating system that maintains it, or the kind of computer it is stored on. SQL is suited for this purpose because it provides a concise, nonprocedural method of requesting data.

Using SQL for client/server applications offers a number of benefits:

- Applications programming is simplified for specifying data requests.
- The language is somewhat portable for applications running on different platforms.

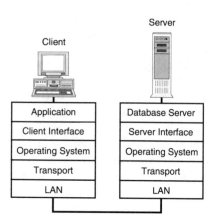

Figure 2.1 The client/server model.

- Network traffic is reduced because only the data request and the requested data are sent out over the network.
- Standardizing on SQL allows different applications to access data stored in the same format—the tables or views maintained by the server.
- Finally, SQL makes the task of accessing distributed database servers possible, because the same database access language is used.

The principles under which SQL operates are sound, but its implementation requires a degree of technical literacy that most people would rather forego in favor of friendlier, off-the-shelf database management products. However, the disadvantage of these products is that their query structure is not transferable across other kinds of databases, which is exactly the problem SQL was designed to overcome.

End-user database query tools are now available that make it easy for technically illiterate users to build queries and generate reports from complex corporate databases without the help of programmers. For example, Cognos Corp. offers Impromptu, an end-user query tool that facilitates the construction of complex SQL queries. DEC offers DEC-Query for Windows, Gupta Technologies, Inc. offers Quest, and Spinnaker Software Corp. offers Personal Access. All of these packages are Microsoft Windows-based query tools that let users query network databases created by such products as Borland International, Inc.'s dBase, build queries to access multiple databases, and perform complex tasks, such as table joins.

Among the most user-friendly SQL front ends is Gupta's Quest. Access to SQL databases is provided through a series of pull-down menus. The first menu lists all available databases. By choosing a database, the user activates a command to connect to that database. Once the connection is made, the user accesses and manipulates the data by working through menus. Quest generates the appropriate SQL statements and commands and activates protocols without further user involvement. The user can query and update tables from multiple SQL databases. Once accessed, information from one database can be copied to another database or to applications residing on the user's PC. Query results can be formatted in tables or as form letters and labels.

Aiming for greater connectivity and integration, to enhance the development of client/server applications, Microsoft Corp. offers SQL Server. Starting with Version 4.2, SQL Server includes integrated, Windows-based (Version 3.0 or higher) server administration, scrollable cursors, distributed data access, fault tolerance, and a built-in facility for integrating external structured and unstructured data. SQL Administrator for Windows lets central site managers dial into remote networks and administer those systems and databases. The managers can use the tool to handle such tasks as setting up, modifying, and updating databases; checking database consistency; solving problems and recovering transactions; and managing the system.

Scrollable cursors provide a fast way to manipulate row-level data, simplifying the development of data-browsing applications for graphical environments, such as Windows. The feature includes forward and backward scrolling, indexing to specific rows, and flexible concurrency control.

SQL is an accepted standard on all computer platforms and has found its way into many database management systems, especially those designed for microcomputers. *Distributed databases,* which store data throughout a system, rather than exclusively on a mainframe computer, created the need for standardized data definition and retrieval processes. SQL, therefore, is a necessity for any company that keeps information in a variety of formats and platforms. Applications created in SQL retrieve data from any platform transparently and safely. SQL code simplifies the programming process because it consists of approximately one dozen statements that accomplish all of its tasks.

There are dozens of database management system software packages that provide data manipulation of varying kinds and to varying degrees. Data manipulation, including viewing and querying, provides users with a way to edit data without having to go to a great deal of trouble creating a special form view and lets users query fields in a standardized manner. To issue queries users select the fields they want to query and then define the criteria, or filter, by responding to the program's prompts or by choosing items from a pick-list presented via a pull-down menu. Users can perform ad hoc queries or save queries so they can be reused.

Viewing, or browsing, allows users to look at a screen full of records or view one record at a time, without having to create a special form view. Generally, users can perform minor tasks, such as editing the data or altering the form views.

All the database management system software programs offer basic browsing functions that let users browse and edit single records. Some go beyond that. For example, FoxPro allows users viewing files in columnar format to resize and reposition browse windows and rearrange fields. FoxPro also has a split-screen mode that displays fields too far apart to otherwise fit on the same screen. Users can freeze one side of the display and scroll through the other, scroll through two views of the same record, or browse one window while editing records in the other.

Paradox allows users to resize columns and to display views from two databases simultaneously. Users can easily switch between single records and columnar views, or toggle from a tabular view to a view of one record in either a default or customized format. A key feature of Paradox is that it lets users create custom form views that display data from different databases. DataEase, too, offers extensive viewing options and lets users toggle between form and tabular views.

The dBase IV, Paradox, and R:Base programs query visually with pull-down menus. A line across the top of the screen displays outlines of the field structures. Users check the fields to include with the cursor, then press a function key. They use pull-down menus to issue the start query command and to define filters, sorts, and links.

When a PC application must access databases residing on other computing platforms, a database management system that supports SQL is recommended. Few programs provide full SQL support as part of the core package. Most of the time, SQL is offered as an add-on module at extra cost. The dBase IV package offers integral SQL support, but SQL commands can only be issued from the dBase IV dot prompt or from within a dBase IV program. R:Base, in contrast, issues queries in SQL, making it easy for nonprogrammers to access data on SQL database servers.

Some products provide a menu-driven query facility that automatically issues a subset of SQL commands; others also include an option that lets experienced users access SQL databases by typing SQL commands at a command line.

2.4 HYPERTEXT

Hypertext is a technical buzzword for a retrieval system that indexes individual words and creates threads between words in a text so that a highlighted word leads directly to another word. This type of retrieval provides virtually unlimited levels of detail and links to related information and ideas.

Hypertext is especially useful in conjunction with massive databases because it takes information retrieval to a new level, making information simpler to find. To create a hypertext system, the contents of the database must be coded to link one subject with another.

In addition to offering simple and complex Boolean searches that can be saved and reused, hypertext allows users to jump from one topic to another, according to their immediate informational needs. By selecting highlighted words or phrases users can access pop-up windows that contain detailed explanations. In other words, users can view related information without having to leave the main text of a document (Figure 2.2). They can access tables and diagrams in the same manner. In multimedia applications they can access related audio messages and video sequences.

One of the criticisms of hypertext is that it is easy for users to get lost or become frustrated because there appears to be no beginning or end to the database. Some hypertext database management systems solve this problem by recording the user's position. When users get lost, they can press a function key that displays a database map. Users can simply back out of the links by using the Escape key or the right mouse button. Alternatively,

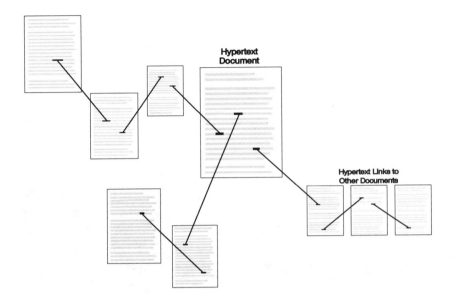

Figure 2.2 Hypertext links to other text files.

they might simply wish to exit the database, which can be done easily by clicking on Exit from a pull-down menu. Upon exiting, users are prompted to leave a bookmark so they can re-enter the database at the point where they left. Other features typically included in hypertext-based applications are online help, notepad, and an import and export facility.

One of the drawbacks to hypertext is that all of the links between ideas, text, documents, files, databases, and audio/visual applications (Figure 2.3) must be created manually. Even with programming experience, this can be a very time-consuming process.

The promise of hypertext tends to fade when users discover how many hundreds of hours it takes to construct a single, complete hypertext document.

SmarText, a product by Lotus Development Corp., greatly simplifies the task of creating and managing hypertext documents by handling many of the tedious chores involved. SmarText comprises two components, the Builder and the Reader, both of which run under Microsoft Windows. Using SmarText Builder, users can convert files created by most leading word processing packages into electronic documents that contain hypertext links to graphics, diagrams, or other objects. The Reader is a run-time program that allows distribution of the hypertext documents for others to use. For example, a hypertext instruction manual can be created with the SmarText Builder and then distributed to clients via the Reader. The Reader only allows users to read the manual and jump from section to section via hypertext links; it does not allow users to modify document contents.

Users begin working with Builder by selecting text and graphics files—in the order in which they will appear—from a list. They format each word processing file with style sheets and then associate the individual styles in the text files with different header levels

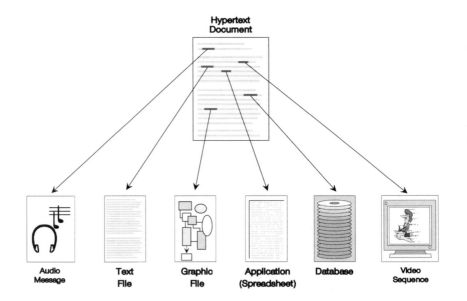

Figure 2.3 Hypertext links to other resources.

in an electronic document. SmarText creates an index of all words that are not included in a customizable list of common words, looks for recurring clusters of words, and automatically links backward from the last occurrence.

SmarText's Boolean search facility consists of a fill-in dialog box that lets users enter words, phrases, and wild cards with Boolean operators. In searching an indexed document, such as a product manual, the Focus Search feature guides users to specific qualifiers by identifying index words related to the search term. A global linking feature links every instance of a word or phrase to a single user-defined location. Users can also zoom in on graphics for a detailed view of the image.

Although SmarText builds basic text and graphics documents, it does not offer the interactive audio and video links other hypertext development packages offer, which limits its usefulness in developing multimedia applications.

2.5 COMPOUND DOCUMENTS

An increasing number of business applications require that documents contain a mix of text, images, and graphic information pulled together from a variety of sources and from a variety of file formats, hardware platforms, and operating systems. These documents are known as complex, or *compound documents*. The documents themselves need not contain images within their files, only links to images, which might be stored on a different database.

Several vendors offer utility programs that can exchange compound documents between the Apple Macintosh and other systems, but a truly universal file format remains elusive. No single standard for document interchange is as widely accepted as ASCII for text-only files, but several platform-independent file formats have been developed by such companies as Apple, Microsoft, IBM, DEC, and Hewlett-Packard. These file formats allow users to more effectively interchange different data types for consolidation into a single compound document, even if this consolidation is only through links.

Apple's Bento lets users find and manipulate just the portion of a document they want to work with, without going through intervening steps to perform file conversions. Bento—the Japanese term for boxed lunch—lets documents contain many different types of data, tagged so applications can find and use just the portions they recognize. With the new technology, users can open a Bento-compatible word processing document—within a graphics application, for example—and edit the text directly, without the intervening steps of publishing and subscribing, importing via the Clipboard, or converting file formats.

A similar document interchange standard is Microsoft's *object linking and embedding* (OLE) protocol, which allows embedded objects within documents. With OLE, users can employ standard copy, cut, paste, and paste-link commands to create compound documents and automatically keep them updated across different application programs. Rather than forcing users to constantly switch applications to edit pieces of compound documents, OLE lets users run one application from within another. With OLE, it no longer matters which application the text or graphic was created in.

OLE makes it possible for users to embed a spreadsheet into a text document, for example, and edit the spreadsheet data without leaving the word processing program. Or, users can launch a drawing program by double-clicking on a PICT image in a word processor document. As a result, within a single document, users can access a text editor, a page-layout tool, a spelling dictionary, and drawing tools, all from different developers—provided their products support OLE.

While several companies offer ways to swap compound documents, through sets of file translators, between Macintosh and a multitude of other systems, what multiplatform users really clamor for is a universal file format. The goal, which has been taken up by international standards bodies and systems architects, is a document representation—readable on a wide variety of systems—that preserves and transfers document structure as well as content.

The U.S. Department of Defense, several other branches of the federal government, the aviation industry, and a number of large corporate users have officially standardized on the *Standard Generalized Markup Language* (SGML), a structured authoring environment and data format that allows information in documents to be shared across platforms and applications. This so-called "metaformat" uses a series of extendable tags to indicate the format and structural relations of individual elements in documents.

Because the format can be extended, SGML is not limited to text documents. Hytime, a proposed variant now circulating in draft form before several standards bodies, adds time-based data elements and synchronization.

As an alternative to the often wordy and open-ended nature of SGML, the *office document architecture* (ODA) attempts to correlate the format of all document elements to an enumerated set of definitions. In theory, using a fixed set makes writing the translation routines faster and more efficient. The ODA standard was established by the *International Standards Organization* (ISO), the *Consultative Committee for International Telegraphy and Telephony* (CCITT), and the *European Computer Manufacturers Association* (ECMA), so it has received some support across a broad spectrum of industry participants. However, that support has been concentrated in Japan and Europe, rather than in the United States. Also, ODA is often criticized as being too limiting and not open enough to accommodate current and future document data types.

While ODA made slow gains through international standards bodies, a similar standard developed by IBM for compound documents achieved a greater measure of acceptance in the United States. IBM's *document content architecture* (DCA) documents can be sent in either *revisable form text* (RFT) or *final form text* (FFT), but usually only the RFT format is offered on non-IBM software.

On the Macintosh, DCA/RFT is one of the formats supported by Claris Corporation's core set of XTND translators; System 7 comes with a DCA/RFT translator for the Apple File Exchange utility.

Similarly, DEC's *compound document architecture* (CDA) is a platform- and application-independent data format. DEC offers CDA Invokers, software that works alongside the company's Pathworks for Macintosh, to allow Macintosh users networked with VAXes to create and edit CDA files. A combination of CDA Invokers and DEC's VAX-based CDA Converter Library lets users translate documents from the Macintosh to CDA and from there to other formats, such as ODA.

In an attempt to create an improved across-platform standard for text only, Apple and some third-party applications developers in August 1991 announced their collaboration on a *rich-text* (RTXT) format. RTXT is intended to ease the movement of formatted text among Macintoshes, IBM PCs and compatibles, and UNIX workstations. At the time of the announcement Apple indicated that RTXT support would come from applications developers and would not be built into the Macintosh operating system.

Hewlett-Packard and Simpact Associates offer the Remark! voice integration product for creating, editing, and playing back voice messages within Hewlett-Packard's New-Wave desktop environment. Remark! is comprised of hardware and software that lets NewWave 3.0 for Windows users who are on any NetBIOS LAN capture voice messages, display them as desktop icons, and share them with other network users. Users can also use Remark! to include voice in compound documents and multimedia presentations.

DEC's All-in-1 integrated office system features a *graphical user interface* (GUI) that allows users to browse compound documents, spreadsheets, memos, and personal calendars and also helps users edit compound documents using DECwrite.

DEC's DECwindows Motif, another GUI, uses a hypertext system called Link-Works to allow developers to design an information network across applications. Information can be linked to several applications so that one entry on a calendar might be linked to a Cardfiler card, a mail message, and an image file. The links are created by attaching the source record to the target record. There is no difference between the target and the source, because the information can be accessed either way, from target to source or source to target. Information about the links is stored in the Linknet, which functions like a mail folder and is managed with the LinkWorks Manager. Using the LinkWorks Manager, users can open linkbase windows, set hyperapplication defaults, add and remove objects from the hyperinformation environment, and display information about objects. However, links cannot be created to applications that do not support LinkWorks.

Once a link has been created between two objects, it is easily followed. The Link menu has two options that take the user to the other end of a link, Go To and Visit. The Go To option shrinks the current hyperapplication to an icon and summons the hyperapplication and object at the other end of the link. The Visit option accomplishes the same task without iconifying the hyperapplication that is being used to traverse the link.

The true power of LinkWorks will come as DEC and third-party developers use the product to enhance new applications—multimedia, in particular. To encourage this, DEC offers a LinkWorks developer's toolkit, which provides access to the features of the Link-Works Manager.

2.6 GRAPHICS FILES

With every advancement in storage media comes the corresponding need for a faster method of file search and retrieval. This is especially true for graphics files. Graphics files not only consume huge amounts of storage—because of their large file size, which is often a megabyte or more—but the files themselves tend to accumulate very rapidly. According to graphics professionals and desktop publishers, organizing and finding such files is not as easy as acquiring them.

A number of low-end products, costing as little as $99, offer the means to catalog and retrieve graphic images. Typically, they provide miniatures of the graphic images, in either black and white or color. These thumbnail-size images are stored in 8-bit format to save disk space, but enough of the image is retained to represent and identify the original. By double-clicking on any thumbnail, the image is displayed in full size in its own window. Although the images cannot be edited, they can be cut and pasted.

Multiple users can access the catalogs at one time, and several images can be cataloged simultaneously. A catalog can hold tens of thousands of images in a variety of standard and proprietary formats. It can take as little as one hour to catalog 50 MB of graphics files.

Because there is generally no way to categorize or filter the unstructured data that make up a graphics file, key words still play an important role in the cataloging process. The size and location of the original files are tracked, and the database can be searched with standard or user-defined key words, which are short descriptions that identify each graphic. Key words also provide a convenient way to catalog numerous images at once by letting the user choose folders and subfolders for processing. Users can opt to print catalogs containing thumbnails, double-size thumbnails, or the actual images.

2.7 THE FUTURE OF IMAGE RETRIEVAL

Every year, people spend billions of dollars and millions of hours searching for and manipulating images. The *Massachusetts Institute of Technology's* (MIT) Media Lab is working in partnership with British Telecom, and they are among the organizations researching the development of tools that will enable computers to "see" and "understand" visual images. With this technology, users will one day have the ability to access and search databases of images based on their actual visual content, rather than on textual descriptions or file names appended to them. This would reduce by orders of magnitude the time and expense of managing image databases.

Everything done with computers so far has been based on letters and numbers. The next step is to teach computers to understand what they see based on visual content. This would allow a user to "show" a computer a photograph, for example, and ask it to find all occurrences of that image. The computer would then retrieve all the pictures, images, and video files that contain the same visual.

But images pose a special problem: their storage and retrieval is best done systematically, but they lack syntax as we have come to know it in a written language. Consequently, the single biggest breakthrough needed is computer understanding of content. In an effort to achieve this breakthrough, the MIT Media Lab's research consists of two major components. The first is the development of advanced image analysis tools that will allow computers to search for and track events captured in visual form. The second is the development of multimedia management systems based on state-of-the-art knowledge representation and presentation technology.

Practical consumer applications of this research could include video catalogs that allow users to access sophisticated image databases via phone lines. Users could, for instance, search for a rug with the same pattern as their drapes or a jacket with a texture that matches a particular pair of slacks. They could then order those items electronically.

Another possible application is crime prevention. For example, a digitized image stored on a credit card could be used by a computer to verify that the card was being used by the right person. The card user would stand in front of a camera while the computer compared the image it was "seeing" to the one stored on the credit card. Fuzzy-logic principles could compensate for superficial or cosmetic differences between the person and the photo. Alternatively, a credit card could contain a thumb print that could be compared to the user's thumb pressed against the camera lens.

Such a system could also be used to browse through movie segments. For example, a user could ask the system to find video clips of Indianapolis auto racing. Such a system would make it much easier to view and edit commercial videos and develop multimedia applications.

The technology for organizing and searching images based on their content is still in its infancy. The cost and difficulty of searching and editing image data are the chief obstacles in the development of advanced multimedia applications.

2.8 CONCLUSION

As information continues to be collected and stored in electronic form, users are looking for better ways of organizing and retrieving it to meet their application needs. The technologies are now available for sifting through massive amounts of text, graphics, and images stored on any database, anywhere on the enterprise network. These traditionally separate data types can even be combined into compound documents. Within these documents links can be created to other documents, files, and databases. Documents can even be linked to other applications, where specific processing, graphics, or formatting capabilities can be accessed and used.

The latest view of information management entails integrating multiple document formats, graphics, images, and applications into existing information systems, rather than isolating them in so-called "electronic filing cabinets." In fact, many document imaging applications and tools are evolving away from the dedicated electronic filing cabinet model and toward the approach of *image-enabling* existing information systems and are extending their capabilities to include digital image storage and retrieval.

Chapter 3

Imaging Applications

3.1 INTRODUCTION

Imaging technology is rapidly changing the way companies do business. When coupled with workflow software, an imaging system constitutes a business strategy that can reduce costs and improve customer service, while ensuring the quality and timeliness of organizational response. These improvements are achieved by zeroing in on the principal cause of lost productivity: paper. It is paper that forces people into unproductive pursuits that hamper organizational performance and growth. Paper must be sorted, filed, retrieved, routed, and filed again by hand. This process is repetitive, tedious, time-consuming, and demoralizing.

Not only does this process have no end, but more paper is continually absorbed into the maelstrom, making it ever more difficult for the organization to extricate itself when pressed by market forces or economic conditions to improve performance. More importantly, such activities tend to sap the energy and creativity of employees, whose time and talents can be better used elsewhere.

3.2 APPLICATION OVERVIEWS

The relevance of imaging is not limited to any specific industry. Hospitals, for example, are turning to document imaging systems to better organize files and reduce retrieval time, especially during emergencies, when fast access to patient data is essential. Along with eliminating file bottlenecks that can jeopardize patient care, imaging systems allow hospitals to trim administrative staff, thereby eliminating unnecessary overhead that tends to inflate the cost of medical services.

In the pharmaceutical industry there are a variety of applications that can benefit from document imaging systems. Clinical data submitted by physicians and research institutions must be processed quickly to discover trends in drug treatment tests. Organizing this massive data is critical to the marketing success of new drugs, since approval by the *Food and Drug Administration* (FDA) can be delayed if the supporting documentation is incomplete or inaccurate. Not only can unnecessary delays cause the company to lose millions of dollars, they can also prolong the release of important new drugs to patients who might be in desperate need.

Telephone companies are using document imaging systems to improve customer service by enabling representatives to retrieve documents instantly via workstations in response to customer inquiries. Images of purchase orders, shipping statements, invoices, and other administrative documents are retrieved virtually instantaneously from *optical jukeboxes*, which are capable of holding as many as several hundred optical disks. Instead of losing up to 30% of documents through data entry errors, companies can hold document losses to 2% or less with a document imaging system.

Airlines, too, are making good use of document imaging systems. Maintenance operations alone can generate over 30,000 purchase and repair orders per year, each requiring ten or more supporting documents. Most of these documents must be stored for several years, as required by law. This can quickly add up to millions of documents that must be stored and retrieved. The maintenance manuals and parts catalogs for the Boeing 727 aircraft, for example, total 50,000 pages. Even when the catalogs are stored on microfiche systems, highly paid maintenance crews must take time out to search for the right document, a process that is neither efficient nor economical.

Government agencies and regulatory bodies rely heavily on paper documents. When they are not requiring paper documents from businesses, they are generating mounds of their own. Among the top federal imaging applications are records management and retrieval, electronic publishing, archiving, and applications associated with engineering drawings. Government demand for imaging is diverse but stems largely from the need to provide faster access to information at a reasonable cost. Among the types of information collected by state government agencies and municipalities on a continuing basis are: birth, death and marriage certificates; maps; deeds; environmental impact reports; building permits; police and court records; voter registration information; and corporate filings. An imaging system that delivers such frequently requested information to the public in 15 minutes, rather than two or three hours, is representative of such a need.

State motor vehicle departments will one day rely heavily on document imaging systems for issuing driver's licenses. On California licenses, for example, a color photograph, fingerprints, a signature, and text information are combined with a security hologram of the state emblem and a data-packed magnetic stripe containing such information as date of birth, license plate number, and license expiration date. All this information is stored on an image database and is available on line to law enforcement and government agencies, which together generate 20,000 to 30,000 requests a month.

Under the old microfilm record system, searches were quite labor-intensive and, therefore, expensive. Another problem was the poor quality of the two-inch-square black-and-white photographs. By comparison, the new image system produces crisp color images that can be viewed on screen or output to a color laser printer in less than a minute. Already, spin-off applications are being developed that make use of the magnetic stripe on the new licenses. Police officers will one day fill out tickets simply by passing the magnetic stripes of the licenses through a hand-held device that will issue a printout to the traffic violator. The hand-held device will also download accumulated citations into the traffic ticket system, eliminating the need for paper records.

There are other reasons why businesses of all types and sizes are turning to imaging systems for document storage and retrieval. Records managers are responsible for ensuring that documents are kept long enough to satisfy the legal requirements of various government agencies. Failure to produce relevant documentation at the required time can result in huge fines or even criminal charges—if it is found that records were carelessly or deliberately destroyed.

Satisfied with the integrity of document imaging systems, government agencies are now more willing to accept documents in electronic form. For example, on December 31, 1991 the *Internal Revenue Service* (IRS) adopted Revenue Procedure 91-59. Accordingly, the agency no longer requires companies to store paper documents, as long as their electronic equivalents provide the same level of detail as the originals. There are other conditions attached to electronic storage. Documents must be kept as long as their contents might be relevant to tax laws, records created on older systems must be retrievable by replacement systems, and documentation—including software changes and security controls—must be maintained on the electronic filing system. And should IRS examiners show up, the company must provide all computer resources necessary for them to audit the electronic books.

Actually, it was inevitable that the IRS would come to accept the validity of imaged documents, since for years it had been accepting—even encouraging—the filing of tax forms in electronic form. To file electronically the user sends a file via disk or modem to a third party, called an *electronic return originator* (ERO), usually specified by the tax program. The paper forms are also sent, separately. These forms include the U.S. Individual Income Tax Declaration for Electronic Filing (form 8453, included in the software) and the W-2 forms. The ERO sends back a receipt, which serves as a bill to the IRS if taxes are owed, and sends the IRS the return. If the user is owed a tax refund, the IRS sends a check or makes an electronic deposit into the user's checking account, usually in a matter of a few weeks. ERO charges for this service are between $20 and $30.

In addition to allowing users to file tax forms electronically and enabling the IRS to process the information and issue refunds faster, tax preparation software offers users several other advantages. Some programs interview users to determine filing status and the forms that must be used. Some help the users get organized by providing a series of prompts and fields that must be filled in via keyboard entry. The programs plug each item into the correct form and schedule and then total the entries. An audit feature alerts users to incorrect or missing data, as well as excessive deductions. Modules for filing state taxes electronically are usually available separately.

The tax programs not only guide users through the maze of forms, but also assist them in figuring out what deductions to claim. Many of these programs include online tutorials, documentation, and context-sensitive help. In addition to suggesting possible deductions, some programs offer what-if analyses and provide financial planning and investment advice for the next tax year, taking into account such factors as inflation and cost-of-living increases.

Businesses, government organizations, and tax payers are not the only groups who stand to benefit from document imaging. Perhaps the most information-intensive organizations are libraries and universities. They, too, are abandoning microfilm and microfiche systems and moving to optical disk-based imaging systems. Some college dormitory rooms are wired not only for phone service, but also for a LAN connection for plug-in computer access to the university library and to other research facilities where data and imaged documents can be accessed from optical disk storage.

Public libraries are also implementing optical disk storage systems. Records of books and their locations are distributed via optical disk to all libraries belonging to the state system. Optical disks are also starting to replace the traditional card catalog for listing books by title and author. Some libraries are preserving historical documents by capturing them in image form for storage on optical disk. Researchers, instead of poring over old originals—and, in the process, inadvertently contributing to their destruction—can obtain the same information by scanning *imagebases*. And they can find what they want much faster than with microfilm and microfiche.

Eventually, financially-strapped universities and public libraries will awaken to the possibilities of using document imaging technology to offer value-added research services to such niche markets as the scientific, medical, law, and engineering professions. For example, a lawyer representing a client in a malpractice suit might need background information on a particular medical procedure. From a modem-equipped computer, the lawyer could dial up the library's optical disk server and initiate a key-word search to obtain the required information. The information could be in the form of images of medical journal pages or papers delivered by experts at various symposia. If the local library did not have the requested item, the request could be passed on to a library that did. The library could not only charge an access fee for the imagebase, but also charge for printing out hard copy from a particular imagebase—with a portion of the printing charge going to the copyright holder.

State and local government agencies could also increase their revenues by offering value-added services. An architect looking for a specific building design that meets stringent state codes for earthquake tolerance, could, for example, access the Building Department's image files for the blueprints. By seeing how another architectural firm met the state requirements, the architect could get an idea of what was actually involved before submitting planning and cost information to a client.

This chapter explores the following real-world applications of document imaging and workflow software: technical documentation, credit card operations, accounts payable transactions, loan processing, and insurance claims processing. From these examples the reader can gain insight into how document imaging and workflow software can be applied to other applications.

3.3 TECHNICAL DOCUMENTATION APPLICATION

Most companies develop and issue technical documentation to acquaint users with how to assemble, install, operate, and maintain their products. The amount of technical documenation varies from company to company, depending on the sophistication, number, and diversity of products offered. Many companies also document their own manufacturing operations, processing operations, and quality control procedures.

The types of information that comprise the technical documentation might be quite diverse and could include internally generated drawings, photographs, customer specifications, parts lists, schematics, blueprints, memos and correspondence, and vendor manuals. The sources of these items might also be diverse; the information could come from customers, suppliers, subcontracters, strategic partners, government agencies, and standards organizations.

3.3.1 The Problems

Typically, different groups in an organization will make use of its documentation; however, the groups will customarily use different parts of the information, depending on what is relevant to their job duties and responsibilities. Some of these groups include purchasing, manufacturing, quality assurance, maintenance, engineering, customer service, document control, and training. Each group is usually aware of the existence of other, related information—it is just a matter of tracking the information down, if and when it is needed. It would be unthinkable to provide every group with its own copy of all documents, even if that were possible. So, when one group needs information held by another group, a lot of time is wasted in pursuing it.

Logistical problems aside, it would not be very practical to distribute documentation to all groups within an organization. The reason is that the information typically exists in many different forms. Much of it might exist electronically in the form of word processing files, CAD/CAM drawings, or compound documents that contain text, graphics, and images. Information distributed in these forms requires specialized workstations and software. And because these types of documents typically do not use a common interchangeable format, multiple workstations and software would be required—an expensive proposition for most companies.

Even if a company could afford to equip each group with all the specialized hardware and software needed to view multiple document types, the problem becomes one of change management. It would be necessary to have procedures in place to ensure that any changes made to one copy of a document were carried over to all other copies of the document, which might be scattered around the world via the enterprisewide network. Furthermore, it would be necessary to have in place a mechanism for approving change requests, so that all parties impacted by the change could be made aware that a change was being considered and have a chance to add their own input to the change process. Depending on the procedures in place (Figure 3.1), the whole approval cycle could take weeks or months. And there is always the possibility of documents getting delayed or lost. To implement such procedures would require a document control group, which often makes the problem worse. In a competitive environment, the whole process of changing and approving documents can result in lost business opportunities.

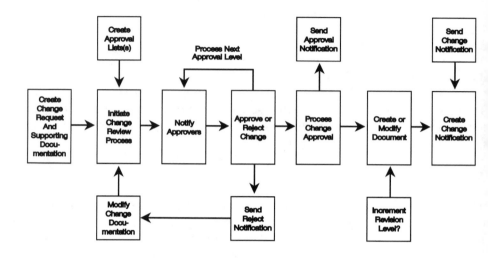

Figure 3.1 The typical document-change control process. *Source:* ACCESS Corp.

3.3.2 The Solutions

Document imaging systems bring together a number of technologies that allow users to capture, store, manage, retrieve, display, distribute, and print information that originates on paper or film or is generated by computers.

The imaging process starts with a scanning of the document, which is similar to photocopying. Then each scanned image is indexed by using automatic character recognition or by reading the punched Hollerith data on an aperture card.[1] The scanned images are stored in digital form on magnetic or optical disks. Computer-generated files, such as CAD/CAM files, can also be stored on the system. Often these files are stored in both native file format and raster format, which allows viewing on either the original CAD system or any workstation capable of viewing scanned images.

A number of different types of scanners are available to handle documents of different paper sizes and weights, documents that are bound or double-sided, large engineering drawings, photographs, aperture cards, jacketed microfiche, and film.[2] Some scanners can handle a duty cycle of tens of thousands of pages daily. (By way of comparison, Hewlett-Packard's market-leading LaserJet IIIp printer has a maximum duty cycle of only 8,000 pages per month.)

---

[1]Aperture cards combine the attributes of punched cards and microfilm. The punched card contains a description of the document and acts as a frame for holding a strip of microfilm. The cards can be processed to yield full-size paper copies of the microfilm image.

[2]A variety of media are used for document images, including opaque, translucent, linen, vellum, clear, or matte-finish film. Some scanners can accommodate all of these media types, in sizes of up to 35 in wide.

The disks are housed in optical storage and retrieval libraries, or *optical jukeboxes,* consisting of multiple 5.25-in or 12-in optical disks. The stored documents can be retrieved in a matter of seconds for display on high resolution workstations or PCs. Multiple jukeboxes can be connected together, allowing an organization to expand its storage facilities incrementally as needs dictate.

Once in digital form, the documents can be managed more effectively and at a single point. Documents are indexed—manually or automatically—by the imaging system's software at the time of scanning. The index information is written to a relational database. When users request a document, they can be sure of getting the most up-to-date copy. Distribution employs digital networks and standard telecommunications facilities, which also allow multiple users to view the same document simultaneously. When T1 lines are used, an E-size engineering drawing in raster form can be sent within ten seconds of the request. Over fiber facilities, the same document can be sent in a fraction of that time.

Because raster images are used, it is possible for most types of workstations and PCs sold today to be used for document display—even low-end displays costing only a few hundred dollars—particularly when such displays are used only for checking the quality and alignment of scanned images.[3] Thus, expensive high-resolution displays and CAD/CAM software are not necessary to view such documents. Because of the wide availability and low cost of the software needed to view raster images, these images are the most practical form for the widespread electronic distribution of documents An authorized user can make changes at a CAD/CAM-enabled workstation and work with a file in its native format. Others can overlay annotations at image-enabled PCs.

Once scanned, oversized documents of C-size and larger are stored in tiled raster image format. In this format, each image is saved as a set of logically connected square tiles, invisible to the user upon display. This is done automatically, without operator involvement. Tiling large documents provides more efficient and faster retrieval of the desired viewing area.

Each document stored as a tiled image has an associated preview image created at scan time. This preview image is a reduced image of the document that allows a user to see each sheet or page without having to pan from side to side or up and down if a total document exceeds the viewing area of the display. When retrieving a large document stored as a tiled image, it is the preview image that is seen first by the user. This permits the user to find the desired page for viewing without wasting time looking at each page in turn. The user selects the area to be viewed by using a mouse to point to the area of interest. The tiles for this area are then retrieved and displayed at full size, without any visual indication of the tile boundaries.

The user can toggle between the preview image and the full-size image, selecting the desired viewing area interactively. The user can browse between documents or pages within a document, move up and down or side to side, and use the zoom feature to view

---

[3]A good argument can be made for providing more expensive, high-quality displays for operators who work with images all day long as part of workflow processing applications. Better displays would greatly reduce eye strain and fatigue.

details within a document. The images can be rotated by keyboard command or can be made to rotate automatically upon display, if that feature is selected during scanning. Users can select from rotation values of 90°, 180°, and 270°.

The imaging systems software includes capabilities that allow users to perform redlining (Figure 3.2), markup, and editing on the document images. Each user's modifications to the image document occupy a separate layer, which can be distinguished by color. The various layers can be saved and managed along with the underlying document and later merged with the underlying raster image. The comments, sketches, and geometric shapes entered by users in the various layers can be cut and pasted to the image, area-shaded, or block-erased. Users can modify the image by selecting edit symbols from a raster library. Users who are not authorized to initiate document changes would only be allowed to review the documents and would be locked out of the raster symbols library.

Storing documentation as image files can save a lot of time and money spent in finding, accessing, viewing, and editing individual items—time and money that would normally be wasted if the documents were available only in paper form. And, for organizations involved in preparing technical proposals to government agencies and commercial vendors, document imaging systems can greatly reduce the time spent in finding and consolidating information from diverse sources and locations.

3.4 CREDIT CARD APPLICATION

In today's troubled economy businesses of all types and sizes are wrestling with ways to stay afloat without jeopardizing their competitive positions over the long term. The banking industry is no exception. To survive in the recession, banks too are streamlining operations and cutting back staff. Along with dealing with the vagaries of the recession, banks are being compelled to offer more and better services to retain existing customers and attract new ones. Not only are banks competing with each other for a larger share of the credit card market (Figure 3.3), but nonbanking institutions are also entering the market and competing against banks.

3.4.1 The Problems

Credit cards are one of the vehicles banks are using to improve their competitive positions. In the span of a decade credit cards have replaced the checking account as the banking industry's most profitable product, responsible for 30 to 60% of an average institution's total profits. Credit card operations are also among the most costly services to maintain, because of huge amounts of money lost on bad credit, fraud, and delayed resolution of customer billing disputes. State and federal laws ensure fair and timely reporting of credit information and protect consumers against inaccurate and unfair billing practices.

Moreover, credit card issuers must resolve inquiries and disputes in a timely, efficient manner. All of this has forced banks to take steps to reduce the financial risks associated with this type of product and to increase the level of service, to maintain strong revenues from their credit card programs. This is hard to do because credit card operations

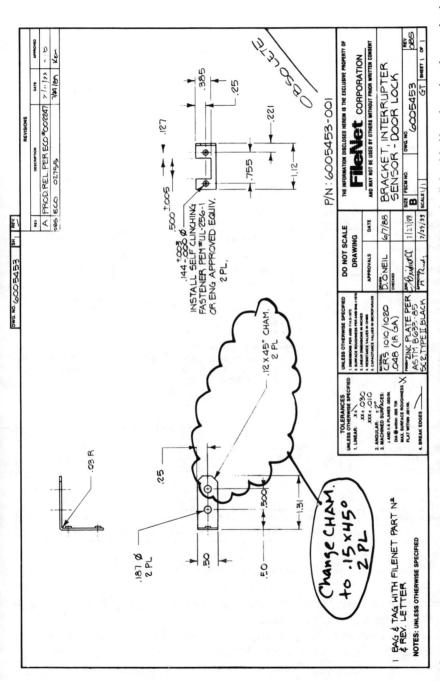

Figure 3.2 Sample redlined drawing. *Note:* The revision to the original image occupies a separate layer, which can be distinguished by color and can be erased and changed again without permanently altering the original. *Source:* FileNet Corp.

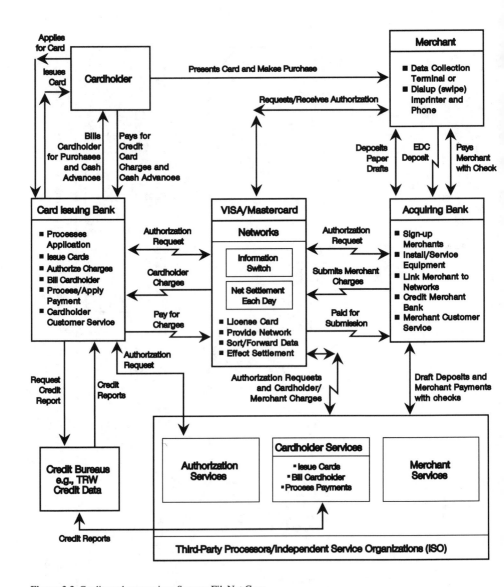

Figure 3.3 Credit card processing. *Source:* FileNet Corp.

are highly paper-intensive. On the other hand, this type of operation is a prime candidate for integrated image processing solutions.

Mainframe computer systems are capable of automating only approximately 10% of the information involved in credit card transactions. The other 90%—chargebacks, balance requests, address changes, finance charge adjustments, payment disputes, and card applications—all involve continuous streams of incoming paper.

Imaging systems that make use of optical disk technology, high-resolution workstations and PCs, and powerful process-automation software can work with an organization's existing mainframe programs to further automate the numerous paper-intensive tasks involved in credit card operations. An imaging system can bring together the different types of information for online access from a single workstation. That way, customer service representatives can resolve inquiries during initial calls, without having to track down the required information and call customers back.

3.4.2 The Solutions

A typical credit card transaction begins with a bank customer submitting an application for credit. Based on the available information and the use of various scoring and reporting systems, the bank decides to approve or deny a credit card to the applicant. The less information available, the more risk involved in the decision process, both in approving the wrong applicant and denying the right one.

An imaging system can speed up the entire application processing cycle. Since all applications are scanned into the system, the need for data entry is greatly reduced, eliminating keying errors. Manual data entry can be confined to taking phoned-in applications. Once scanned, all applications are immediately available for online access and can be automatically routed to the appropriate representatives for processing. Representatives can track application status from their desk on an initial call, rather than having to call the customer back days or weeks later.

Fraud, which can cause extensive financial loss, is a major concern of most credit card issuers. Imaging systems can reduce fraud risks by allowing banks and other institutions to increase the quality of approvals. When an imaging system is connected to a mainframe, decision makers can receive the most up-to-date information on each applicant, including online fraud files, customer histories, and third-party scoring and credit reporting data—all information that might be located on different hosts. Users can access all of this information—and update it instantly—from an imaging system workstation.

Organizations can also use the imaging system to enhance customer service. Most credit card issuers receive thousands of inquiries daily from cardholders and merchants who honor the cards.[4] Billing disputes, balance requests, address changes, finance-charge adjustments, requests for new cards, and statement and insurance questions are among the types of calls that banks receive. These inquiries generate callbacks, outgoing correspondence, customer file and history updates, and billing adjustments. In addition, credit card issuers must honor requests for original sales slips by either keeping the paper sales slips, keeping a microfilm version of slips on file, or requesting copies from merchants.

To retain customers and gain new ones in a competitive market, inquiry resolution must be fast and the results satisfactory. However, paper files and microfilm tend to inhibit quick inquiry resolution.

---

[4]A large bank like Chemical Bank in New York—the nation's sixth largest—receives 60,000 inquires by mail and phone each month. The bank uses an imaging system from FileNet Corp.

When a cardholder disputes a charge on a monthly statement, the credit card issuer temporarily credits the cardholder's account until the dispute is resolved. If the merchant bank has proof of charges, the merchant represents the charge amount back to the issuing bank. A merchant might resubmit a transaction deposit up to three times for payment and, if not satisfied, might request a final arbitration hearing. The dispute is resolved when either the amount is permanently credited to the cardholder's account or the cardholder pays the amount to the issuing bank to be credited to the merchant account.

This process is complex, and there are strict time limits for processing chargebacks and guidelines for submitting supporting documentation if errors are claimed by either side. If these time requirements and guidelines are not met, the issuing bank might be forced to credit the cardholder, regardless of who is at fault.

Imaging allows multiple users immediate workstation access to all files (Figure 3.4), resulting in the resolution of most problems during the initial call. Imaging also enables

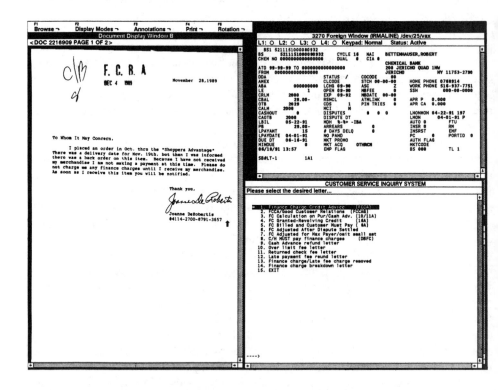

Figure 3.4 Multiple views of customer information. *Note:* Incoming mail is scanned, indexed, and stored. When a customer calls with a problem, a customer service representative can quickly resolve the problem with an automatic display of customer information in multiple windows: card-holder correspondence (left side), a mainframe window with card-holder account history (top right), and a control window that guides the operator through the inquiry resolution steps (bottom right). *Source:* FileNet Corp.

credit card issuers to meet processing time limitations on disputes, easily handle the numerous types of outgoing correspondence to customers, update customer and fraud files in real time, and eliminate expensive microfilm and paper storage facilities.

An imaging system can be used to store customer signatures and geographic data, thereby helping users track customers and confirm proof of legal debt responsibility. In the past when a credit card account defaulted, the bank would search for the original signed application in paper or microfilm files, then make paper copies for distribution to the collections group. When an unresolved collection problem went to court, lawyers required the original applicant signatures as evidence. At some banks half the time the original documents could not be located for presentation in court, resulting in lost revenue from increased chargeoffs. With image processing lawyers always have the collection documentation they need when they go to court.

Image processing can help prioritize work, reducing the organization's exposure to financial loss from the untimely resolution of chargebacks. Each stage in the work process can be assigned a specific time frame for completion. If a document does not progress past a particular stage within its assigned time frame, it can be brought to the attention of the appropriate customer service representative or automatically routed to a supervisor.

In addition to controlling the movement and processing of work, an imaging system automates a number of other management tasks and can provide a significant reduction in the time needed to handle inquiries and resolve disputes within legal-charge time limits. For example, an imaging system can monitor the number of outstanding disputes and track the progress, age, and resolution of disputes through a number of productivity reports. These reports allow supervisors to adjust employee workloads and schedules to ensure timely processing of all work.

The workflow scripts that make all this possible can be developed by the customer with assistance from the imaging system vendor. Simple inquiry operations can be fully automated within 30 days, while more complicated operations, such as chargeback processing, can be automated in two or three months. Other operations, like fraud analysis and security, can be phased in later.

One leading vendor of imaging systems, FileNet Corp., claims to have helped banks dramatically improve a variety of operations with its FileNet imaging solutions. According to the company, FileNet provided these improvements:

- Increased application approvals by 50% or more;
- Resolved chargebacks in half the time;
- Doubled the number of resolved inquiries;
- Reduced fraud cases by as much as 45%;
- Reduced required training time by 50%;
- Eliminated microfilm resource requirements and maintenance costs;
- Reduced data entry by 50%:
- Improved document retrieval by 99%;
- Improved general productivity by an average of 40%;
- Provided savings to clients of from 30 to 60% per item processed.

An added benefit of imaging systems is increased job satisfaction for customer service representatives—they are freed from the daily burden of paper files and dissatisfied customers. Instead of looking for paper files, they spend more time helping customers, providing them with personalized attention and service and enhancing corporate image in the process. The lower stress levels also result in a decrease in employee turnover, saving the company hiring and retraining costs. Not only can fewer staff handle more work, but, when hiring does become necessary, the time it takes to train new customer service representatives is greatly reduced. With an imaging system in place, a trainee can become productive in a week instead of months.

3.5 ACCOUNTS PAYABLE APPLICATION

Organizations tend to think of their accounts payable operations as quite different from those of other organizations, despite the similarities in transaction types and accepted accounting principles. The common denominator, of course, is paper.

3.5.1 The Problems

Each day invoices arrive in the mail and must be matched with original purchase orders and delivery receipts. A Fortune 500 company can pay one million bills or more every year for goods and services and can handle more than 80,000 invoices per month. An accounts payable workload of this magnitude requires automation.

Although financial application programs run on mainframe systems make purchase order information available on line and eliminate some of the paper in accounts payable departments, a substantial number of invoices still remain on paper. The management of that paper continues to consume corporate resources and delay timely payments to vendors. Even without exceptions, it is not uncommon for vendors to wait three months or more for payment, with two months being the average wait.

In addition to coping with paperwork, some common problems accounts payable departments face include:

- Incorrect or duplicate payments;
- Invoices that get lost or left unpaid;
- Failure to prioritize invoice processing to meet vendor payment terms and take advantage of associated discounts;
- Failure to match invoices with supporting documents;
- Failure to answer vendor inquiries in a timely manner.

3.5.2 The Solutions

Although a mainframe can handle 90% of the transactions in an accounts payable department, it contributes little to resolving the remaining 10% of transactions, called "exceptions." These are the transactions that involve out-of-file, misfiled, or lost paperwork.

Clerks can spend an inordinate amount of resources finding, routing, and finally processing the paper originals.

Typically, the accounts payable process starts with the generation of a purchase requisition for goods or services. The purchasing department then reviews the available vendors, selects a vendor, and generates a purchase order, specifying the items required, purchase prices, and shipping and billing information. When the goods are shipped, the vendor mails the customer an invoice requesting payment. The amount of goods received might be entered into the mainframe inventory control database, or the paper delivery receipts might be filed in a storage cabinet, to be retrieved later when payment is requested.

The accounts payable department, usually a centralized accounting function, receives the invoice and is responsible for matching at least three items: proofs for goods or services purchased, received, and billed.

Most organizations have clearly defined policies and procedures to guide personnel through much of this paper-intensive workload (Figure 3.5). Handling exceptions, however, can cause significant delays in vendor payment because of the paperwork required and the number of people who need to get involved in resolving the problem. Some examples of exception cases include overshipment of goods, incorrect shipments, price discrepancies, overbilling, and duplicate invoices.

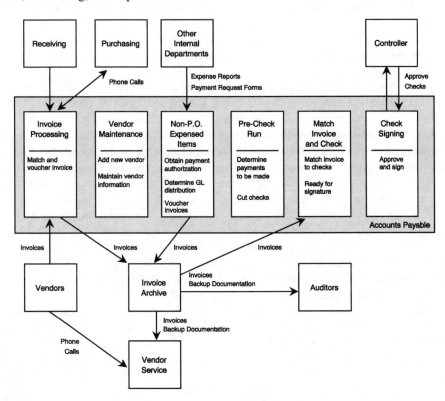

Figure 3.5 Typical accounts payable process. *Source:* FileNet Corp.

In addition to processing invoices from vendors, the accounts payable department is also responsible for processing such payouts as employee expense reports, rents, utilities, taxes, and other nonpurchase-related expenses.

Procedures for controlling, monitoring, prioritizing, and handling exception cases can be automated with an imaging system. Invoices can be automatically matched with delivery receipts. With immediate access to invoices and backup documentation, accounts payable personnel can provide better service to vendors on initial phone calls, without leaving their work areas. The following scenario illustrates how an exception case is resolved with the aid of an imaging system.

Invoices entering the accounts payable department are batch-scanned and date- and time-stamped (Figure 3.6). The scanned invoices are then indexed with vendor codes and routed to the appropriate accounts payable clerk. The clerk reviews the invoice and enters invoice data into the mainframe accounts payable system. In this case, internal checks show a difference between the billed amount and the purchase order amount. Further investigation reveals an item price discrepancy. The clerk calls the buyer for resolution and puts the invoice "on hold" for one week, using the imaging system's holding queue. The clerk then moves on to the next invoice in the electronic in-basket.

Workflow software manages the storage, retrieval, processing, display, communication, printing, and routing of all information required to process work. After one week, the imaging system's workflow software automatically selects the problem invoice and routes it to the supervisor at a high priority. The invoice moves to the head of the supervisor's in-basket for processing. The accounts payable clerk is free to work on other activities, and the invoice is not lost or forgotten.

Many times purchase orders, contracts, invoices, and receiving documents must be matched up to assure that materials or services have indeed been received. The imaging system's workflow software provides a "rendezvous queue" that holds scanned documents until receipt of other appropriate supporting documents. The workflow software tracks outstanding items and notifies the accounts payable clerk when all documents have arrived or when the document has been on hold beyond its pre-assigned time limit.

In cases in which the various documents are scattered among several mainframes, the imaging software's terminal emulation capability allows clerks to look up vendor information in one or more of these systems to complete invoice processing. Because the imaging system can be integrated easily with mainframe accounts payable applications—often without requiring any changes to the mainframe programs—clerks can access inventory and customer data, as well as document images of invoices, through multiple windows opened at the same workstation. This feature allows clerks to compare documents from various sources without leaving their workstations.

The workflow software also includes a variety of system-generated reports that allow supervisors to monitor the productivity of each accounts payable clerk. This permits the reallocation of work among employees to balance their workloads. In addition, the imaging system can produce an audit trail of documentation flow, which aids dispute resolution with vendors.

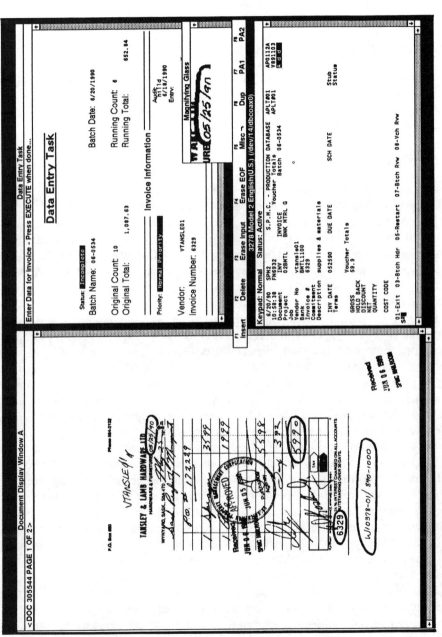

Figure 3.6 Data entry screen. *Source:* FileNet Corp.

An added benefit of imaging systems is that they can retrieve documents for auditing purposes without disrupting the daily operations of the accounts payable department.

3.6 INSURANCE PROCESSING APPLICATION

Underwriting, which is one of the most critical functions in the insurance business, is the interface between the insurance company and the customer. It is performed by either an independent agent or a policy holder. It is the principal means by which insurance companies gain new revenues and minimize risk.

3.6.1 The Problems

The underwriting process usually requires an inordinate amount of clerical and professional resources. Depending on the insurance product, client files can grow to include hundreds of documents. The files can be physically passed dozens of times between various professional and clerical personnel before a single application is fully processed. Paper files are often suspended in tubs while awaiting the arrival of other required documents and are not readily available to representatives handling customer requests. In addition to consuming a lot of space, even the best managed paper-based system makes the information in each file available to only one person at a time.

Claims processing is another important activity of insurance companies, and it usually requires ongoing interaction with customers. Customer satisfaction is determined by the insurance company's speed and efficiency in processing claims, as well as by its ability to accurately respond to questions about customer status. The insurance company's ability to perform in these areas determines whether customers stay with the insurer or transfer their business elsewhere. If, for example, the insurance company administers the employee health care plan for a Fortune 500 company, employee dissatisfaction with the claims process could result in the loss of a sizable key account.

Prompt customer service can be difficult to achieve if paper files are tied up in the claims department. Such delays could result in duplicate files being created, further extending work backlogs and possibly resulting in duplicate claim checks being issued.

For customers who are independent agents, the tasks of the insurance company are to track the agents' state licenses and credentials and keep the agents up-to-date on the various policy types and services. All this work can add up to a major paper trail, which must be managed to ensure timely service and new revenues. Some insurance companies have licensed and contracted 20,000 or more agents and do business with them on a regular basis.

Annuities represent another booming business for insurance companies. This area also produces an incredible stream of documents, including: account and loan applications; payment amount changes; withdrawal requests; account balance requests; fund transfers; name, address, or beneficiary changes; and numerous other documents associated with pension plans. Literally millions of sheets of paper can be accumulated pertaining to "live" executive pension plans. In addition, every shift in the economy produces a flood of phone calls from investors requesting changes in their annuity plans.

3.6.2 The Solutions

Voluminous files are digitized for permanent storage on high-capacity optical disks, where they can never be lost or misfiled and are accessible to multiple users simultaneously (Figure 3.7). Workflow software can be programmed by the user to emulate and improve established paper-processing flows.

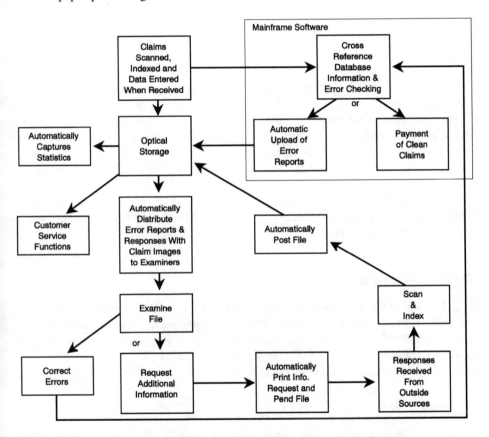

Figure 3.7 Typical claims process as handled by an imaging system. *Source:* FileNet Corp.

Some workflow software includes features specifically designed for insurance companies, such as the ability to rapidly group together documents into folders. The underwriter can browse quickly through the folders, marking or tabbing documents as needed to note important items, even magnifying hard to read sections, and electronically paper-clipping notes to any document or file.

An imaging system allows users to view portions of documents within a file, access a mainframe computer for additional data, and generate and automatically print form letters for routine requests or customized letters for unusual requests. All these tasks can be accomplished without clerks having to leave their workstations.

Often insurance companies' information databases contain sensitive information that must be protected by law, such as HIV test results for AIDS. Imaging systems can provide multiple levels of password protection to control access to certain functions or files.

Workflow software can also manage the state licensing of independent agents, by keeping track of the receipt and status of all necessary documents and the distribution of documents to service representatives for processing. The software can generate custom reply letters, electronically annotate special conditions or circumstances in documents, and distribute correspondence from the agents. With all documents stored in digital format, files are available anytime the agent calls to request status or other information.

In the very competitive annuities market, insurance companies must struggle to maintain consistent profit margins and keep levels of customer service high—in the face of rising clerical costs for managing all the paperwork. An imaging system with automated workflow capabilities can facilitate processing of all the necessary documents, from initiation to final disbursement. The system can interface with the mainframe computer to track account balances, master indexes, and all the intervening documents. Complex transactions can be completed in parallel by several departments because each department has simultaneous access to the same information.

Some imaging systems also offer interfaces to facsimile, so transactions can be entered directly into the imaging system via fax transmission and confirmed via fax, without creating additional paper records.

3.7 LOAN SERVICES APPLICATION

In the last few years the recession, increased competition, and a plethora of variable-rate loan products have combined to shrink profit margins in the loan servicing industry. Lenders are being challenged to access documents more quickly in answer to a barrage of questions from consumers regarding a wide variety of products. While striving to improve customer service, these institutions have also had to cope with escalating labor costs.

3.7.1 The Problems

Since economies of scale are important factors in determining loan servicing profitability, experts predict a trend toward greater industry consolidation in the years ahead. In the short term, however, lenders must attempt to service larger volumes of mortgage, home equity, consumer, and student loans. Many long ago automated their operations with computers. But this step only automated about 10% of the information needed to support their business operations. The remaining 90% of information originates outside the organizations and enters through the mail room. A huge volume of information must be sorted, routed, processed, filed, retrieved, and refiled in original paper form. The collected information does not readily lend itself to traditional data processing; it is in the form of typed and handwritten documents, graphics, and photographs.

Over the life of a mortgage or home equity loan it is not uncommon for the loan file to quadruple in size. And, because an office can hold only a certain amount of paper files, the records management center is often at a different location than the department requiring the documents. Off-site record storage substantially increases file retrieval time.

To further complicate matters, loan servicing activities are controlled by the availability of documents in the loan folder files. A high percentage of loan documents are out-of-file when requests are made—another clerk has the file. Sometimes two clerks are processing the same document without knowing what each other is doing. Overall processing time to complete departmental transactions is delayed by the lack of an organized and controlled document routing system. As a result, multiple copies of the same document are made to satisfy the requirements of several departments simultaneously, which frequently causes more confusion and delay, not to mention problems associated with determining which copy is the most complete and updated.

The ramifications of such file-processing inefficiencies can be quite serious. Taxes and insurance might not be paid on time from escrow accounts, which might result in interest penalties and, in extreme cases, property liens. Also, prompt processing of insurance renewals and policies is needed to protect lenders from loss. If complete, error-free loan documents are not presented to investors in a timely manner, lenders could face interest penalties or cancellation.

3.7.2 The Solutions

Many lending institutions are turning to advanced imaging technology to cope with the avalanche of paper and to increase staff productivity and responsiveness.

Instead of having to locate, move, track, copy, box, ship, and refile paper-based loan files—often under extreme time constraints—the imaging system allows documents to be retrieved in seconds, so that responses to customer inquiries can be handled quickly, efficiently, and economically. Imaging also leads to improved management of the volumes of paper required to process and track tax and insurance payments in a timely manner, reducing the risk of penalties.

Lomas Mortgage USA, holder of one of the nation's largest mortgage loan portfolios, valued at $20 billion, reports an improvement in document retrieval time from four and one-half days to 10 seconds, using an imaging system provided by FileNet Corp. The processing error rate for records management declined from 2.4% to 0.4%, while the unit cost per loan dropped from $1.85 to $1.39. With the streamlined workflow and efficiency provided by image processing, Lomas was able to reduce the staff headcount by half.

3.8 CONCLUSION

The potential of imaging technology to radically transform a business from a lethargic, marginally profitable operation to a thriving, highly profitable one has been amply demonstrated over the years. Examples abound from virtually every sector of the economy of companies that have improved performance and cut costs to stay competitive in dynamic markets.

Improvements such as these are achieved by attacking one of the most persistent root causes of poor performance: paper. Dealing with ever increasing volumes of paper is counter-productive. It forces organizations to maintain artificially large staffs and to continually replace people who are lost to job stress or want to pursue more challenging careers elsewhere. Paper slows response time to customer inquiries, which not only encourages customers to do business with competitors, but also prevents organizations from successfully pursuing new business opportunities. If allowed to continue, the limitations imposed by paper hamper not only organizational performance, but long term growth as well.

Imaging systems can impose order on the chaos created by paper. In this sense, imaging is not just a technology, but a key business strategy that can enhance an organization's future competitiveness—to say nothing of its short-term survival.

PART II
IMAGING SYSTEM PLATFORMS

Chapter 4

Desktop Imaging Systems

4.1 INTRODUCTION

In the 1980s the first wave of document imaging systems was targeted at banking, health care, pharmaceutical, and insurance industries, as well as government offices. The sheer size of these operations, along with the high volume of paper used, made them the most likely beneficiaries of document imaging. Today, because capabilities for full document image processing can now be added to existing PCs and LANs, the technology is a viable and affordable option for paper-intensive businesses of all sizes.

Now just about any kind of business can benefit from document imaging systems. Manufacturing, transportation, publishing, and other enterprises are implementing imaging solutions. Small businesses, too, are turning to document imaging to avoid being squeezed out of their offices by file cabinets, which are considered a wasteful use of valuable floor space. For organizations of all types and sizes, document imaging is rapidly shaping up as the office automation solution for the 1990s.

Low-end desktop imaging solutions are an inexpensive way for companies to experiment with the technology before committing to it in a big way. These systems can provide the means for exploring new information management strategies and designing or restructuring workflow. They can provide the means for understanding what is involved in making the transition from complete paper storage to electronic filing and, in the process, speed up document retrieval and provide access to the same information by multiple users.

Document image processing can potentially benefit any business that needs to save original documents with graphics, photos, handwritten data, or signatures for contract and other legal purposes. Most paper-intensive office environments are prevented from throwing away hard-copy documents because of the office computer's inability to store anything except the typed word.

Until recently there was not a cost-effective way for most small offices to computerize documents containing visual elements. Now, after input, documents are stored, filed, retrieved, and output just like any other type of data—and they retain their original format. Such processing once required the addition of expensive, stand-alone proprietary systems and extensive staff training. Thanks to advances in image processing technology, that situation is changing.

Getting started with document imaging is surprisingly affordable. Today's imaging products make use of either the PC, the work group LAN, or both and inexpensive off-the-shelf components, such as scanners and high-capacity disk drives. For long-term storage requirements, an optical WORM disk drive unit is typically used. Each WORM disk can hold as much as 650 MB of information.

Since optical WORM disks cannot be overwritten, they provide an unalterable audit trail back to the original document. This is an important requirement for such businesses as accounting firms, banking and financial services, and health care providers, who must comply with IRS codes, government regulations, and industry rules that require unambiguous audit trails.

4.2 FUNCTIONAL COMPONENTS

In addition to differing in price, high-end and low-end imaging systems also differ in the volume of documents they can process in a duty cycle, their storage capacities, and the degree of automation they bring to bear at each step of the document imaging process. Another difference is that low-end imaging systems use off-the-shelf scanner, printer, facsimile, and storage devices, while high-end imaging systems tend to be turnkey offerings. These systems rely on the vendor's own brand of components or components purchased from other manufacturers under various licensing arrangements.

There are several basic features that are common to any imaging system:

- Image capture
- Indexing
- Compression
- Storage
- High-resolution display
- Management

Although laser printers and facsimile machines also play an important role in supporting imaging applications, these devices require no special consideration here. The merits of one brand over another are well documented elsewhere; and performance comparisons are published frequently by the leading computer magazines. There are literally hundreds of printer and facsimile machine models to suit virtually any budget.

4.2.1 Image Capture

The first step in the document automation process is called *image capture*. Input devices for image capture include scanners, digital cameras, and video recorders. Scanners and digital cameras input images directly into an application. Input from video recorders must be passed through special video boards known as *frame grabbers*.

4.2.1.1 Scanners

Most image capturing involves using a scanning device, which produces an exact likeness of the document, including illustrations, text, and handwritten information. Most low-end desktop scanners recognize 256 gray scales, with an optical resolution of 300 *dots per inch* (dpi). In some cases, hardware and software enhancements can boost resolution to 600 dpi. The image (text, photo, or drawing) on the document is composed of *pixels*, or dots. Tighter clustering of the pixels corresponds to the darker parts of the image. The arrangement of the pixels gives the image its contrast.

Scanners use a *charge-coupled device* (CCD) to sense images. Light reflected off a scanned document is converted by this component into electrical signals. The CCD image sensor contains an array of tiny photodiodes, one corresponding to each pixel in a horizontal line of the scanned image. This means a device capable of scanning a standard 8.5-in-wide page at 300 dpi has at least 2,550 photodiodes.

Flatbed models use an internal light source mounted on the carriage mechanism; the carriage moves underneath the scan bed during a scan. A series of mirrors carry the light reflected from the document to the CCD image sensor, which remains fixed. A scanner's horizontal resolution depends on the density of the photodiodes in the image sensor itself. Its vertical resolution depends on the speed of the light source. Together, image/sensor density and carriage speed determine *optical resolution,* which is the maximum number of pixels the scanner can capture per square inch.

In older gray-scale scanner design, the photodiodes only measure the intensity of the light reflected from the document's image, or text. The computer stores the result, using up to 8 bits of digital information: 8 bits produce 256 possible shades of gray. Today's color scanners measure not only the intensity of each pixel area, but also its color value. Up to 24 bits of color information can be captured for each pixel: 8 bits each for *red, green,* and *blue* (RGB) light. With 24 bits, a pixel can be any one of a possible 16.7 million colors—more than the human eye can detect.

Users need not always capture the full 24 bits of information. They can reserve high-quality scans for professional reproduction, thus saving substantial disk space. Depending on the software, users can vary the bit depth of the scan to create formats that match specific application and output needs. Color scanners can also produce gray-scale images of various bit depths. The depth can range from the 1-bit scans used for OCR to a full 256 levels of gray.

Scanners themselves come in several hardware configurations: hand-held, flatbed, automatic sheet-feeding (for continuous, high-volume scanning), and overhead. Hand-held scanners are the least expensive—only a few hundred dollars—and are only worthwhile when the volume of document scans is very low. They do have one advantage over other types of scanners in that they can input oversized documents. The user merely scans one column at a time until the whole document has been input. A light or beep indicates if the user is scanning too fast or too slow. When the user finishes scanning, the automatic stitching feature pieces together the image fragments into a coherent whole. Without this feature, the user would have to manually match up and align each of the scanned areas—a tedious and time-consuming process.

Flatbed scanners are more expensive, costing between $1,000 and $4,000. But, because documents lay flat against the units, flatbed scanners capture higher quality images than hand-held devices can. Many flatbed scanners accommodate only regular-size paper (8.5 by 11 in), posing an obstacle when legal and other oversized documents must be scanned. And, because each document must be manually positioned on the flatbed, these scanners are useful only for low-volume image operations.

Ranging in price from $2,500 to $5,000, automatic sheet-feeding scanners can handle larger image volumes. Depending on the capacity of the paper tray, and assuming there are no paper jams, these scanners can operate unattended for long periods. The image quality is similar to a flatbed scanner. Via software commands or physical adjustment of the front panel, sheet-feeding scanners can even be made to accommodate legal-size documents.

Finally, there are overhead unit scanners, which are similar to flatbeds in price. These devices require that users position documents under a fluorescent lamp for scanning. Unfortunately, documents must be perfectly positioned under the lamp, which tends to waste a lot of time. Also, the quality of the images might not be consistent from one document to the next, due to reflections and interference from other light sources.

Some scanners come with software that permits users to edit acquired images by cropping, focusing, tinting, and rotating. In addition, users can adjust acquired images for brightness and contrast or draw on them to highlight important areas. Alternatively, users can employ a graphics editing tool in conjunction with the scanner to achieve the desired level of editing control.

When OCR software is used in conjunction with the scanner, the contents of a document can be stored in ASCII format or entered directly into a word processing format. In either case, the text can be stored, edited, or merged with existing files.

Many vendors claim 99% reading accuracy in their OCR packages, but actual results will depend on the quality of the documents being scanned. Some OCR packages can recognize image resolutions as low as 100 dpi, making them useful for scanning faxes, dot-matrix printouts, and light photocopies—which are normally troublesome to scan.

4.2.1.2 Digital Cameras

Digital cameras allow images to be imported directly into an application or database. This capability is especially useful in the real estate and insurance industries, where appraisers and agents regularly take photographs and store them in their records and files.

Digital cameras take pictures in the same manner as conventional Polaroid cameras. Users look through a viewfinder, line up the shot, and push the button. Like a Polaroid, the digital camera has a built-in, automatic flash. Outdoors, it automatically varies exposure time in response to changing conditions. But, instead of using film, this camera saves digital images in its RAM or on a proprietary floppy disk that can hold 32 to 50 digital photos. The digital images can be loaded directly into a computer via a serial connection. Once they are in the computer, the images can be retouched, duplicated, integrated into other document image files, even transmitted by facsimile or electronic mail.

The digital camera has four distinct components: the camera itself, the in-camera software, the retouching software, and the battery charger. The lens is permanently set at f/4.5, with a focal length of 55mm in a 35mm format. There is no focusing or depth of field to be concerned about, as long as the subject is at least three feet away. Some digital cameras include an adapter ring that lets users attach camcorder-size 37mm macro and wide-angle lenses.

Images are captured with a light sensitivity roughly equivalent to an *International Organization for Standardization* (ISO) film speed of 200—the same as Polaroid's "One Film." A neutral-density filter can be attached to the lens to reduce light evenly throughout the spectrum, resulting in an ISO equivalent of approximately 25. The camera varies electronic shutter speed from 1/30 to 1/1,000 seconds.

Digital cameras capture images in the same manner as scanners. The ones and zeros, or bits, that make up the picture are stored in compressed format in the camera's memory chips, which also hold the camera's software. The rechargeable batteries power the flash and hold the images in RAM for as long as 24 hours. Photos are downloaded from the camera through a serial connection to the PC. Images can be saved in PCX, BMP, and TIFF PICT, PICT2, Paint, and *encapsulated PostScript* (EPS) formats. The camera's application software runs under Microsoft Windows and permits the photos to be displayed as thumbnails, which are laid out like a photographer's contact sheet. To view a full-size image, the user simply highlights one of the thumbnail images and presses the Enter key.

Digital images can be retouched, saved, stitched to other images, or deleted. During retouching, a photo can be enlarged on-screen for pixel-by-pixel editing, which includes brush, draw, crop, cut, and paste functions. Images can also be scaled, rotated, and adjusted for contrast and brightness.

Digital cameras are available from a variety of sources, including Canon USA, Eastman Kodak, Logitech, and Dycam, Inc. Prices start at $600. Continued refinements in technology will result in improved image quality, larger data storage capacity, and more advanced features, such as adjustable shutter speed and aperture settings.

4.2.1.3 Video Frame Grabbers

Image capture boards, or frame grabbers, convert the signals from video cameras and *video cassette recorders* (VCR) into arrays of data points and store the arrays digitally. Software manipulates the data to fit specific applications and the image display board allows the images to be viewed on the PC's video monitor. Frame grabbers and image display boards are available from a variety of vendors. Several vendors have combined the functions on one board, along with the *video RAM* (VRAM) needed to store the images for conversion.

There are two types of frame grabbers. One type allows a single video frame at a time to be digitized from any *National Television Standards Committee* (NTSC) or *Phase Alternative Line* (PAL) source and stored on hard disk in compressed form. The image can then be integrated into an image document or used in another application. The second type of frame grabber is the full-motion video board. It can capture, digitize, compress, and store multiple frames, for the purpose of playing back an entire video sequence. This board is useful for creating multimedia applications. Both types of boards usually include software for basic cut, copy, and paste operations. The boards accept third-party application programs for more advanced image manipulation, even allowing users to choose from a selection of compression algorithms. Within the application program, users grab a still image simply by clicking in the recording window and dragging the image to create a new window for the still. The still can be saved as a PICT file.

Add-in TV boards are also available. These boards display video inside a moveable, resizable window on the PC screen, just like any other application. Users choose from menus to adjust color saturation, hue, RGB balance, brightness, and contrast; to frame-grab; and to select from among three NTSC or PAL video sources (camera, VCR, videodisc, etc.). These products provide a pass-through connection between a computer's *video graphics array* (VGA) card and monitor. This eliminates the problem of computer-system bus and memory speeds being too slow to display full-motion images in real time. The board communicates with its companion software to determine the size and position of the on-screen window, and whether the image that will occupy the window should be the full-screen or a zoomed-in image of a selected area. A jack on the board allows users to attach external speakers for sound.

Add-in TV boards could be useful in a variety of applications, including litigation support and insurance claims processing. Paralegal clerks can grab and integrate critical video frames into case files and store them in the imagebase. Insurance offices can view adjuster-shot tapes of accident or disaster sites while working on claims reports and grab and electronically paste specific frames into the reports. In both applications, this method replaces the Polaroid photographs that are usually clipped to reports. With frame grabbing, there is no chance of a photo becoming separated from the case file or claim report.

Most video boards cost well under $1,000. At the high end, there are NTSC video board sets costing $4,000 and more that can compress real-time video and capture video at 30 *frames per second* (fps). Sampling rates can be adjusted downward to reduce disk storage requirements.

An image capture standard has recently been adapted by an industry group called the TWAIN Coalition, a consortia of more than 175 companies, including Aldus Corp., Hewlett-Packard, Eastman Kodak, and Logitech, Inc. Formerly called the *connecting link for applications and source peripherals* (CLASP), TWAIN is an important API and protocol because it facilitates both the capturing of images from scanners, frame grabbers, video, and digital cameras and the integration of those images into files created with imaging software. The imaging software must also support the standard.

With TWAIN, any application—from word processing programs to image editing tools—can communicate directly with such input devices as scanners, video boards, and digital cameras. And the applications and peripherals can communicate without the complexity and bother of users having to scan and save images and import them into applications. Users can capture images from *within* the applications, simply by selecting the scanning menu choice in the program.

The TWAIN API runs under Macintosh operating systems 6 and 7 and Windows 3.x. TWAIN sets certain conventions for linking software to the various input devices. Software developers can use the standard to write programs that support a number of input devices directly, without having to program drivers for each. This simplifies things for users too, since they do not have to install specific drivers for each input device and keep up with the latest driver versions.

Hewlett-Packard's ScanJet IIp, a 300-dpi, 8-bit (256 grays), monochrome flatbed scanner, is among the first scanners to support the TWAIN imaging standard. Within an application users select an option such as Scan Text or Acquire Image and click on the Scan button. Within minutes the scanned image appears at the location indicated by the cursor.

4.2.2 Indexing

Scanned documents can be indexed by key word, to facilitate retrieval from the imagebase. The maximum number of key words that can be used to identify each document varies according to the software package used, from 10 to 20 or more. A number of indexing systems can be devised, according to the needs of the organization. The index can include key words found in the document itself, after it has been scanned with OCR software. Entire documents and case files can also be indexed by project, account number, department, or division. Another way to index documents and case files is by topic.

In addition to indexing, documents can be customized with notes. Each user who accesses the document can append his or her comments, questions, and instructions to the file, so that further action can be taken in processing the transaction. Other document images and text files can also be appended. This allows a case file to be built.

Documents do not have to be indexed individually or on a discretionary basis. A number of documents can be indexed together in a process called *batch indexing*. With batch indexing, a number of documents are collected in an electronic version of an in-basket for processing according to predefined indexing rules. This speeds up the indexing process and eliminates the confusion that can result from individual indexing preferences. Once a document is properly indexed, individuals are allowed to customize it with preferred key words that will aid search and retrieval and to append notes.

Once all the images are indexed and stored in the imagebase, users with the proper access rights can retrieve them from any PC on the network via standard browse or custom search routines. Custom searches look for images whose fields meet certain predefined criteria. Figure 4.1 summarizes the document imaging process.

4.2.3 Compression

Because image documents are much larger than ordinary text or binary files, most desktop imaging systems support one or more compression schemes, including their own proprietary methods. Compression allows images to be stored on the PC's hard drive until the in-

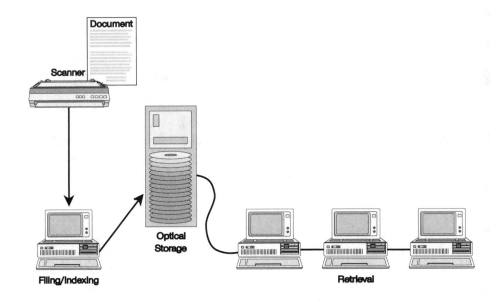

Figure 4.1 The document imaging process.

creasing volume justifies moving to more expensive optical WORM units or tape storage systems.

Compression is typically a function of software that is bundled into the imaging software. A compression board can be used to offload the function from the PC's main processor and thus provide a substantial performance boost. Compression software can also be purchased separately from the imaging software. Two popular off-the-shelf compression products are Stacker and SuperStor, which can increase hard disk capacity by two or three times. Images and text are stored in compressed form and transparently restored when accessed. (When a database consists mostly of images, however, more sophisticated compression products are available that provide much higher compression ratios.)

A service is said to be *transparent* when it is provided without an explicit request from the user. Stacker and SuperStor both operate in the background and have no noticeable effect on the requesting program or any other application, including the operating system. Both products use a technique known as *lossless compression*. This type of compression works as follows:

- The data is examined to identify patterns.
- To each identified pattern, a unique code is assigned that consists of significantly fewer bytes.
- The unique codes are substituted for the corresponding patterns.
- The data is then stored in its new format.

When the compressed file is accessed, the encoded data is replaced with the original strings of data, completely restoring the image. Of course, the degree of compression achieved varies according to the characteristics of the data being compressed. Table 4.1 summarizes the typical compression ratios of various file types that can be achieved using SuperStor.

Table 4.1
Compression Rates on Various File Types

File Type	Typical Lossless Ratio
Executable program	1.4:1 to 2:1
Word processing	2:1 to 4:1
Database	2:1 to 8:1
Spreadsheet	2:1 to 4:1
Video image	2:1 to 8:1
CAD/CAM	3:1 to 8:1

Source: AddStor, Inc.

A key advantage of SuperStor over Stacker is that the former allows files to be downloaded to a floppy disk in compressed format and then decompressed on another PC, regardless of whether or not that PC also uses SuperStor. With Stacker, the second PC must also have Stacker software installed on the hard drive.

Other compression techniques are integrally supported by desktop imaging products, including the *Consultative Committee for International Telegraphy and Telephony's* (CCITT) Group 3 and Group 4 compression standard, which is used for facsimile transmission at 9.6 Kbps and 64 Kbps, respectively. The highest levels of compression are offered by products that adhere to the *Joint Photographic Expert Group* (JPEG) and *Motion Picture Expert Group* (MPEG) compression standards. These are typically supported via add-in compression boards or included with specialized graphics or multimedia boards.

The JPEG standard is designed for compressing more complex gray-scale and color images. The lossless method allows the application to compress data without any data loss. The lossy algorithm provides higher levels of compression, but at the expense of some data loss. Such losses vary widely for different types of images, producing results that might be acceptable for certain types of applications but not for others. For example, a claims adjuster at an insurance company who views scanned images of documents, diagrams, and photographs from a terminal can accept relatively high levels of data loss without losing pertinent visual information. On the other hand, an engineer examining critical elements of a product design will accept no data loss because of the potential for error that such a loss represents.

Compression through these techniques ranges from approximately a 5 to 1 ratio for lossless compression to a 100 to 1 ratio for "lossy" compression. However, LEAD Technologies claims a 255 to 1 compression ratio with its LEAD Compression Card for PCs. The card can compress megabyte-size image files to about 5K at almost real-time rates. The board works with such image file formats as TGA, TIFF, GIF, PICT, and PCX. It features selectable compression ratios (5 to 1 to 255 to 1), supporting and extending the JPEG standard. Up to 160 images can be stored on a single 3.5-in floppy disk, with minimal image degradation, compared with 30 images using standard compression techniques.

A process called *forms removal* can improve compression ratios, regardless of the algorithm used. When scanning forms it is the data that is important—not the form itself. By eliminating the repetitive forms and saving only the data, compression ratios can be vastly improved. For example, a standard dental claim form scanned at 300 dpi and compressed using CCITT Group 4 typically uses 73 Kb of disk storage. When the form is removed, the same image file occupies only 13 Kb in compressed form (Figure 4.2). When the form is called up for display on a workstation monitor, the data is overlaid on an image of an empty form. The file containing the empty form can be stored locally, while the data can be retrieved from a database server.

4.2.4 Storage

After documents have been scanned and indexed, they must be moved to a storage facility, from which they can be retrieved as needed by multiple users. In other words, the image files must be moved from the scanning station's own hard disk to a server on the network. In a small office, the server might be just another PC with a high-capacity hard disk. Other PCs can be cabled to the server using relatively inexpensive off-the-shelf LANs, such as those offered under Artisoft's Lantastic product line.

Companies supporting high-volume image processing operations might be better off with a dedicated server that provides access to image files stored on optical disk. Optical disks are available in three configurations: *compact disk read-only memory* (CD-ROM), *write-once read-many* (WORM), and *compact disk recordable* (CD-R).

4.2.4.1 CD-ROMs

CD-ROMs are similar to the 4.7-in CDs used for music. As its name implies, the CD-ROM is a read-only medium that can contain up to 600 MB of data. CD-ROMs are inexpensive to manufacture and easily duplicated. This combination makes CD-ROMs an ideal medium for database publication. However, their read-only nature makes them unsuitable for imaging applications, since they do not allow changes to be written to the optical disk.

4.2.4.2 WORM Optical Disks

WORM disks come in three sizes: 5.25-in disks, which hold approximately 400 MB; 12-in disks, which hold 3500 MB; and 14-in disks, which hold 5000 MB. Although the WORM

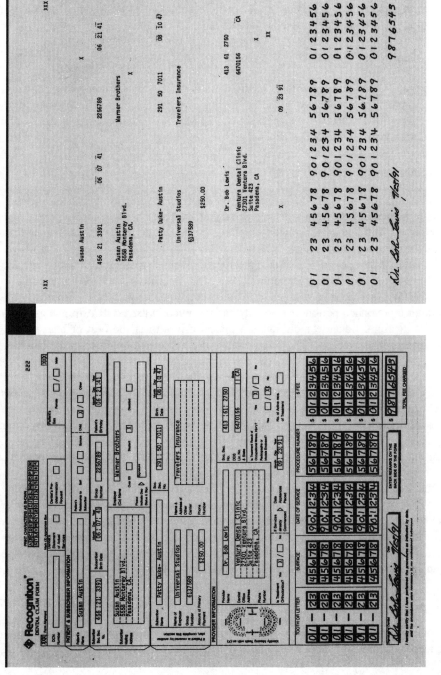

Figure 4.2 Forms removal. *Source:* TiS America, Inc.

configuration is useful for storing documents that are not expected to change and that need to be archived for retrieval, it too is unsuitable for an imagebase. This is because data can be written to it only once. After that, it essentially becomes a CD-ROM, until the contents of the entire disk are logically deleted and rewritten.

4.2.4.3 Magneto-Optical Disks

Magneto-optical disks are a rewritable medium; these disks can be written to over one million times, making them ideally suited for storing a large imagebase. Rewritable drives come in a one-sided, 3.50-in size, which stores 128 MB of data, and a 5.25-in size, which stores approximately 300 to 500 MB per side.

4.2.4.4 Multifunction Optical Drives

A recent addition to the market is the 5.25-in multifunction drive, which can support WORM disks and CD-Rs from the same drive unit. Performance is comparable to single function drives, and the price is slightly higher. At this writing, there are no standards or compatibility among multifunction drive types.

Despite the absence of standards, multifunction optical drives are attractive because they offer users a two-for-one opportunity. For large imagebases, the ability to write to disk many times is a virtual requirement. At the same time, image files that should be archived after a prolonged period of inactivity can be stored in the WORM format as a precautionary measure. Because multifunction optical drives offer the best of both worlds, they are ideal for imagebases. They also remove the element of doubt from the purchase decision.

Although optical disks are typically 10% slower to access than magnetic media, the ability to maintain image files virtually on line is worth the slight difference in access time. Continued refinements in drive technology are rapidly narrowing the performance gap between hard and optical disks. Hewlett-Packard's C1716C multifunction drive, for example, has a 35-ms access time, compared to the 95-ms access time of older drives. In the near future, optical drives could get close to the 15 to 18 ms access speeds of magnetic media and provide the added benefit of removability.

The *American National Standards Institute* (ANSI) is considering establishing Hewlett-Packard's file format—*optical systems architecture* (OSA)—as a standard. OSA already has the support of other vendors and optical technology is still in its infancy stage. This situation provides an opportunity to create a file format standard that would permit just about any system to read data off any given disk. Hewlett-Packard expects ANSI to reach an agreement on the standard within the next two years.

4.2.4.5 Optical Jukeboxes

High-volume image applications collect multiple 12- or 14-in optical disks in automatic changers, or optical jukeboxes. A large jukebox can contain more than a terabyte of image data, equivalent to more than 10 million pages of text. Smaller jukeboxes hold 5.25-in optical disks. Because it can take 15 to 30 sec to access disks in large jukeboxes, many systems employ caching systems to speed access.

4.2.4.6 CD-Recordable

A new technology, *CD-recordable* (CD-R) holds the promise of providing a cost-effective and standards-based alternative to WORM. Meridian Data, Philips, Sony, Sun Microsystems, Kodak, and others have formed a consortium to establish standards for the new writable CD-ROMs. The group wants to ensure that users can place an optical disk in any CD-R drive and know that it will work, regardless of who manufactured the drive or the media. The members of the consortium want to eliminate the interchangeability problems that continue to plague current WORM technology.

4.2.4.7 Optical Tape Drives

The capacity of optical tape is unmatched and therefore might very well become the standard methodology for recording and archiving entire libraries of image databases. 35mm optical tape has a storage capacity of 1 TB (1,000 GB) on an 880-m (approximately 2,800 feet), 12-in reel. Its data storage capacity is equal to 5,000 conventional magnetic tapes, or 1,000 double-sided 5.25-in optical disks. It can store the amount of data contained on approximately one billion sheets of standard-size paper.

4.2.5 High-Resolution Displays

Another important component of a document imaging system is the high-resolution display. The image workstation should be equipped with a high-resolution display to improve the image quality of both graphics and text. A sharp display will give users a better idea of how image documents will look printed, especially if the documents consist of detailed blueprints and CAD/CAM drawings. A high-resolution display can also reduce eye strain, an important consideration when operators must view screens of data for most of the working day.

On-screen sharpness is defined primarily by resolution, a term that usually refers to the graininess of the on-screen image; that is, the number of dots, pixels, that comprise the image both horizontally and vertically. Resolution can also be described by the video standard that produces it. Today's most popular standard, for example, is VGA, which produces a display resolution of up to 640 by 480 pixels and a text resolution of up to 720 by 400 pixels.

Nearly every VGA adapter sold since 1988 can display resolution of at least 800 by 600 pixels. The latest PCs often have built-in capabilities of 1,024 by 768 pixel resolution and better. Almost any display adapter that produces VGA resolution, other than the very cheapest adapters, will probably handle VGA 800 by 600 pixel resolution as well as Super VGA 1,024-by-768-pixel resolution.

An important issue is the color capability of the display adapter. The more colors the display adapter can produce, the more realistic the image will be. In fact, a wide range of colors will actually make a display adapter seem to produce a sharper image. The most realistic looking images are obtained only when a display adapter generates a complete spectrum—as in true color or 24-bit color systems. In such systems, 16.7 million colors can be displayed.

As *graphical user interfaces* (GUI) gain acceptance, *graphics accelerators* are becoming increasingly important. A graphics accelerator—a special chip on the video graphics board—is especially adept at handling the needs of applications programs that make use of GUIs, such as Windows. Performance increases of 100 to 1600% or more are possible when GUI-oriented programs are running.

A graphics coprocessor can boost speed even more. This is a programmable special-purpose microprocessor that operates in a manner similar to a graphics accelerator. Because of its programmability, a graphics coprocessor can be adapted to handle virtually any display function, plus much of the number-crunching required in generating on-screen images, which the computer's main processor otherwise handles.

A potential problem of display systems is *flicker*, which is an unsteady flashing of the image on the monitor. The VGA standard specifies a refresh rate of 70Hz; that is, the full-screen image is drawn on the screen 70 times a second. In most cases, this is quick enough to eliminate flicker. In high-resolution mode, however, the refresh rate of the display adapter can diminish to 60Hz or less, producing noticeable flicker and causing severe eye strain during prolonged viewing.

Today's better quality display adapters follow the recommendation of the *Video Electronics Standards Association* (VESA) for vertical refresh rates: 72Hz for 800 by 600 pixel resolution and 70Hz for 1,024 by 768 resolution. Some boards support higher refresh rates at these resolutions. Older boards follow VESA's manufacturing guidelines, which call for a 56Hz or 60Hz refresh rate at 800 by 600 resolution. For imaging applications, especially workflow processes that require continuous viewing, such slow display adapters should be avoided.

4.2.5.1 Monitors

The choice of a monitor is especially important in imaging applications. Screen size, for example, is important when the imaging application makes use of multiple windows simultaneously—such as when a user is displaying one or more mainframe sessions in separate windows, along with the forms and other pertinent data required to handle a customer inquiry. Clearly, the size of a monitor's viewing area can impact productivity. A 17-in monitor provides up to 60% more viewing area than a 14-in monitor.

A monitor's dot pitch is another characteristic to consider. For example, an imaging application that involves detailed drawings of the kind used in CAD/CAM would be better served by a monitor that offers a very low dot pitch. The minimum dot pitch required for Super VGA resolution or better is 0.31 mm, but 0.28 mm is recommended. There are some monitors capable of even finer resolutions of 0.26 mm and 0.25 mm.

Most PCs sold since 1990 have Super VGA or better display capabilities built in, so it is only a matter of choosing a higher quality monitor that will take full advantage of these capabilities. There are a few monitor standards for resolutions higher than Super VGA. They include IBM's 8514/A and XGA, as well as the nonstandard, high-resolution products known as multiscanning monitors. Although more expensive, this type of monitor represents the best choice for a high-resolution display system when the image application requires the sharpest display.

4.2.6 Management

Imagebases are managed much like any other databases. There are software-defined provisions for controlling user access with passwords, assigning various access privileges, and logging access, which further enhances security by providing an audit.

When access to an imagebase requires a password, users are allowed a specified number of attempts before access is permanently denied. Unsuccessful attempts are logged so the office administrator can be informed of possible security breaches. Upon successful entry, users might be prompted for personal identification numbers, which are structured for certain access privileges. For example, a user might be allowed to view documents but not allowed to change the index or add key words.

Depending on how image documents are indexed, it is even possible to allow a user access to the imagebase, but not to a particular file in the imagebase. This is accomplished by setting up access privileges that are associated with specific index fields. Thus, when the user tries to search for documents that correspond to a restricted index field, access will be denied and logged.

4.3 CONCLUSION

No longer is image processing synonymous with expensive, stand-alone proprietary systems and extensive staff training. Desktop imaging systems can be custom-built from off-the-shelf hardware and software to suit just about any business need and budget. Imaging systems are finding practical uses among many types of businesses, regardless of size. Inexpensive desktop imaging solutions—requiring only a scanner and some image management software to start—provide even the smallest organizations with the means to test the viability of the technology. As the technology proves itself, additional resources can be budgeted for expansion.

Continued technology innovation is improving the performance and price of all system components. The software—when integrated into industry-standard windowing environments—is becoming more powerful and easier to use. Without exaggeration, document imaging is rapidly advancing to become the office automation solution for the 1990s.

Chapter 5

Considerations for LAN-Based Imaging

5.1 INTRODUCTION

Today's document imaging systems allow businesses and government agencies to move closer to a paperless office environment by providing the means to digitally store documents in massive image databases. When implemented over a LAN, storing documents on an image server can solve many of the problems commonly experienced with paper files, including multiple access, while streamlining business operations by automating workflow (Figure 5.1).

In combination with workflow software, the LAN makes possible an efficient assembly-line approach to document image handling, whereby each workstation operator processes a portion of the information contained in the image file before passing it on to another workstation operator. When the various steps are completed, the file is stored at an imagebase server, where it can be identified and retrieved by such means as key word, file number, or customer account. Even when the workflow is not automated, LANs facilitate the exchange of image files between processing points, eliminating the delay inherent in paper-based file systems.

If an existing LAN will be used to support imaging, the impact that imaging traffic will have on current applications must first be determined. When expanding existing LANs or building new ones to support imaging applications, there are a number of factors to consider that can impact overall performance. These factors include network topology, access method, and media type. Although these are important considerations, a decision must be made at the start of any LAN project about which implementation approach will best satisfy the immediate as well as long-term needs of the organization.

5.2 LAN APPROACHES

A *local-area network* (LAN) is a high-speed connection between workstations, servers, and other types of devices that enables users to share resources, exchange files, and send messages efficiently. This distributed computing environment virtually eliminates the in-

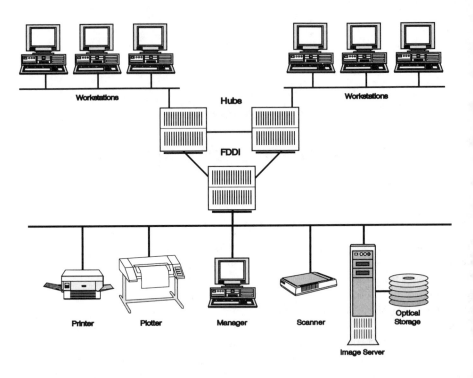

Figure 5.1 Document imaging over the LAN.

formation bottlenecks that are common with centralized mainframes. With information instantly available to individuals who are empowered to fully exploit it, the quality and timeliness of decision making is improved, which, in turn, permits a more effective corporate response to dynamic business conditions and provides numerous opportunities to improve customer service. These benefits coincide with the advantages that can accrue from effective document imaging system implementation.

There are several approaches to LAN implementation. The preferred approach is dictated by such factors as bandwidth availability, connectivity requirements, and economics. LAN implementations include:

- PBX LANs. Some digital PBXs, such as InteCom's IBX, are capable of implementing—via plug-in modules—Ethernet and token-ring LANs. The PBX acts as a wiring hub, connecting all stations in a star configuration with twisted-pair telephone wire. This can be an effective approach for supporting imaging applications, but only if the PBX can support Ethernet and token ring at their optimal speeds.
- CO LANs. Central office LANs provide Centrex users with rudimentary local-area connectivity. CO LANs have a top asynchronous speed of 19.2 Kbps and a top synchronous speed of 64 Kbps. Instead of investing heavily in on-site hardware and ca-

bling, users with low to moderate data-networking needs can tie into the CO LAN by installing inexpensive *data over voice* (DOV) multiplexers at each station. A similar device at the central office separates the two types of traffic for routing to their respective destinations. Despite the convenience and low cost of this arrangement, the maximum available bandwidth is not enough to support most imaging applications.

- Baseband LANs. Most of the popular LAN technologies fit into this category, including Ethernet (10 Mbps), token ring (4 Mbps and 16 Mbps), StarLAN (1 Mbps and 10 Mbps), and ARCnet (2.5 Mbps and 20 Mbps). All of these LANs are suitable for supporting image applications, but they differ in their performance characteristics (discussed later).

- Broadband LANs. This category of LANs provides the highest capacity, up to 100 Mbps. Several LAN standards provide such capacity, including the *fiber-distributed data interface* (FDDI) and the *shielded twisted-pair distributed data interface* (SDDI), which is advocated by a vendor coalition led by IBM. For organizations with an installed base of shielded twisted-pair wiring, SDDI not only meets the immediate bandwidth requirements of imaging applications, but also accommodates long-term growth.

- Wireless LANs. Most wireless LANs employ infrared, spread-spectrum technology or microwave. Infrared systems use a part of the electromagnetic spectrum located just below visible light. Infrared signal frequencies are too high to transmit data in the same way that radio frequencies can, limiting transmission to about 1 Mbps—which is not enough to support most imaging applications. Spread-spectrum technology operates just below 900 *megahertz* (MHz) at the upper end of the *ultra high frequency* (UHF) band used by television, cellular, and FM radio. With a potential bandwidth capacity of 10 Mbps, this type of LAN can support most imaging applications. Potential drawbacks to wireless communication include limited range, line-of-site requirements, and possible interference with the operation of other office equipment. Microwave operating in the 18 to 19 *gigahertz* (GHz) band range is useful for linking LAN segments in a campus or metropolitan environment, provided that rights of way for equipment and line-of-site for transmission are available.

- LAN Services. Telephone companies and interexchange carriers offer services that are ideally suited to extending the reach of LANs. These services include frame relay and *switched multimegabit data services* (SMDS), which are capable of transporting data at T1 and T3 speeds, 1.536 Mbps and 44.736 Mbps respectively. Of the two types of facilities, T3 is recommended for image applications, since it can accommodate baseband LANs without the down-speeding of traffic that T1 facilities cause. (These services are discussed in Chapter 12.)

5.3 LAN CHARACTERISTICS

Although the LAN concept has been well articulated since the mid-1970s, early developers had no universally accepted standards to work from. Without such blueprints, each vendor developed its LAN a little differently. Multiple LAN topologies emerged—bus, ring, and star. LANs have other differing characteristics as well, such as access methods and media types. These differences impact installation, expansion, and operating costs.

5.3.1 Topologies

Network topology is very revealing; whereas a telephone or computer network has a hierarchical form, LANs use flat topologies for distributed computing and peer-to-peer communication. The flat topology is exactly what is needed to effectively implement document imaging, especially when automated workflow is an integral part of the application. There are three basic LAN topologies in common use today: bus, ring, and star. Each topology has strengths and weaknesses that should be considered in the implementation of LAN-based imaging applications.

The *bus* topology, typified by Ethernet, is limited by distance—approximately 2500 meters (1.5 miles). Although signal strength can be boosted when repeaters are used to connect LAN segments, the nature of the access method (discussed later) imposes a practical limit on the total length of bus networks. Theoretically, the ring network is not limited by distance, although its token-passing method of granting access might eventually impose a practical limit before access delay becomes a problem. The advantage of the bus topology is that it costs less to implement than the ring or star. Because each device on the network operates independently of the others, the failure of one does not necessarily disrupt the operation of the others. In automated workflow imaging applications, this is an important consideration. Furthermore, devices can be added or deleted from the network without disrupting service.

In the *ring* topology, the failure of one device can break the ring and render the entire network inoperable. This scenario can be avoided, though, if each station is equipped with bypass circuitry. Bypass circuitry allows the token to pass through a faulty station unimpeded so that access to the ring by other stations is not disrupted. It also allows stations to be added or deleted from the ring without disrupting service. Other stations are automatically informed of address changes so that network resources can continue to be allocated proportionately.

The principle advantage of the *star* topology is network management. With all links radiating from the central node, LAN administration, diagnostics, fault isolation, and component swaps are much easier to implement. The obvious limitation of the star topology is that all communication must pass through a central node. If that node becomes inoperable, the entire network is put out of commission—unless steps are taken to equip the node with fault tolerance.

5.3.2 Access Methods

The access methods for LANs can be categorized as contention-based (probabilistic) and deterministic. *Ethernet* is an example of a contention-based LAN: all the stations on the LAN contend for the available bandwidth on a first-come, first-served basis. If two or more stations access the LAN at the same time a "collision" occurs, whereupon all stations back off and try again at staggered intervals.

Token ring exemplifies the deterministic method of access: each station is allocated a slice of the available bandwidth and is guaranteed access to the LAN when its turn comes. Transmission is controlled by a continuously circulating "token." Each station in turn recognizes the token, seizes it, and replaces it with a packet of data. After the packet of data is transmitted, the station reinserts the token onto the LAN for pickup by the next station having data to transmit. This process continues in round-robin fashion.

The deterministic method of access (token ring) is desirable when any of these conditions exist: most of the users require guaranteed access to the LAN; the applications need a specific amount of bandwidth (and no less); or host sessions cannot tolerate too much delay (caused by retransmissions that often plague contention-based networks). The contention-based method of access (Ethernet) is best suited for applications that require only brief, intermittent use of the LAN, or whose users are few and require large amounts of bandwidth for long intervals.

For some imaging applications both Ethernet and token ring methods of access might be applicable. For example, the average scanned document consists of 50 to 100 KB, which can take one second or longer to transmit over a fully loaded Ethernet. A compound document that includes a CAD/CAM drawing might consist of 5 MB or more and take approximately 45 minutes to transmit. These applications will have a direct bearing on the size of the network. In the first case, the short transmission time means that more stations can be connected to the Ethernet. In the second case, the long transmission time means that fewer stations can be connected to the network.

However, if the imaging application entails virtually continuous use of the Ethernet for brief transmissions—to support a workflow process, for example—this will also put a practical limit on the number of workstations on the network. Conversely, if CAD/CAM transmissions are not very frequent, more stations can be connected to the network.

Another factor that must be included in this equation is compression. If the network is becoming saturated with imaging traffic, then compression, which increases throughput and reduces delay, is a virtual necessity.

5.3.3 Media Types

Today's LANs can be run over any type of media (Table 5.1). Early LANs used thick coaxial cabling that was inflexible and difficult to install. Later, thin coaxial cabling was developed, which made installation a lot easier. Today, it is common to find LANs operating over both shielded and unshielded twisted-pair wiring. LANs that take advantage of twisted-pair wiring are less expensive to install than LANs using thick and thin coaxial cabling, mainly because excess twisted-pair wiring already exists in most office environments.

Fiber-optic cabling, which is used to interconnect LANs between floors or between buildings, offers total immunity against *electromechanical interference* (EMI) and *radio frequency interference* (RFI). Wireless LANs use radio waves to connect stations on the

Table 5.1
Recommended LAN Cabling

| | | Twisted-pair | | | |
| | | Unshielded | | | |
Application	In Place	New	Data Grade	Shielded	Optical Fiber
Dial data	X	X	X		
Data/voice to 64 Kbps		X	X	X	X
Token ring - 4 Mbps			X	X	X
Ethernet					
Token ring - 16 Mbps				X	X
FDDI					X

Legend
  Unshielded in-place: 24 to 26 *American Wire Gage* (AWG)—a minimum of 2; often 25-pair telephone
    company cable already installed.
  Unshielded new: D-type inside wiring—24 AWG; minimum of 3; 4 recommended.
  Unshielded data grade: AT&T 1061, Belden Wire and Cable Co. 1455A; 4 pair.
  Shielded twisted-pair: IBM Type 1; 2 pair.
  Optical fiber: 62.5/125 micron multimode.

Source: East Coast Corp., Trenton, NJ

same floor. Although there is the potential for EMI and RFI, security is enhanced through the use of spread-spectrum technologies and can be increased further through the use of encryption algorithms.

5.4 TYPES OF LANS

There are several types of LANs. The most popular are Ethernet and token ring; less common are ARCnet and StarLAN. In addition, there are two standards for high-speed backbones that are used to interconnect multiple LANs, high-performance workstations, or both: the FDDI and the SDDI. Table 5.2 summarizes the important characteristics of these LANs.

5.4.1 Ethernet

Ethernet is one of the best known examples of a LAN based on a bus topology. It is contention-based, meaning that stations compete with each other for access to the network. Each station "listens" to the network to determine if it is idle. Upon sensing that no traffic

Table 5.2
Characteristics of LANs

LAN Type	Speed (Mbps)	Topology	Access Method	Media
ARCnet	2.5 or 20	Hub	Token passing	Coaxial (thick and thin); twisted-pair (shielded and unshielded)
Ethernet	10	Bus or hub	CSMA/CD	Coaxial (thick and thin); twisted-pair (shielded and unshielded)
Token ring	4 or 16	Ring	Token passing	Coaxial (thick and thin); twisted-pair (shielded and unshielded)
StarLAN	1 or 10	Hub	CSMA/CD	Coaxial (thick and thin); twisted-pair (shielded and unshielded)
FDDI	100	Bus	Token passing	Single- and multimode optical fiber
SDDI	100	Hub	Token passing	Twisted-pair (shielded), preferred by IBM
TPDDI	100	Hub	Token passing	Twisted-pair (shielded and unshielded), under consideration by ANSI

TPDDI = Twisted-pair distributed data interface

CSMA/CD = Carrier-sense multiple access with collision detection

is currently on the line, the station is free to transmit. When several stations try to transmit at the same time, a collision results, forcing the stations to back off and try again at staggered intervals.

The longer the bus and the more stations that are connected to it, the higher the probability that such collisions will occur. For this reason, the maximum usable bandwidth is considerably less than 10 Mbps. In fact, over the years various studies have indicated that the maximum available bandwidth of Ethernet is only 30 to 50% at any given time. This translates into a throughput rate of only 3.33 Mbps to 5 Mbps, versus the maximum rate of 10 Mbps. This is an important consideration, especially when adding imaging applications to an existing Ethernet, because the additional burden of the imaging application can bring down overall network performance to an unacceptable level for all applications.

If the bus network remains fairly static, traffic is uniform over time, and users can tolerate some delay from retransmissions caused by collisions, Ethernet might be an economical choice for a LAN, even with the addition of imaging applications. But networks have a tendency to grow as organizational needs become more varied and sophisticated. As the number of workstations increases and the volume of traffic grows, so does the possibility of collisions, which will slow down the network with retransmission attempts.

When delay becomes a problem, consideration should be given to putting the image application on its own LAN. This can be accomplished very economically over the same type of unshielded twisted-pair wiring that already connects telephones to the corporate

PBX. Enough excess wiring exists in most offices so that, usually, no additional installation is required. Under the LAN standard known as 10Base-T, unshielded twisted-pair wiring might become the preferred transmission medium for Ethernet. The ability to network devices in this manner is a way to save on LAN installation costs, as well as moves and changes.

Compatibility is another advantage offered by *10Base-T*. Although vendors have been offering Ethernet products that use unshielded twisted-pair wiring for quite some time, there have always been compatibility problems among vendor offerings. Under 10Base-T, products that adhere to the standard will be interoperable over the unshielded twisted-pair Ethernet. This will give users more flexibility in mixing and matching products from multiple vendors.

Implementation of 10Base-T does not require that existing Ethernet installations be retrofitted with special adapters at the wall and wire closet; it works with standard *Institute of Electrical and Electronics Engineers, Inc.* (IEEE) 802.3 Ethernet interfaces and the eight-pin modular jacks typically found on most business telephones. Centralized 10Base-T hubs can be created to compress and route image traffic, provide network management capabilities, and provide access to the WAN via integral bridge/routers.

5.4.2 Token Ring

An alternative LAN topology is token ring, which is the preferred LAN for the IBM operating environment. Operating at rates of 4 Mbps or 16 Mbps, the "ring" is essentially a closed loop—although various hardware configurations and wiring schemes might cause it to resemble a star. A set of bytes called the "token" is circulated around the ring, giving each station in sequence a chance to put image traffic on the network. A token holding timer controls the maximum amount of time a station can occupy the network before passing the token. The image data is passed from station to station. Only the addressee retains the image before passing the token on to the next station.

Among the advantages of token ring over Ethernet is that access is not contention-based, but deterministic, meaning that each station has guaranteed access to the ring network in turn for a specified time. Therefore, a higher throughput rate is possible on the token ring in heavily loaded situations, limited only by the slowest element—sender, receiver, or link speed.

However, an aspect of token-ring operation that bears special consideration for imaging applications is that transmission takes place in only one direction. This entails the image data being transmitted a number of times, from station to station, before finally reaching its destination. Since the token ring frame size is only 4,000 bytes at 4 Mbps and 17,800 bytes at 16 Mbps, while image files can be 50,000 bytes or more, it will take several passes of the token to complete the transmission of a single image file. In a large network, this can pose significant delay.

Fortunately, another feature of the token-passing method of access is that the token can accommodate priority levels, allowing high-priority traffic to take precedence over lower-priority traffic. Only if a station has traffic equal to or higher in priority than the priority indicator embedded in the token is it allowed to transmit. In a network supporting multiple applications, image traffic can be given priority so that intolerable delays can be avoided. This assumes, of course, that other applications do not require continuous use of the network.

The token ring in its pure configuration is not without liabilities, however. Failed stations and faulty links can break the ring, preventing all the other terminals from using the network. At extra cost, a dual-ring configuration with redundant hardware and bypass circuitry is effective in isolating faulty nodes from the rest of the network, thereby increasing reliability.

Through the use of bypass circuitry, physically adding or deleting terminals to the token-ring network is accomplished without breaking the ring. Specific procedures must be used to ensure that the new station is recognized by the others and is granted a proportionate share of network time. Each station becomes acquainted with the address of its predecessor and successor on the network upon initialization (*power-up*) or at periodic intervals thereafter.

Token rings are also vulnerable to anomalies that can tie up the network for indeterminate periods. This alerts all other stations on the ring that the token protocol has been suspended. If a terminal fails before it has a chance to pass the token, the whole network is out of commission until a new one is inserted. The token might even be corrupted by noise to the point of becoming unrecognizable to the stations. The network can also be disrupted by the occasional appearance of two tokens or by the presence of a continuously circulating data packet. The latter can happen when data is sent to a failed terminal and the originating terminal gets disabled before it can remove the packet from the ring.

To protect the token ring from potential disaster, one terminal is typically designated as the control station. This terminal supervises network operations and does important housecleaning chores, such as reinserting lost tokens, taking extra tokens off the network, and disposing of "lost" packets. To guard against the failure of the control station, every station is equipped with control circuitry, so that the first station detecting the failure of the control station assumes responsibility for network supervision.

Overall, token ring has a lot to recommend it for image applications. At 16 Mbps, it exceeds maximum Ethernet performance by 63% and overcomes the distance limitations of Ethernet through token regeneration at each station. Unlike Ethernet, token ring provides every station with guaranteed access to the network, instead of making each station wait for access until the network is idle.

5.4.3 ARCnet

The *attached-resource computer network* (ARCnet) was introduced in 1977 by Datapoint Corp., making it the first commercially successful LAN. Although it operates at only 2.5 Mbps, in many ways ARCnet is more reliable, flexible, and economical than Ethernet or token ring.

ARCnet uses a token-passing protocol. When an ARCnet station receives the token, it is permitted to broadcast image traffic to other stations. While the token ring protocol passes its token around a physical cable ring from one device to the next, ARCnet passes its token from station to station in order of address.

ARCnet has been over-designed to achieve a higher level of robustness than Ethernet or token ring. For example, ARCnet works well even when connectors are loose, cable runs are too long and out of specification, or grounds are faulty or absent. When ARCnet is configured around "active" hubs, the network will not go down when a station becomes disconnected or when an installer forgets to terminate a cable. Since ARCnet uses a modified token-passing protocol, which requires that the hardware acknowledge every transaction, including passage of the token, successful message delivery is virtually assured.

The flexibility of ARCnet is demonstrated by the many ways it can be configured. ARCnet was originally designed to be configured as a distributed star, which entails each station being directly connected to a hub, with several hubs connected to each other. This design suits organizations that terminate cables in centrally located wiring closets. An Ethernet-like bus topology can be implemented with ARCnet, which allows stations to be interconnected via a single run of cable. The two topologies can even be combined for maximum configuration flexibility. For example, instead of connecting a single ARCnet node to a port on an ARCnet hub, a bus cable with a maximum of eight nodes attached can be connected.

An improved version of ARCnet—ARCnet Plus—offers 20 Mbps performance. ARCnet Plus is downward compatible with ARCnet, allowing a mix of ARCnet and ARCnet Plus equipment to share the same network—something that is not possible with 4 Mbps and 16 Mbps token-ring stations. When the network starts up, each ARCnet station broadcasts its capabilities in turn, letting the others know what transmission speed it can handle. This permits ARCnet Plus stations to communicate at the maximum rate. If an ARCnet Plus station encounters a slower ARCnet station, the network steps down to 2.5 Mbps.

ARCnet Plus uses packet lengths of up to 4,096 bytes, versus 508 bytes under ARCnet. This makes ARCnet Plus more suited to handling image applications than ARCnet. ARCnet, on the other hand, is best for applications that involve the exchange of many small packets, such as data entry and terminal emulation.

Despite its claim to fame as the first commercially available LAN, ARCnet never achieved the market success of Ethernet and token ring. ARCnet currently holds less than 20% of the base of installed LAN connections. In addition to ARCnet's obvious speed limitation, another reason that it was not more successful is that, in the early years, Datapoint never actively marketed ARCnet. While sponsors of Ethernet and token ring participated in meetings of the IEEE that led to the standardization of these LANs, Datapoint was content with using ARCnet to support its own business computing systems.

ARCnet Plus seems well suited for supporting some imaging applications; it offers higher speed, greater configuration flexibility, and more immunity from faults that affect other networks. But thought must be given to LAN interconnection; ARCnet Plus cannot currently be interconnected with other types of LANs, limiting where images can be transferred. On the other hand, there are numerous ways to interconnect token-ring and Ethernet LANs, as well as Ethernet and StarLAN.

5.4.4 StarLAN

The star topology consists of a central node, or *hub*, to which all devices on the network are connected. This topology is familiar in the office environment, where each telephone is ultimately tied into the PBX. Another example of a star network entails several terminals sharing a single host. The star and the ring network have the same disadvantage: the failure of a single node can result in the failure of the entire network unless provisions are made for hardware redundancy or bypass. In the star topology, it is the reliability of the hub that is critical, since all the network interface units and the interconnecting media are contained within a single cabinet.

NCR offers two versions of StarLAN: StarLAN 1, which operates at 1 Mbps, and StarLAN 10, which operates at 10 Mbps. StarLAN was originally developed by AT&T to satisfy the need for a low-cost, easy-to-install LAN that would offer more configuration flexibility than IBM's token ring. And because it is based on IEEE 802.3 standards, StarLAN offers interoperability with the embedded Ethernet base. When AT&T bought NCR Corp. in 1990, it transferred its computers and LAN products to NCR.

Unlike the bus and ring, which distribute intelligence throughout the network, the star network concentrates all of the intelligence required to run the network at a central hub. The star wiring configuration of StarLAN is compatible with the telephone closets found in most offices and can use the existing telephone wiring, as well as fiber-optic cabling. The hub monitors network traffic to prevent collisions between workstations trying to access the LAN. And since the hub knows the paths to all of the devices on the network, as well as the address of each device, data routing is fast and efficient.

The failure of one node on the star network does not affect the operation of the others, unless, of course, the faulty node happens to be the hub. Because network intelligence is centralized at the hub, safeguards must be taken to protect it from catastrophic failure. Such measures might include an uninterruptible power supply, an alternate hub on hot standby, or a hub that is equipped with redundant subsystems.

5.4.5 FDDI

FDDI is a 100 Mbps fiber-optic LAN that addresses the bandwidth, distance, and fault recovery issues that limit Ethernet LANs. In the corporate and campus backbones especially, users are looking to FDDI for a more robust, long-term solution than current networks can provide.

What makes FDDI so compelling? First, it is the only standard LAN platform currently available that has a total bandwidth capacity greater than that of Ethernet (10 Mbps) or token ring (16 Mbps). When users begin to reach the limits of current LAN technologies and decide to invest in a new LAN, they look for standards and for an investment that will not run out of capacity in two or three years. Conventional LANs might not have enough bandwidth capacity and growth potential to meet these long-term needs, especially when image applications are implemented. FDDI provides the needed capacity and added throughput by a deterministic token-passing access method, which makes for a high level of network availability.

FDDI uses a timed token-passing access protocol for passing frames as large as 4,500 bytes. The standard permits support of up to 1,000 connections over a fiber path of 200 km (approximately 120 mi) in length, allowing as much as 2 km (1.2 mi) between stations. Each station regenerates and repeats frames sent to it, which also serves as the means for identifying newly attached devices on the network. FDDI includes built-in management capabilities that detect failures and reconfigure the network automatically.

FDDI provides an optional bypass switch at each node to overcome a failure in the node. In the event of a node failure, it is bypassed optically, removing it from the network. In the event of a cable break, the dual counter-rotating ring topology of FDDI allows use of the redundant cable to handle normal 100 Mbps traffic. If both the primary and secondary cables fail, the stations adjacent to the failures automatically loop the data around between rings, thus forming a new C-shaped ring from the operational portions of the original two rings. When the fault is healed, the network puts itself back into the original configuration.

FDDI and Ethernet can be implemented together to form an enterprisewide network that supports imaging and many other applications simultaneously. For example, all image-enabled workstations can be connected together in a star topology with twisted-pair wiring. The hub can be connected to other hubs via an FDDI backbone.

Several vendors offer such hubs, which feature backplanes that support gigabit speeds. In addition, these hubs offer multiple modules for Ethernet. Each module is equipped with as many as eight ports, each of which supports an independent Ethernet segment connecting workstations and servers. Such hubs are also equipped with two FDDI modules, which are used to form the high-speed backbone.

5.4.6 SDDI

A new de facto industry standard for high-speed LANs can provide users with a more economical alternative to FDDI. The SDDI, endorsed by IBM and other companies, allows users to run the FDDI standard 100 Mbps transmission speed over shielded twisted-pair wiring at a distance of up to 100m (328 feet) from station to hub, which is enough to reach the nearest wiring closet on most office floors.

Ostensibly, SDDI is being promoted as a way to help users make an easy, economical transition to 100 Mbps at the workstation, in support of such bandwidth-intensive applications as imaging. Products based on SDDI are available now, but they benefit mostly IBM customers who already have shielded twisted-pair wiring in place.

At this writing, however, ANSI is considering the recommendation of its X3T9.5 Committee for a single standard for 100 Mbps operation over twisted-pair wiring— shielded and unshielded. The ready availability of unshielded twisted-pair wiring in most organizations is expected to spur market acceptance of products based on the ANSI standard. In terms of upgrading existing LANs or building new ones to handle imaging applications, the imminent ANSI standard offers more configuration flexibility and, in many cases, better economic justification than SDDI.

5.5 THE ROLE OF HUBS

The fact that LANs are becoming more complicated at the physical and management levels has created the need for intelligent hubs that not only facilitate the management of sprawling LANs by providing real-time status information and compiling statistical reports, but that also prevent relatively simple problems from bringing down the entire network. Enterprise reliance upon LANs for critical information continues to grow. But LAN availability is estimated to be only 94% at best, which translates into three weeks of downtime each year. Yet physical wiring problems cause over 60% of LAN failures. This is exactly the type of problem that intelligent hubs are intended to solve.

It is a typical occurrence with LANs that, when a problem is found, a qualified technician is not available on site to correct it. The remote management capabilities of today's intelligent hubs make it easy to remotely diagnose the problem and isolate the fault from the rest of the LAN, eliminating the need to manually repatch cable connections in a wiring closet. From the management console, appropriate corrective action can be taken to restore the faulty component to proper operation.

Intelligent hubs can even recognize the difference between token-ring adapters and associate the right adapter with the ring speed. When a mismatch is detected, the intelligent hub will intervene, reconfiguring the circuitry to prevent the ring from going down.

Other times, a non-token ring device might be plugged into the *multiple access unit* (MAU) by mistake. This is a common occurrence because the PC's DB-9 serial connector or display connector closely resembles the one on the MAU. This can also take down the ring. The trouble is that the token ring's self-healing protocol is not able to force the non-token ring device off the network because it does not recognize the token ring protocol and, of course, cannot interpret it. Consequently, the network will stay down until someone figures out what the problem is and unplugs the cable from the MAU or the PC. An intelligent hub, on the other hand, can instantly recognize that the device is not a token-ring adapter and force it off the ring.

Sometimes cables become just loose enough to pass a phantom voltage that opens the ring connection, but not enough to pass traffic and tokens. This violates token-ring procedures and causes other stations on the ring to beacon, so that self-healing can begin. When the device withdraws from the ring and runs self-diagnostics, no problem will be found. The device will reinsert itself onto the ring, beginning the whole process over again. An intelligent hub handles this problem by reporting to the centralized management station the location of the device that is repeatedly beaconing (to get itself re-established onto the ring). The network manager will be alerted to take action, which entails forcing the device off the ring until someone can address the problem.

In addition to turning offending stations off to prevent them from affecting LAN performance, intelligent hubs also provide access control and improve both cable and overall network management. They provide an array of information that is useful to the network manager. Typically, the hubs provide performance statistics and alarms, which occur on the network as a result of either predefined or network-specific (Ethernet or token ring) thresholds established down to the port and workstation level. A certain degree of report customization and network mapping is available. GUIs that use windows, icons, and pull-down menus make the network management system easier to use, which facilitates problem resolution.

Hubs started as simple devices that imposed order on the cabling mess found in most organizations. Since then, wiring hubs have evolved rapidly to become indispensable components of LANs and internetworks. Eventually, they will assume their place as enterprise-level management systems.

5.6 THE ROLE OF SERVERS

A *server* is a computer that is deployed on the LAN to facilitate resource sharing among nodes by distributing files, messages, and applications to departmental work groups or stand-alone computers (via modem connection) in local or remote geographical locations. Distributing resources on the network via servers also minimizes the disruption to productivity that would normally result if all the resources were centralized and a failure occurred.

Server-based imaging systems are designed to access information from other servers, as well as from scanners and optical libraries on the network. The imaging software offered by Wang Laboratories, for example, provides APIs for image printing, document management, and imaging file access via the *remote procedure call* (RPC) mechanism.

Because all networks are different, configuring the server is essentially a custom engineering job, requiring that the server's capabilities match the needs (and number) of users. Even preconfigured servers might require upgrading before they can live up to performance and reliability expectations in the live environment.

In terms of CPU power and RAM, the server is usually more powerful than any of the client systems it will serve. (Exceptions are some print servers and communication servers that provide narrow functionality.) The server should be configured with at least two to three times the amount of CPU power and input/output bandwidth that the most active user will require. For example, a large network of image-enabled microcomputers should be supported by one or more workstations, minicomputers, or even a mainframe configured as a "superserver."

There are some very sophisticated superservers that use *reduced instruction set computing* (RISC) and multiprocessor architectures. In addition to having multiple CPUs, superservers also differ from the previous generation of LAN servers in other ways. Superservers

- Handle a greater amount of network traffic without slowing down during computer-intensive tasks;

- Have very large amounts of RAM—as much as several hundred MB;
- Have large amounts of disk storage, with large caches.

Superservers are ideal for supporting imaging applications, if only because of the large files that are involved, typically 40,000 to 100,000 bytes—more if complex CAD/CAM graphics and color are involved. In such cases, optical media should be considered, at least for archival purposes.

There are several methods for protecting image files and other data stored on servers. One way is to have the server's operating system use data recovery techniques, such as *hot-fixing*, a method of rerouting data from a disk's bad sectors to good sectors. Another protection method is the operating system's file replication service, which periodically distributes image files and other data to another server on the network. This spreads the risk of loss among two separate servers.

A potentially important method of data protection is known as the *redundant array of inexpensive disks* (RAID). This solution involves using multiple small disks instead of a single large one. Instead of storing all the accumulated image files on one high-capacity disk, distributing it across multiple smaller disks housed in a server offers protection from a crash that could wipe out all data on a single shared disk.

Finally, an *uninterruptible power supply* (UPS) provides a temporary source of power during an outage, until an orderly shutdown of the server can be implemented.

5.7 CONCLUSION

By understanding the impact of imaging on existing networks and carefully evaluating the available alternatives, an organization can arrive at an imaging application that provides high levels of efficiency and economy and ensures the optimal performance of the entire corporate network.

Depending on the existing traffic load, adding an imaging application might require that the LAN be reconfigured or upgraded to maintain an acceptable level of performance for all the applications. A full-time image application that includes document scanning and distribution, file retrieval and annotation, and case file assembly and transfer can easily dominate a LAN and possibly overwhelm it. If the imaging application makes continuous use of the LAN for such activities, a dedicated LAN might be required. Alternatively, the work group running image applications can be partitioned from the rest of the LAN, so that group does not affect the performance of other applications.

Network upgrades can be accomplished in a number of ways, such as by adding higher performance equipment and transmission media to build higher-speed backbone networks or by subscribing to carrier-provided digital services to extend the reach of a LAN. Adherence to media standards positions the LAN to take advantage of more connectivity options than are possible with the so-called de facto standards. These de facto standards are intended, in large part, to provide specific vendors with marketing advantages.

Chapter 6

Considerations for Mainframe-Based Imaging

6.1 INTRODUCTION

Since the 1960s mainframe computers have become a permanent fixture of most large corporations and government agencies, despite repeated predictions of their demise in favor of distributed computing and peer-to-peer networking via LANs. The sizable investment in software applications alone is enough to keep mainframes entrenched in many organizations for the foreseeable future.

According to the META Group, a research firm in Westport, Connecticut, corporations worldwide have invested $750 billion on software applications for IBM or IBM-compatible mainframes. And, despite the recession, users spent $26.6 billion in 1991 for 14,000 new mainframes. According to Dataquest International, this represents a drop of 6.4% from the previous year.

In addition to being the only platform many companies trust to run their mission-critical applications, there are several other reasons why companies are not quite ready to jettison their mainframes.

First, mainframes are capable of handling enormous transaction volumes—as much as 20,000 to 25,000 per hour—in addition to other applications, such as materials management, receivables, payables, payroll, and electronic mail. Adding document imaging to the existing host environment is relatively easy and permits many corporations to further leverage their investments in mainframe systems.

Second, because the mainframe offers a single repository, data is more readily consolidated, updated, and protected. Moreover, access to the data is more effectively controlled. The same levels of data integrity and access control in a distributed environment require resource-intensive software and continuous vigilance on the part of the LAN administrator.

Third, the mainframe can help an organization keep pace with user application needs. Although centralized host environments have long been criticized for application backlogs, this is becoming a nonissue with the continued evolution of host-based *computer-aided software engineering* (CASE) tools and *fourth-generation languages* (4GL).

91

The availability of such tools is also making the development of custom applications easier and faster. Whereas users of microcomputers and workstations tend to rely on off-the-shelf software that is immediately available and provides a common feature-function set, it is the custom applications developed for mainframes that often translate into competitive advantage.

Finally, over the years many organizations have developed a wealth of application code for their mainframes. Moving to a distributed systems architecture would mean rewriting or possibly throwing out major portions of that code. In most cases recompiling mainframe programs for a distributed environment is fraught with problems, making success difficult, if not impossible. On the other hand, it is a relatively simple matter to run third-generation application code through a machine filter to prepare it for migration to the 4GL environment.

The question that begs an answer is why sales of mainframes have experienced slow growth in recent years. There are three reasons. First, slow growth is the natural result of a maturing industry. With the majority of batch processing demand largely satisfied, future growth will come primarily from customer service and from vendors meeting the increasing demand for information processing and office automation applications, such as document imaging.

Second, the role of the mainframe is changing. It is evolving from a back office, number-crunching behemoth to a highly flexible, intelligent hub for corporate networks. In fact, the emphasis of vendors, including IBM and Unisys, is on improving the connectivity of their mainframes for enterprisewide computing. There are several components to this concept, including:

- Client/server computing, in which UNIX-based mainframes act as information hubs, serving the diverse needs of all departments;
- Mainframe channel extension over WAN facilities that support network-routing capabilities for resource sharing and disaster recovery;
- Interoperability between the host environments of different vendors, such as Unisys connectivity to IBM's SNA.

When this emerging role of mainframes is better understood and appreciated among users, mainframes will again experience healthy sales, although probably not on the scale witnessed in the early to mid-1980s. Already, however, mainframes are supporting document imaging applications, including those of Amdahl, Bull HN Information Systems, Hitachi Data Systems, IBM, Tandem Computers, and Unisys.

Third, the recession has affected the sales of mainframes in recent years, as it has for other types of computer and communications products. And, while fewer mainframes have been sold, they are also getting more powerful and less expensive, giving buyers more bang for the buck. According to a report by the research firm Computer Intelligence, the power of mainframes in terms of *millions of instructions per second* (MIPS) tripled between 1988 and 1991.

However, a more important measure of performance, from an imaging perspective, is total system bandwidth. This refers to two things: the amount of data that can move across the system's *backplane* (the computer's major internal communications path) and the total input/output bandwidth of the system for network and peripheral connections. When optical fiber is used for the backplane, internal throughput is measured in terms of gigabits per second, instead of megabits per second, which is used with conventional metallic backplanes.

A variety of fiber-optic channel extenders are available to support high-speed connectivity between the mainframe and remote peripherals and networks. Channel extenders based on the FDDI provide host-to-host or host-to-LAN connectivity at up to 100 Mbps. Channel extenders based on the *high-speed serial interface* (HSSI) provide the same type of connectivity at up to 52 Mbps. And channel extenders that support T3 offer connectivity between the hosts and remote peripherals at up to 44.736 Mbps over the WAN.

The T3 channel extender allows the mainframe to support multiple sites over high-speed lines, such as T1 and T3. When the host needs to communicate with a remote peripheral, it encapsulates the data in a packet, along with the target device's subchannel address, and routes it to the extender serving the remote site (Figure 6.1). In a full mesh network of channel extenders connected by T1 or T3 lines, switching channel extenders permits traffic to be automatically routed around failed communications links.

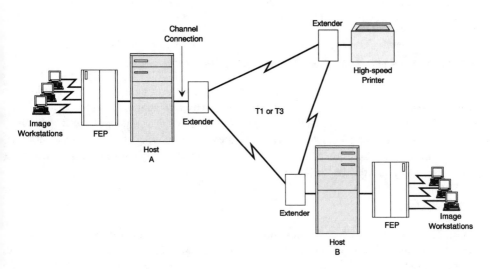

Figure 6.1 Wide-area channel networking.

The performance and networking capabilities of today's mainframes have vendors recasting their machines as LAN servers, performing such rudimentary services as file storage, print serving, and backup services.

6.2 ROLE OF THE MAINFRAME

In supporting high-volume document imaging applications, the mainframe essentially performs the functions of a file server and workflow manager. As a file server, the mainframe is functionally positioned at the center of the document imaging system; it coordinates the activities of the system's major components and manages vast amounts of imaged documents generated by the workstations. The mainframe receives new imaged documents from scanner-equipped workstations, distributes processing tasks to individual workstations, collects the results, and performs any necessary file consolidations. The mainframe also receives user requests for display, print, facsimile, and other processing functions.

As a workflow manager, the mainframe matches documents in need of processing with the appropriate or next available workstation operator. Routing is determined at the time the document imaging system is configured for operation and is based on such factors as user profiles, which describe the categories of work each user is trained to handle. Alternatively, the supervisor can create or change the user profiles to balance the work load. Either way, the workflow manager uses this information, along with information provided by indexing, to determine who processes what documents. To keep track of work in progress, the workflow manager maintains a processing history for each document, which is available for display at an operator's or supervisor's workstation.

In addition to functions for queuing and routing documents, workflow management can also include such functions as user- and document-access security, and support for backup and recovery procedures.

6.3 MAINFRAME IMAGE SYSTEM COMPONENTS

High-volume image processing and distribution in the mainframe environment involves the use of many types of equipment that are already used to support existing applications. In addition to the mainframe itself, these include terminals or workstations, printers, communications controllers and LAN or WAN connections, and magnetic and optical storage. Of course, the document imaging application must include a high-speed scanner, which is the one piece of equipment that usually needs to be added to a workstation.

6.3.1 Workstations

Most workstations will be used for viewing imaged documents. There are a variety of monitors available for this purpose. Color display monitors from 14 in to 20 in can display up to 256 colors simultaneously. These are useful for image applications that include artwork, color photographs, or CAD/CAM drawings. Otherwise, high-resolution gray-scale or monochrome monitors are adequate for most document imaging applications.

Monitors are available in portrait or landscape orientation. There are full-page portrait monitors that are vertically oriented to provide a maximum viewing area of 8.5 by 11.8 in. Portrait monitors are used when it is important that the user be able to view an entire page of an imaged document at one time, rather than having to scroll to view portions of a page. Most monitors are horizontally oriented, or landscape. A virtual requirement for viewing engineering models, blueprints, and CAD/CAM drawings, a landscape monitor also provides a number of viewing options for the display of data and images (Figure 6.2).

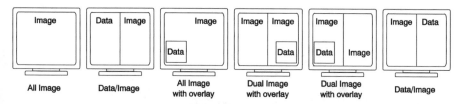

Figure 6.2 Data and image display options on landscape monitors. *Source:* IBM Corp.

Split-screen landscape monitors can display coded data and imaged documents side-by-side in separate display areas, allowing users to view host application and image sessions simultaneously.

In the IBM environment a display configuration called the *dual-headed configuration* has two monitors sharing the same workstation. Certain IBM monitors (models 8506 and 8508), when used for image display, do not permit the simultaneous display of host application coded data. This requires a second display monitor attached to the same workstation or a separate IBM 3270-series terminal (Figure 6.3).

6.3.2 Scanning Equipment

The scan workstation provides the means of capturing paper documents electronically. Capture can be performed either in a batch mode, in which all pages are continuously scanned with high-speed equipment, or interactively, with the pages being scanned and viewed individually. Interactive scanning allows users to display documents on the screen to check resolution and alignment and then make equipment adjustments prior to the high-speed batch scanning of similar-quality documents.

An optional component of the scanner is software that provides OCR. This software allows the scanner to read and extract typed data from the imaged documents—the entire page or particular zones—and convert it into ASCII text or a supported word processing format for editing at the workstation. Most standard type fonts are supported by the OCR software, including those printed in dot matrix format. OCR software flags characters it cannot recognize with a symbol such as the pound sign (#) so the operator can easily find them and make the corrections manually. OCR software can even be "trained" to recognize fonts or nonstandard symbols it does not normally support. This is done by scanning a training page containing such fonts and symbols and entering a string for the OCR program to use when it encounters them during scanning.

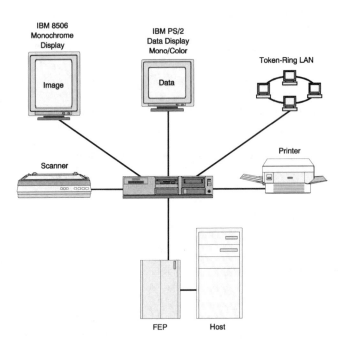

Figure 6.3 IBM's dual-headed monitor configuration. *Source:* IBM Corp.

Mainframe-based imaging systems excel at high-volume transaction processing. This starts with the rapid automatic capture and indexing of paper documents. The scanner can include the capability to read bar codes and imprint the sequence number on each image. Another advanced capability of high-speed scanners includes duplex scanning with single-pass transport. This allows two-sided pages to be scanned in a single pass. Without this capability, the page is flipped over and then rescanned. Either way, sides one and two are marked as such, and the images are collated by the system.

Output from the high-speed scanner can be used as input by the imaging system's folder application. This application uses a batch storage process to index and store documents and optionally route them for processing through workflow queues.

Other technologies can be combined with scanning to further automate document processing. Transaction-intensive environments, such as the banking industry, need very sophisticated systems for check processing. The discrete steps that must be performed include capturing the image; performing character recognition, endorsement, and encoding; and sorting the documents into separate pockets. The NCR 7780, for example, accomplishes this by performing high-speed *magnetic ink character recognition* (MICR) and OCR, enabling the system to interpret the code lines on a document. The NCR 7780 also uses *character amount recognition* (CAR) technology, which allows the system to scan, read, and store handwritten numbers on a document.

In addition, the NCR system performs "power encoding," which allows a large number of documents to be encoded at high speed. The NCR 7780 captures images, performs recognition and encoding, and endorses checks without the need for operator interaction. In the power encode mode, the NCR 7780 can process full payments as well as minimum payments at rates up to 10,000 transactions per hour.

5.3.3 Printers

Band printers, which are capable of operating at 70 lines per minute and more and use fan-folded paper, are common in mainframe data processing environments; but most imaging applications require the high resolution of a laser printer. A variety of laser printers, desktop and system-oriented, are supported by mainframe-based imaging systems.

Since document imaging systems are used ostensibly to eliminate paper, when printing is necessary, a conventional desktop laser printer offering 300-dpi resolution should be adequate for most applications. For image applications that demand higher resolutions, such as commercial publishing, 600-dpi, 800-dpi, 1000-dpi, and 1200-dpi printers are available.

Lasermaster Technologies' Unity 1000, for example, is a multiplatform printer that provides 1,000-dpi printing in minicomputer and mainframe environments (and also supports Macintosh and IBM-compatible PCs). The printer includes an internal hard disk with 35 preinstalled typefaces and features an Ethernet expansion port, automatic port switching, and halftone enhancement technology, which improves the appearance of halftone images by providing increased gray levels at higher screen frequencies.

Such high-resolution printers typically cost two to 10 times that of a 300-dpi laser printer, which averages $2,000. Printer economics will change significantly in 1993, however, when Hewlett-Packard releases its 600-dpi desktop laser printer. The price tag is expected to be under $3,000.

Most laser printers handle both standard and legal-size sheets, although a few printers that are based on RISC architecture, from QMS and others, output documents measuring up to 11 by 17 in at 20 pages per minute.

If color is important, there are a variety of color printers, starting at $5,000, that print up to seven colors by thermal transfer or ink on plain paper, with a resolution of 300 dpi and better.

While most desktop printers perform at four to eight pages per minute, a printer in the mainframe or LAN environment would have to perform at 20 to 30 pages per minute, possibly more. There are new laser printers that can output 100 pages per minute with a 2 million-page per month duty cycle. Such a printer, the 300-dpi HP-F100 Jumbo Jet, is available in Europe. Developed by Hewlett-Packard and marketed by Fareham, Hampshire-based European Business Group Ltd., the Jumbo Jet supports all major minicomputer and mainframe hosts.

Users can print imaged documents in a variety of ways; they can print a single page from a folder, the entire folder, or several folders in batch mode. Not only can individual pages be printed, document-related notes, annotations, and document forms within a page can also be printed. Print commands are selected from a menu at the view workstation. When set by the supervisor, a print request banner identifying the job owner is printed with each job. The supervisor can modify the list of print jobs, release jobs from queue and inquire as to the status of jobs. The supervisor can also prefetch documents during nonpeak hours for high-volume retrieval and printing requirements.

6.3.4 Communications Controllers

The mainframe environment is no longer isolated from the rest of an organization's computer resources. In fact, an enterprise can greatly benefit when mainframe image applications can be extended via the wider connectivity offered by LANs and carrier-provided facilities. LAN support is a feature that is now available with most communications controllers or front-end processors, as is X.25 and, increasingly, frame relay.

Communications controllers are devices that sit in front of the mainframe and control access to a relatively limited number of ports. The communications controller can provide connections to remote communications controllers at other hosts via such carrier-provided services as X.25 and frame relay, or private facilities such as T1.

Via plug-in interfaces, communications controllers can provide access to both Ethernet and token-ring LANs. In addition to token-ring support, IBM's 3745 communication controllers, for example, support Ethernet LANs that run the *transmission control protocol/internet protocol* (TCP/IP). This enables Ethernet-attached workstations to access IBM host resources, such as database information and applications, and provides backbone support for connecting Ethernet LANs across an IBM WAN. The 3745 also provides access to frame-relay networks, which provide more efficient data transport than T1 alone.

Another type of communications controller found in the mainframe environment is the *front-end processor* (FEP), which provides more configuration flexibility. The front end is connected directly to the mainframe, while the back end provides connections to various communications channels. The controller transmits and receives messages, assembles and disassembles packets, and detects and corrects errors. In the LAN environment these functions are provided by the network adapters. FEPs also perform polling, allowing a large number of devices to share a relatively small number of mainframe ports.

FEPs provide *systems network architecture* (SNA) connectivity over services like X.25 and frame relay via routers. Of the two services, frame relay is preferred for image traffic. The FEP passes the SNA traffic to the router, where it is encapsulated in the frame relay protocol. At the remote location another router performs the process in reverse.

6.3.5 Storage Facilities

Although desktop, LAN, and mainframe imaging systems use essentially the same magnetic and optical media for storage, there are some storage configurations used more often in the mainframe environment that can effectively support document imaging applications. These include magnetic tape and optical libraries, as well as *direct-access storage device* (DASD) and *redundant arrays of inexpensive disks* (RAID).

5.3.5.1 Library Facilities

High-end library storage facilities are complete installations potentially consisting of thousands of individual tape cartridges or optical platters, which are retrieved by robots.

IBM, for example, offers its 3496 Tape Library Dataserver, an automatic loading tape cartridge retrieval system. The Dataserver consists of an enclosed structure along which a robot runs. Up to 64 tape transports can be attached along one side of the enclosure. From 5,660 to 18,910 cartridges can be installed—and operate unattended—up to 14 mi from the host, through the use of fiber-optic channels available under Escon.

IBM's online optical disk subsystem, the 3995 Optical Library Dataserver, can store up to 181.6 GB of images and other information on erasable optical platters. This is a greatly expanded version of the optical jukebox used on LANs.

IBM is not the only vendor who offers library storage facilities. StorageTek offers products for robotic tape libraries. The company also offers *Expert Library Manager* (ExLM), a software product that automates movement of tape cartridges used in its 4400 and 9310 *automated cartridge systems* (ACS). Cartridges are exchanged at a rate of 175 and 350 cartridges per hour, respectively.

Another StorageTek product, ExtendedStore, is a library that archives tapes containing less frequently used data. The product does not include tape drives. ExtendedStore, which can handle about 6,000 tape cartridges, keeps the data available for easy access. When data from ExtendedStore is needed, it is moved via StorageTek's pass-through port system to a standard library, which has an attached tape drive from which the data can be read or written.

For companies with less voluminous storage needs, StorageTek offers TimberWolf and WolfCreek, smaller-capacity libraries that handle 500 and 1,000 cartridges respectively, with a cartridge exchange rate that starts at 350 per hour. Each product can be upgraded in increments of 500 cartridges and can be attached to any StorageTek library. The open architecture of the StorageTek products makes them compatible with numerous IBM and non-IBM vendor platforms.

For organizations that want to file their image documents separately from other corporate data, there are tape jukeboxes that accommodate 10 to 20 tape cartridges. When 8mm tape cartridges are used, a tape jukebox of 10 cartridges can store 50 GB of image files. These units allow users to automate unattended backups and recoveries.

Sheer storage capacity is an important difference between the disk and tape media typically used in the PC and mainframe (and LAN) environments. With regard to tape, several vendors offer the new 8mm magnetic tape systems, which provide up to 5 GB of storage capacity per cartridge. Such systems have a data transfer rate of 500 KB per second and a search rate of 37.5 MB per second, allowing any image file on a 5-GB cartridge to be located within 85 seconds.

These 8mm tape systems use the licensed technology developed by Exabyte, which is the lone supplier. The ISO recognizes Exabyte's 8mm data format—used in its EXB8200 8mm Cartridge Tape Subsystem—as a worldwide standard. When used with an optional data compression module that is based on IBM's *improved data recording capability* (IDRC), 5 to 1 compression is available, which the user can turn on and off. When on, a single 8mm cartridge can have a capacity of 25 GB, making such systems viable alternatives to more expensive optical disk technologies.

Vendors are enhancing the file search capabilities of 8mm tape systems. Winchester Systems, for example, offers Flash8mm, which incorporates Touch Technologies' Dynamic Tape Accelerator to increase backup rates by allowing the tape to stream in one direction continuously, instead of back and forth, in the manner of reel-to-reel tape systems.

With price performance continually improving, 8mm tape systems are migrating from mainframe, midrange, and LAN environments down to the work group and individual user levels. There, they are replacing the long popular *quarter-inch cartridge* (QIC) tape systems.

6.3.5.2 Direct-Access Storage Device

Another type of storage facility commonly found in mainframe and midrange environments is the *direct-access storage device* (DASD), originated by IBM. Although the market for DASD is dominated by IBM, there are several third-party DASD suppliers, including EMC, IPL, Memorex Telex, and StorageTek.

In essence, DASD provides consistently fast access to data, regardless of its location in massive databases. Typically, the available storage space of DASD is allocated to specific applications, so that frequently used information is made immediately available. Less frequently used information is stored on less expensive archival media. In an imaging application, for example, active documents and file folders would be stored on DASD for quick retrieval, while inactive files might be stored on magnetic tape. Files that are considered closed would be permanently stored on optical media, such as WORM disks.

Organizations that use DASD also most likely use IBM's *Database 2* (DB2), a relational database management system. (IBM recommends DB2 for use with its ImagePlus document imaging systems.) However, the problem with DB2 is that it has a large appetite for DASD space. Considering the storage requirements of image files, any needless use of DASD space can greatly inflate the cost of imaging operations. According to a 1991 survey by Candle Corp., DB2 wastes large amounts of DASD space at an annual cost of between $40,000 and $100,000 per organization. On very large systems the cost of wasted DASD space can run into millions of dollars.

Not coincidentally, Candle offers a utility program that generates a financial analysis of how much money the DB2-allocated space that goes unused costs to maintain per month and recommends ways to reclaim unused DASD space. This is particularly useful because IBM's DB2 provides no way to determine the amount of storage space that is over-allocated or unused. The utility, DB/DASD, also provides an automatic allocation feature, which allocates the available space more efficiently, freeing database administrators from the time-consuming, laborious task of manually reallocating DASD space when they do discover unused DASD.

IBM does offer *system-managed storage* (SMS) products to assist database administrators in managing DASD use, but they do not support DB2 files. This forces database administrators to use third-party DB2 DASD management solutions.

DB/DASD does not, however, compress the database or otherwise reduce the amount of storage space that DB2 takes up. For these tasks database administrators must turn to products like DB2 Reduce, from Boole & Babbage, and Shrink/DB2, from Sterling Software. These products compress DB2 tables during the read/write process from and to DASD so the tables take up less space. But the products do not address the problem of how to reduce the amount of unnecessary space allocated to DB2. Instead, they reduce the amount of space a particular DB2 application uses within the allocated DB2 data partition.

For example, an image database might reserve 40 MB of DASD space at the time is set up. The actual DB2 files might take up only 20 MB when the database is put into operation. With compression that 20 MB might be squeezed into 10 MB—but there will still be the original 40 MB of DASD reserved for DB2 that cannot be used for image documents and files. This means that the effective use of DASD requires both a management utility and a compression product.

For disruptions caused by internal problems, there are three recovery techniques commonly used with DASD: journaling, checksum, and mirroring. *Journaling* is a system function that provides an audit trail of activity on physical files. It allows users to save files faster by saving only changed records and provides recovery of individual files to the point of failure.

Checksum protection is a system function that can help avoid a time-consuming system reload, even when a failed disk drive must be replaced. The system is able to reconstruct the data on any failing drive on the checksum set after a single drive failure.

Mirroring provides automatic duplication of data on separate storage devices. This ensures that the system will continue to operate and the data will remain completely intact when one of the devices fails. This approach allows users to keep the system available during and after DASD or other storage hardware failure, reducing or eliminating downtime for repair or recovery. However, mirroring does not eliminate the need for backup or guarantee continuous, uninterrupted operation. Nor does it make journaling obsolete. In fact, mirroring uses twice as much DASD, which is already expensive.

Channel extenders can support remote DASD over a metropolitan area, via high-speed private lines or carrier-provided services, or in campus network facilities, via such interfaces as FDDI, HSSI, or T3. These arrangements allow DASD to reside in remote locations as far away as 8 to 10 km, which, in turn, permits DASD to be used for electronic vaulting. In *electronic vaulting* a duplicate image of local DASD is maintained at a remote site to act as backup system.

6.3.5.3 Redundant Arrays of Inexpensive Disks

Redundant arrays of inexpensive disks (RAID) is an emerging storage technology designed to address the data reliability deficiencies of DASD. In essence, a RAID configuration consists of multiple small disks. Instead of risking loss from a crash that could wipe out all of the image documents and files on one high-capacity disk, an organization can use RAID to distribute the image files and documents across multiple smaller disks (Figure 6.4).

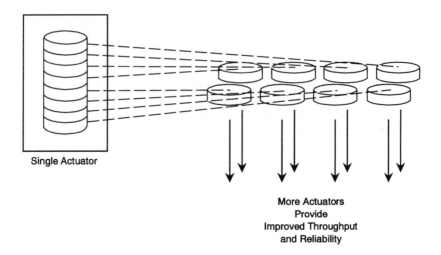

Single Actuator

More Actuators
Provide
Improved Throughput
and Reliability

Figure 6.4 Concept of redundant arrays of inexpensive disks.

RAID configurations are as applicable to workstations and LANs as they are to mainframes. While more economical safeguards are available, the mission criticality of information stored on mainframes often makes RAID more relevant for that environment than workstations and LANs.

RAID devices use a software technique called *striping*, which spreads data across multiple disks. Multiple small disk drives operate with a single controller and appear to the host system to be a single logical disk drive.

There are no standards for RAID, but there is general agreement in the industry about the configurations and the functionality associated with each configuration. Generally, the RAID configurations fall into the following categories:

- RAID Level 0 products are technically not RAID products at all, since they do not offer parity or error-correction data, which would provide redundancy in the event of system failure. Although data striping is performed, it is accomplished without fault tolerance. Data is simply striped, block by block, across all the drives in the array. There is no way to reconstruct data if one of the drives fails.
- RAID Level 1 products duplicate the data that is stored on the separate disk drives. This mirroring approach ensures that critical files will be available in the event of individual disk drive failures. Each disk in the array has a corresponding mirror disk and the pairs run in parallel. Blocks of data are sent to both disks at the same time. Highly reliable, Level 1 products are also costly, since every drive requires its own mirror drive, which doubles the hardware cost of the system.
- RAID Level 2 products distribute the code used for error detection and correction across additional disk drives. The controller includes an error-correction algorithm, which enables the array to reconstruct lost data if a single disk fails. As a result, no

expensive mirroring is required. But the code does require that multiple disks be set aside for the error-correction function. Data is sent to one array disk at a time.

- RAID Level 3 products store user data in parallel across multiple disks. The entire array functions as one large logical drive. The parallel operation is ideally suited to supporting imaging applications that require high data transfer rates when reading and writing large files. RAID Level 3 is configured with one parity (error-correction) drive. The controller determines which disk has failed by using additional check information recorded at the end of each sector. However, because the drives do not operate independently, every time an image file must be retrieved all of the drives in the array are used. Other users are put into a queue.

- RAID Level 4 products store and retrieve data using independent writes and reads to several drives. Error correction data is stored on a dedicated parity drive. In level four, data striping is accomplished in sectors, not bytes (or blocks). Sector-striping offers parallel operation; reads can be performed simultaneously on independent drives, thus allowing multiple users to retrieve image files at the same time. However, multiple writes are not possible. The parity drive must be read and written to for each write operation.

- RAID Level 5 products interleave user data and parity data, which are then distributed across several disks. Because data and parity codes are striped across all the drives, there is no need for a dedicated drive. This configuration is suited to applications that require a high number of input/output operations per second, such as transaction processing tasks that involve writing and reading large numbers of small data blocks at random disk locations. Multiple writes to each disk group are possible because write operations do not have to access a single common parity drive.

RAID Levels 1 through 5 enable the array to recover data from a single failed drive, but not from two failed drives. Some vendors are working on additional RAID levels to increase data security and throughput. One of these, RAID Level 6, can recover from a double-disk failure.

For document imaging applications within a work group, a RAID Level 0 configuration might be appropriate, since it supports high data rates for very large files. If continuous availability is a requirement, fault tolerance becomes more important, in which case RAID Level 1 is a better solution. But RAID Level 5 is more economical.

IBM is one of several storage technology vendors supporting the RAID concept. IBM's RAID Level 3 configuration for the RS/6000 workstation, for example, includes as many as 40 5.25-in *enhanced small-device interface* (ESDI) disk drives, which operate at a sustained data rate of 18 MB per second.

6.4 IMPLEMENTATION ISSUES

For many organizations, adding or integrating document imaging applications with existing data processing applications makes good economic sense. However, this decision must rest on other factors as well, such as:

- The degree to which existing applications can benefit from document imaging and the extent to which existing workflows must be redesigned to accommodate a mainframe-based solution;
- The load already being handled by existing data processing resources;
- Availability of spare disk space, memory, and off-line archival facilities to accommodate and protect the image files, as well as the management software;
- Availability of network facilities or spare bandwidth to accommodate the transport of image files between corporate locations and provide alternate routing in case of network failures;
- Availability of in-house staff to develop routines for specialized document processing, using APIs;
- Continuity of data processing staff in following through—from design to implementation of a mainframe-based imaging system.

While adding or integrating image applications to existing data processing applications might seem economical initially, adding the necessary resources to implement document imaging can raise the price considerably. Proper planning will reveal all costs at the start, preventing cost overruns that can damage the credibility of the project and the people involved. The organization might benefit from a workflow study and resource audit, performed by an outside consultant or the professional services group of an imaging system vendor.

6.5 CONCLUSION

The mainframe has proven itself a reliable platform for mission-critical applications. Far from being ready to scrap their mainframes, many companies are looking for ways to extend their investments in hardware and software by taking on additional enterprisewide applications. For many companies, document imaging fits the bill.

Incorporating document imaging into the existing host environment can be relatively easy with proper planning. And—compared to the up-front cost of equivalent amounts of processing power, memory, and disk storage in a distributed environment of microcomputers, workstations or both—implementing an imaging system with existing data processing resources can be economical as well.

The mainframe offers the advantage of a single repository where access to sensitive information can be controlled and data can be consolidated, updated, and protected more readily than in a distributed-computing environment. With the aid of CASE tools, 4GLs, and APIs, data processing staff can keep pace with special image processing and management requirements, which, in turn, often translate into competitive advantage. With vendors emphasizing the connectivity and interoperability aspects of their systems, the mainframe is rapidly evolving into an enterprisewide information hub that is fully capable of supporting a wider range of applications, including document imaging.

Part III

VENDOR IMPLEMENTATIONS

Chapter 7

IBM Imaging Systems

7.1 INTRODUCTION

Despite declining revenues in recent years, a 10-year low stock price, loss of its triple A credit rating and continued staff reductions, IBM Corp. is still the world's dominant computer manufacturer. Its hardware offerings span the three major business platforms: mainframe, midrange and microcomputer. With many business applications moving off the mainframe and onto the other platforms, IBM has had to depend more on the growing outsourcing and systems integration markets, where its revenues grew almost 35% in 1991. IBM also offers a number of software products that together have experienced modest revenue growth. This emphasis on service and software bodes well for IBM's success in the document imaging systems market. Another bright spot in IBM's product portfolio are its token ring networks, which have finally reached market parity with Ethernet.

7.2 IMAGING SYSTEM OFFERINGS

IBM's imaging systems span the three major hardware platforms. The ImagePlus family allows users to tie a number of products together to interact with existing business applications, whether implemented at the work group or enterprise level.

For mainframe environments, IBM offers the *systems applications architecture* (SAA) ImagePlus *multiple virtual storage/enterprise systems architecture* (MVS/ESA), which supports high-volume operational and production applications, providing large organizations with centralized, enterprisewide document, folder, and workflow management.

For midsized businesses or large departments, IBM offers ImagePlus/400 for *Application System/400* (AS/400) environments. The ImagePlus/400 is designed for medium- to high-volume document storage and retrieval, automated workflow processes, and integration with other business applications. The ImagePlus/400 system takes advantage of the IBM SAA ImagePlus Workflow Application Facility/400 and ImagePlus workstation programs, as well as AS/400 hardware and software.

For PS/2 LAN-based environments running *OS/2 Extended Edition (OS/2 EE)*, IBM offers SAA ImagePlus/2. Jointly developed by IBM and Eastman Kodak, ImagePlus/2 is designed to meet low-volume needs of departments in large organizations, as well as the needs of small- to medium-size businesses that handle several hundred documents daily.

Although IBM would prefer that its customers use OS/2 in conjunction with Image-Plus/2, it offers a version of the workstation program that operates under DOS. The DOS version is command driven, whereas the OS/2 version uses Presentation Manager with full SAA-compliant screens. At this writing, IBM has demonstrated a version of ImagePlus/2 that works under Windows 3.1. The primary advantage of using OS/2 is that it offers powerful multitasking capabilities and the ability to window multiple sessions. For many image applications this is an important capability to have.

The components of an ImagePlus system are the same as those found in most other vendors' systems: scanner, display workstations, storage devices, and printer. The system application software implements folder and workflow management. Optional components include facsimile, OCR, and bar code recognition.

For users who want to manage image documents and workflow under IBM's UNIX-based *Advanced Interactive Executive* (AIX) operating system, IBM recommends Im-ageSystem, which is offered by Image Business Systems, an IBM business partner. ImageSystem works on IBM's RISC System/6000 processors and uses the PS/2 as a high-function image workstation.

A related IBM offering is the ImagePlus *high-volume transaction processing system* (HVTPS), which provides high-volume image processing for medium to large financial institutions with MVS/ESA environments. Normally, the ImagePlus systems do not read and interpret the contents of documents, but the HVTPS is an exception—it reads written amounts on checks. The product extends image processing to IBM's check-processing control system to provide faster, more efficient financial document handling capabilities.

7.3 IMAGEPLUS OVERVIEW

The high-end ImagePlus system operates on IBM System/370 or System/390 processors capable of running MVS/ESA. Four system components run on the host processor:

- Folder Application Facility (optional), which includes the Folder and Workflow Application, Folder and Document Management APIs, and Document Services APIs;
- Object Distribution Manager;
- Data Facility Product (DFP) *Object Access Method* (OAM);
- Optical storage subsystem.

7.3.1 Folder Application Facility

The Folder Application Facility is a panel-based, menu-driven, front-end application. It automates the traditional systems of filing, retrieving, and processing documents and folders and offers online help.

7.3.1.1 Folder Management

The Folder Management function of the Folder and Workflow application maintains on-line information about each document, once the ImagePlus system identifies the document. It also provides an indexing function for images, as well as folder and document security-level assignment functions.

Users can create unique identification schemes for storing scanned documents (image objects[1]) in electronic file folders. They can choose from any number of ways to identify folders, including an account number, customer number, student number, part number, or claim number. In addition, the folders can be categorized by type, such as graduate and undergraduate student folders. The folders can be subdivided with file tabs. For example, a student's folder can be subdivided by such tabs as "Admission and Application," "Medical Records," and "Academic Transcripts," so users can access appropriate records quickly. When the tabs are used to identify and retrieve specific records, they can be displayed side by side with related data files.

With a secondary indexing function, users can consolidate up to three different folder types under one heading, and they can list all folders grouped under a particular secondary index. Users can give each folder type a default value that specifies the folder description and security level. Separate security levels can also be given to each document in a folder.

The Folder and Workflow application provides users with a variety of maintenance options to view and modify image objects and the information about image objects. Folder processing can be suspended at any time, if a user needs to wait until more information can be supplied or additional action taken. When the additional information—a delayed form or signature, for example—becomes available, the user can resume processing at the point at which it was suspended.

The Folder and Workflow application allows batch storage processing of many documents at once. The batch storage process consists of validation, storage, and index updating, as well as document purge or delete from storage. The input to the batch process is usually provided by the high-speed capture subsystem of the Object Distribution Manager, which scans and stores documents in high volumes.

7.3.1.2 Workflow Management

The Workflow Management function of the Folder Application Facility automatically routes documents to the various operators, based on categories of documents and definitions. The categories are established in the user profiles created by supervisors at the time the ImagePlus system is configured for operation. When the imaging system is operational, users are only given work that is defined in their profiles. This feature can, for example, prevent inexperienced users from getting high-priority work or prevent users from

---

[1] An *object* is anything a user can manipulate as a single unit, such as an icon, form, window, text, font, graphic, image, or formatted data.

getting work that is more appropriately handled at a higher level of decision making. The function also tracks the status of work awaiting processing.

The supervisor functions that create user profiles can also be used to grant supervisory authority or folder-routing capabilities to users and to view and manage various work queues. To enhance security, a sign-on feature prevents a single user from signing onto the imaging system at multiple workstations. The system can validate passwords to allow only authorized personnel access to the Folder and Workflow application.

7.3.1.3 Application Programming Interfaces

The optional Folder and Document Management APIs are a collection of programmable commands that provide the functions for indexing, retrieving, and maintaining documents in the ImagePlus system. The APIs support the Folder and Workflow application. They also permit the Folder and Document Management functions to be extended to include the variety of documents that an organization might be storing in other systems or generating in other applications.

The Folder and Document Management APIs provide the following command processing functions to applications developers:

- Folder management commands that create, delete, retrieve, and update folder information;
- Object management commands that manage individual objects and groups of objects;
- Note management commands that add, count, and retrieve folder note entries;
- Object history commands that add, delete, and retrieve object processing events;
- Object pending commands that delete, retrieve, and resend pending object entries;
- Storage management commands that change storage management information.

The Folder and Document Management APIs also have command interfaces that use the Object Distribution Manager to perform synchronous storage and retrieval of objects in the CICS[2] environment.

A migration utility—including source code—is provided with the APIs. This utility automates the conversion of *Data Language 1* (DL/1) databases to DB2 tables, which are used by the Folder Application Facility. DL/1 is the data-manipulation language used in IBM's *information management system/virtual storage* (IMS/VS) environment, whereas DB2 is IBM's relational database management system.

The Document Services APIs provide a set of programming interfaces that allow developers to design applications that are specific to an organization's image processing requirements. The APIs permit the development of a wider variety of specialized, or selective-use, front-end applications.

---

[2]CICS is IBM's *customer information control system*, a program environment that allows transactions entered at remote computers to be processed concurrently by a mainframe host.

The document services APIs provide the following object command processing requests: store objects, display objects, print objects, and delete objects. They communicate these requests to the Object Distribution Manager.

Distributed with the Document Services APIs (as well as the Object Distribution Manager) is an *Interactive System Productivity Facility* (ISPF)-based application, which provides panels that can be used to maintain the support tables for the Folder and Document Management APIs, the Document Services APIs, and the Object Distribution Manager. This support table administration facility allows the user to view, add, and update data in a support table.

7.3.2 Object Distribution Manager

The Object Distribution Manager works as a file server for image objects and for nonimage objects, such as coded data. Positioned at the functional center of the ImagePlus system, the Object Distribution Manager coordinates the activities of the system's major components. It receives new image objects from the scanner-equipped user workstations and routes these objects to the OAM or to a sequential file for future batch or coded-data storage processing. The Object Distribution Manager also receives user requests for display, print, and other object processing functions. It passes these requests to the system's storage components, receives the requested objects, and routes the objects to the appropriate workstation or LU 6.2 application.

In conjunction with the APIs, the Object Distribution Manager supports the generation of the object name, collection names, user transaction handling reference, and symbolic host/symbolic workstation reference.

7.3.3 Object Access Method

The OAM provides the means for moving data between the peripheral devices and the host operating environment. By supplying storage criteria for the types of documents that will be processed and the rules that must be used in processing them, the OAM provides system-managed storage for objects and allows the storage management cycle to be controlled by the user. The OAM then automatically stores, retains, and subsequently migrates and deletes objects according to user-defined document processing cycles.

The OAM uses the storage criteria to store objects in a storage hierarchy consisting of a high-speed magnetic disk and a high-capacity optical disk. It maintains an object directory, which allows access to every object stored in the system, regardless of where in the storage hierarchy the object currently resides.

The OAM stores new objects and frequently accessed objects on high-performance magnetic *direct-access storage devices* (DASD), such as the IBM 3390. It migrates objects to an optical disk library when the objects reach the user-defined migration criteria. Image document retrieval from DASD takes from four to six seconds, whereas an image document retrieved from the optical disk library takes approximately 30 seconds.

If the document processing cycle includes the eventual deletion of archived material, the OAM simply erases the expired object's address information, resulting in its logical deletion. The OAM also supports the option of concurrently writing the object to a backup optical disk, which IBM calls *image shelf storage*.

The OAM tracks all magnetic and optical storage disks on the ImagePlus system, including all library and shelf optical disks. It also directs the mounting and removal of these disks, in answer to user needs, and the staging of objects between magnetic and optical storage, for enhanced response time.

The IBM 9246 Optical Library Unit is the centerpiece of the optical storage system. It includes FileNet's Optical Disk Storage and Retrieval Library Unit (OSAR 64 Model 1100) and two *Laser Magnetic Storage International* (LMSI) LaserDrive 1250E optical disk drives. The library unit also contains a mechanical accessor, to retrieve and mount the optical disks as needed, and storage slots for up to 64 disks. For large organizations, the library unit can be expanded to contain four disk drives.

For storage media, the IBM 9246 uses LMSI LM1200 optical disks. These are 12-in WORM optical disks that are capable of storing 128 GB of information on line, which is equivalent to over 2,500,000 page images at a typical size of 50 KB per page.

Figure 7.1 shows a typical IBM SAA ImagePlus MVS/ESA system and illustrates the various component relationships.

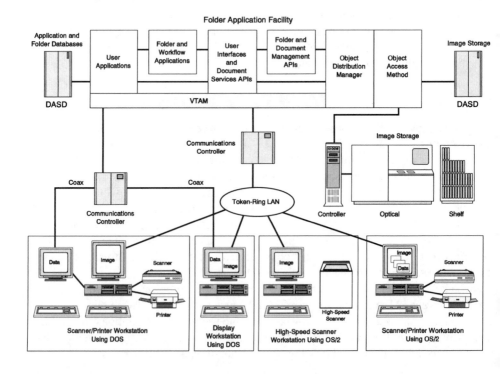

Figure 7.1 IBM SAA ImagePlus MVS/ESA system. *Source:* IBM Corp.

When connected to a token-ring LAN, an image workstation requires two types of cards: an image adapter card and a token-ring card. The image adapter card performs the image compression/decompression processing, to conserve network bandwidth. However, a recent software upgrade now allows compression/decompression to be handled by the workstation's CPU, eliminating the need for a separate card—provided that the workstation is a PS/2 Model 70 or higher. The token-ring card is used to establish an LU 6.2 session over the LAN between the workstation and the host. If the workstation is used to support 3270 sessions, a terminal emulation card is also required.

7.4 DOCUMENT ENTRY

As with any other imaging product, entering paper documents into the ImagePlus system involves two steps: indexing and scanning. These steps can be performed by using a manual process for each page or by using a high-speed scanner to enter large volumes of documents. With high-speed scanning, the batch storage process can be used to validate document indexing information, store the documents, and update the Folder Application Facility index and routing information.

The ImagePlus offers a number of scanners, including flatbeds and automatic sheet feeders from such vendors as Ricoh, Howtek, Bell and Howell, and Kodak. IBM's high-speed capture subsystem uses the Kodak ImageLink Scanner 900. This unit is equipped with a paper stacker for automatic feed and performs single-pass transport and duplex scanning, bar code reading, and page imprinting. The Folder Application Facility batch storage process uses output from the scanner to index and store documents and optionally route them for processing through workflow queues.

With the manual process, index information is entered using Folder and Workflow application panels. The system provides a temporary ID that uniquely identifies the document and associates the document with the folder into which it is to be placed. Then the document is scanned into the system at a scanner-equipped user workstation. The manual process is shown in Figure 7.2.

When documents arrive in the mail, they are taken to an operator workstation where the Folder and Workflow application resides. The operator uses this terminal to index the documents. The operator enters descriptive information about the documents and relates them to one or more electronic file folders.

At this point, the operator can also specify how the new documents are to be routed. The routing information might be indicated by the form number entered for the document. For example, a form number might indicate what department, work group, or individual should get the document first. The operator submits the indexing information to the Folder and Workflow application, which returns a temporary ID. This number is kept with the hard copy of the document. The document is then indexed and associated with a folder, and can be taken to a scanner-equipped workstation.

After the temporary ID is keyed in at the scanner-equipped workstation, each page of the document is scanned into the ImagePlus system. The scanner operator checks the image display to ensure that the resulting image is clear and legible. The collection of

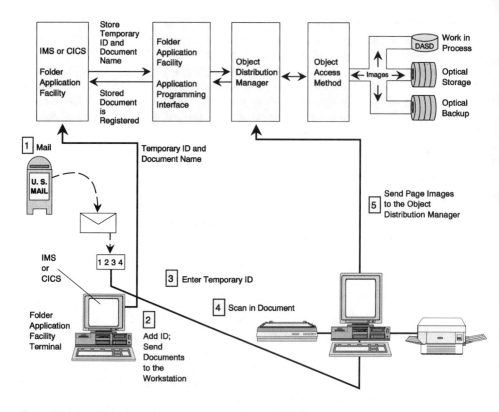

Figure 7.2 Manual indexing and scanning processes. *Source:* IBM Corp.

scanned-page images is then submitted to the IBM SAA ImagePlus Object Distribution Manager MVS/ESA as an image object.

Within the ImagePlus system, the Object Distribution Manager receives the new image object and routes it to the OAM, which stores the new object on magnetic disk. The Object Distribution Manager also notifies the Folder and Workflow application that the document with the temporary ID has been scanned and stored in the OAM.

With the image object now registered in the system, the Folder and Workflow application places the object in a routing queue for subsequent routing to an appropriate user via the Workflow Management function. The Folder and Workflow application then updates the indexes and makes the object available for processing.

7.5 WORKFLOW

Users can process documents that are assigned specifically to them, or they can process work that is defined in their user profiles. In a standard request the user simply issues a command instructing the system to get work and a document is provided for processing.

The Folder and Workflow application determines the kinds of objects the user is authorized to process and selects from this group the object with the highest priority. In a request for a specific object the user views the documents of a folder and selects the desired item. For both types of requests the object and any related data are retrieved and sent to the workstation. This process is shown in Figure 7.3.

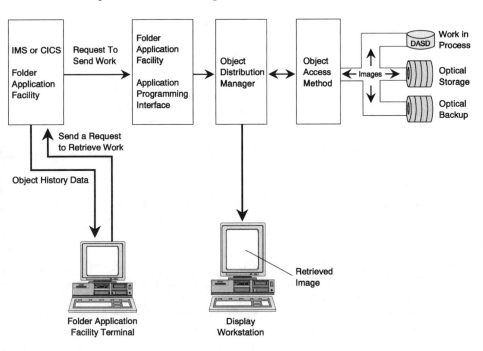

Figure 7.3 Retrieving a document for processing. *Source:* IBM Corp.

The first page of the selected object appears on the workstation's image display monitor. The user is able to scroll through and manipulate the displayed image using the functions provided by the workstation program. The object's processing history can be displayed on the workstation's data display monitor at the user's request. This processing history presents an audit trail of all work performed on the object up to that point. The supervisor also has access to this information, independent of any workstation operator.

Within the Folder and Workflow application objects are either in the routing queue or filed. Objects are filed if they do not need processing or if processing is complete. Filed objects can be put back into the routing queue upon command by a workstation operator or can enter automatically when it is time for processing.

Generally, users will process and then file documents, but they also have the option of holding a document, which delays further processing until a specified date and time. Documents can also be rerouted to other users on the ImagePlus system. Sometimes the supervisor will reroute documents to balance the workload among operators.

The Folder and Workflow application helps users track their assignments. Users can call up a list of documents currently assigned to them or all of the documents belonging to a specific folder currently being routed. When viewing this information users can access the processing history of a document and perform maintenance on the document. Users can manage processing of the document by reassigning it to the person who handled it last or by suspending it for later processing, using the hold capability.

Based on the information entered during indexing, documents can be prioritized for processing. A base priority value is set and incrementally raised each day the document remains unprocessed. When work is requested by a workstation user, the system responds with the highest priority document that user is qualified to work on. This helps assure that work is distributed evenly and that the most critical work is handled first.

The workflow management function can also handle the unpredictable processing requirements of a business. For example, when it is discovered that a document being processed is missing key information, it can be turned back to the previous workstation to have additional work performed before it is processed any further. To accomplish this, the document can be changed from one routing queue to another or assigned specifically to a user for priority processing.

Workflow management provides the best illustration of productivity improvement in the office environment. In large organizations there are tens of thousands of paper documents processed daily, most of them scattered across desks in hundreds of different offices and cubicles. It is impossible to measure the work waiting to be done, let alone check on its progress. With the workflow management software of an enterprisewide imaging system, each document can be individually tracked, assigned a priority for control, and selected for processing from input queues. This allows supervisors to measure the productivity of workers with statistics generated by the system, which in turn allows management to more accurately forecast staffing requirements and make other workload-related decisions.

7.6 FOLDER MANAGEMENT

Documents can be indexed into folders after scanning. Up to three secondary indexes can be assigned to a folder or group of folders to provide alternative means of identification. For example, an employer insurance policy number can be used to group all employee claims for that policy. The workstation user can display a list of folder contents and select a particular document for viewing or printing. Likewise, a list of folders grouped under a particular secondary index can be listed, a folder selected, and a list of its contents displayed. Documents can be moved from one folder to another.

Folders can be created with attributes such as folder type and security level. These attributes can be updated as needs change. Folders can also be created with temporary IDs that can be changed later to permanent IDs. This is useful for a bank or mortgage company, when, for example, customers apply for loans. The folder can be assigned a temporary ID and, when the loan is approved, a permanent ID can be assigned.

As objects are processed history events are created, and the workstation operator can add comments about these events to provide details about processing. These comments can be forwarded with the file to the next workstation operator.

The folder management function maintains information about all image objects, including their relationship to folders. The following folder maintenance capabilities are provided:

- Change folder identification;
- Delete folder notes;
- Display folder note details;
- List folder notes;
- Update folder attributes.

The following maintenance operations can be performed on documents or pages within documents:

- Add a document;
- Append a document;
- Copy a document;
- Display a document;
- Display a document's processing history;
- Display document details;
- Export a document;
- Index and route documents individually;
- Route related documents together;
- List all documents in a folder;
- List document versions;
- Move a document;
- Print a document;
- Update a document;
- Move pages from one document to another.

The following page-related actions can be performed:

- Delete
- Rearrange
- Replace
- Insert

The Folder and Workflow application can be customized to store related folders and their documents for use by a specific organizational function, such as accounts payable, accounts receivable, customer service, or personnel management. Separate Folder and Workflow applications for each of these functions can be defined with their own ID. That way, the folders and documents associated with each organizational function can remain separate and independent of the others. When workstation operators sign on to the Folder and Workflow application, they specify the organizational function they work in by entering the appropriate ID. Once the organizational function is accessed, the operators can view and work with the folders and documents that are associated with it. When a new folder is added, it is automatically identified with that functional area.

Other line-of-business applications can be accessed, unless the workstation operator is locked out of sensitive areas with appropriate security.

7.7 CONVENIENCE FEATURES

IBM's Folder and Workflow application includes a number of convenience features that make daily image processing easier. The application allows panels to be customized by the organization to suit particular work environments. For example, panel titles, data field headings, and data field names on the panels can be changed to match current office terminology. Figure 7.4 shows a sample add and route document panel; the "Routing line of business" field indicates the type of business associated with the document. The example input value is "HOM," indicating home owner, which might be used in an insurance environment. The Workflow Management function uses the field for routing purposes; both the data field name and the input value can be changed to reflect the organization's terminology.

```
F620                Add and Route Document

Type information and then press Enter.
— — — — — — — — — — — — — — — — — — — — — —

   Form number...................          Security class........
   File tab...........................          Date received........
   User defined date............
   Paper kept......................  1. Yes    2. No
   Description.....................

   Comments




   Document Routing Information
      Routing line of business................  HOM
      Transaction type.........................

   Temporary ID for scanning...............


F1=Help  F3=Exit  F6=Routing details  F12=Cancel
```

Figure 7.4 Sample add and route document panel. *Source:* IBM Corp.

Some panels come prefilled with appropriate default values. Whether the panels contain default values or are customized with user-specified values, they can be carried forward to subsequent panels. For example, if index information is being entered for several invoices all belonging to the same customer, selected information for the customer will be carried forward to the related panels. Likewise, in the development of user profiles for new workstation operators, the information from existing user profiles can be used as a time-saving template.

7.8 SUPERVISOR CAPABILITIES

System supervisors build a user profile for each ImagePlus workstation operator. The user profile includes unit codes that specify the categories of documents each person is authorized to process. By specifying these codes supervisors control how the Folder and Workflow application distributes work to system users. Supervisors can modify existing profiles to reflect new workflow requirements or changes to operator qualifications.

The Folder and Workflow application gives supervisors several ways to balance shifting workloads. Supervisors can monitor work queues in several ways that workstation operators cannot; they can even loan workstation users to other departments. Supervisors can view the work pending in any work queue by various categories, such as assigned work, suspended work, and all work related to a specific customer.

At any time supervisors can change the unit codes and other information within user profiles, providing or denying access to users, redirecting or suspending work items, or reassigning documents from one user to another.

In addition to being able to add or delete user profiles on the system, supervisors can add document assignment authority or supervisory authority to a user profile, so that, for example, a senior workstation operator can take over in the supervisor's absence.

7.9 ONLINE HELP

The Folder and Workflow application includes comprehensive online help, which can be categorized as follows:

- Configuration facility help, which provides online help for each configuring facility panel, as well as detailed information about each panel;
- Installation facility help, which provides online help for each installation facility panel, as well as detailed information about each panel;
- Workstation program help, which provides detailed information about scanning, displaying, modifying, and printing documents;
- Message help, which explains why a message was displayed and what the user must do to correct a problem;
- Command help, which lists all the commands and their parameters. The functions of the keys are also explained.

7.10 IMAGEPLUS/2 Application Facility/2

ImagePlus/2 was developed jointly by IBM and Eastman Kodak. The product consists of two parts: Application Facility/2, a system management program; and Services Facility/2, an enabling base.

The Application Facility/2 consists of two parts: a system administration program and an image processing program. The facility provides a system management solution, programming tools for integrating the management system with the users' other business applications, and a development environment for image processing applications.

The system administration program allows the system manager to create and customize the applications provided in the Application Facility/2. The system manager can control access to the system, define workflow for documents, and customize the image processing program to meet departmental needs. A set of APIs can be used to integrate the Application Facility/2 into existing line-of-business applications.

7.10.1 System Administration Program

The system administration program performs the following functions:

- Defines the components of items stored in the "file room," where all documents are held. The administrator uses this program to define index classes and index fields and to associate index fields to each class. In addition, for each user, the administrator establishes processing options, specifies document routing procedures, and determines how documents will be controlled and stored.
- Defines storage classes, which provide the user with the ability to manage where and how long an object resides in the system. A user can control the length of time an object resides on magnetic tape, optical disk, or the shelf.
- Defines work baskets, which are used to store and distribute groups of image items to individual users. To define a work basket, the administrator names the work basket, indicates whether users will select items from the work basket or have items assigned to them, specifies how many items a work basket can hold before notification of an overflow condition, and lists the users who can access the work basket.
- Defines workflow, to control the movement of an image document through a sequence of work baskets. This balances work assignments among operators, reduces backlogs, and allows changing business priorities to be accommodated.
- Specifies security parameters, such as user IDs and passwords, and identifies the types of access and processing options given to users.

7.10.2 Image Processing Program

Users can perform the following operations with the image processing program:

- Capture images via a scanner or facsimile device. Captured mages can be grouped into folders manually or automatically, for concurrent access over the LAN by multiple users.
- Identify documents via indexing, so they can be recognized by the system. Users select from index classes to determine the indexing criteria and storage media for a document. Based on the index class specified, the system displays a set of fields in which the user enters the index information that identifies the item in greater detail for file room storage.
- Add personal notes to the document or folder, which features the author's user ID, date, and time stamp.
- Process documents in the workflow sequence established by the system administrator.
- Store a document or folder on either magnetic or optical media, based on frequency of use.
- Retrieve an item by searching for it in the file room and displaying it on the workstation monitor. Search criteria might consist of one or more of the document's index values. The more values entered, the more precise and efficient the search.

7.11 CONSULTING SERVICES

IBM is devoting more of its resources to general business consulting and systems integration services than previously and has created an Image Solutions Group. The group is geared to offer full life-cycle consulting, from re-engineering business operations to implementing full-blown enterprisewide imaging systems. Interestingly, in its consulting capacity, the company recommends non-IBM components as well as its own components, according to user needs.

7.12 EDUCATION SERVICES

In addition to publications in the ImagePlus system library, IBM provides customers with several educational opportunities, including self-study courses developed by *Science Research Associates* (SRA) and lecture courses by experts, which are reinforced by hands-on laboratory training.

The self-study courses describe all ImagePlus functions, identify the major components of the system and their interaction, determine hardware and software requirements, and provide information for planning, proposing, and designing an ImagePlus system.

The lecture courses and laboratory sessions provide information on how to install, customize, and maintain an ImagePlus system. The specific topics covered include implementing the Folder Application Facility, Object Distribution Manager, OAM, and optical storage subsystems. Backup and recovery procedures are also covered.

7.13 CONCLUSION

From the perspective of IBM, document imaging fits nicely with a software and services orientation, which the company is emphasizing in light of slumping hardware sales. All indications point to IBM's success with the ImagePlus line. The line brought in $605 million in revenues in 1991, and $1 billion is projected for 1992. According to the company, there are about 700 ImagePlus installations, representing 450 midrange and 250 mainframe systems.

Chapter 8

Unisys InfoImage System

8.1 INTRODUCTION

Unisys Corp. is among the top five computer manufacturers. Like IBM and others, Unisys has experienced a serious dip in revenues in recent years, losing $2.4 billion between 1989 and 1991. Starting in 1991 Unisys reorganized itself. The company sold its networking subsidiary Timeplex, removed 20,000 items from its product portfolio, eliminated 10,000 jobs, retrained 25,000 employees, and refocused its global marketing strategy on four industry segments: financial services, airlines, communications, and government.

Unisys is a vociferous advocate of open systems. The company has demonstrated and reaffirmed its commitment to open systems in terms of applications portability, systems interoperability, and products being built in accordance with industry standards and the *open systems interconnection* (OSI) model.

Unisys' commitment to providing open system solutions is best demonstrated by its progress in supporting OSI standards for product, sales, and interoperability testing. Unisys is among the few companies aggressively selling OSI products, and it operates a test facility in Malvern, Pennsylvania, which has an annual budget of $1.5 million.

The *OSI Interoperability Lab* (OSIL) has an 11-member technical staff and is accredited by the *National Institute of Standards and Technology* (NIST). The lab assists customers with interoperability problems, such as when a Unisys customer encounters an interoperability conflict between new Unisys equipment and its installed base of IBM equipment.

The *Unisys Architecture* (UA) is the strategic framework within which the company promises to help users link disparate Unisys processors to one another and—using OSI protocols—to the systems of other vendors. The objective of the UA is to enhance the efficiency, flexibility, and portability of applications while, at the same time, improving the consistency and friendliness of end-user interfaces for accessing applications, databases, and networks.

This commitment to open systems and industry standards is also reflected in the company's InfoImage system for document imaging applications. Unisys workstations use

MS-DOS for the operating system (or UNIX), and the application software takes full advantage of the Windows environment. Although Unisys emphasizes its own hardware, the user is free to mix and match components from other vendors.

8.2 PRODUCT OVERVIEW

InfoImage Folder (Figure 8.1) is the centerpiece of the InfoImage system and comprises modular building blocks that allow users to acquire only what they currently need, with the idea of adding on later to accommodate future growth. This modularity also allows components to be optimally distributed throughout a department without disrupting existing physical arrangements.

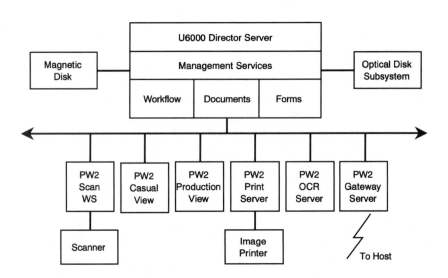

Figure 8.1 InfoImage system overview. *Source:* Unisys Corp.

The folder is the means of organizing documents through the power of the relational database. Folders do not have to contain related documents. Instead, for example, they can be organized to contain different documents for jobs pending. By indexing and then retrieving documents with the same index value, the user has an electronic version of a manila folder. Index data can be entered manually through OCR, *document data exchange* (DDE), or a combination of these methods. Indexes are stored in the relational database on the director server, nonindex data is stored on optical disk.

Through the document assembly process, pages are organized in a specific sequence to form a document. Document assembly can be performed automatically or manually.

Automatic assembly takes place as part of the scanning process, during which the operator chooses such assembly attributes as micrographics patches (i.e., encoded document separators), bar codes, or a fixed number of pages within a document. In manual assembly the operator identifies the documents by indicating to the system where the document separator should be placed. With either method the operator can use edit functions to reorder, copy, cut, paste, or delete pages.

Document assembly has two parts: pre-assembly and postassembly. During assembly the user indicates to the system the pages that make up a particular document and the order of those pages. Prior to assembly the system contains batches with unordered pages. After assembly the pages are ordered to make up a document. Figure 8.2 shows the hierarchy of objects for document entry operations.

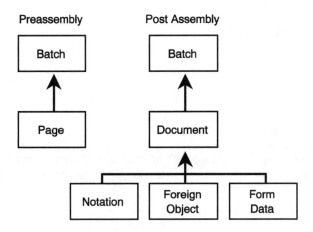

Figure 8.2 Hierarchy of objects for document entry operations. *Source*: Unisys Corp.

Figure 8.3 shows the hierarchy of objects during the document-use, or "postcommittal" phase. Documents can be directly attached to a folder or subfolder. A folder can contain up to eight levels of subfolders. There can be several objects attached to a document, such as a page, a notation, a foreign object, or form data. Notations allow the user to enter general information about a document.

Foreign object refers to any DOS file—such as a spreadsheet, word processing file, or a graphic—that a user might attach to an image document in the windows environment. When a foreign object is imported into a document or folder, it appears as an icon in the window and must be viewed from there. Further manipulation of the foreign object must be done from within the original DOS application.

Annotations are similar to notations, but are associated with individual pages rather than with the entire document. A maximum of 20 annotations can be attached to a page. Form data includes index and nonindex data.

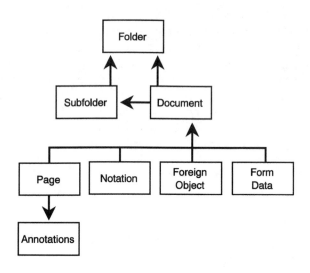

Figure 8.3 Hierarchy of objects for document-use operations. *Source:* Unisys Corp.

8.3 SOFTWARE COMPONENTS

The InfoImage Folder system is comprised of four software components: Folder application software, Director software, Database software, and Event Manager software.

8.3.1 Folder Application Software

The Folder application software runs on Windows-equipped Unisys Personal Workstations (PW2) or DOS-based microcomputers. Two software modules comprise the Folder application: the Folder Manager and the Forms Creator. The Folder Manager works with Windows and provides the user interface. The Forms Creator allows the user to set up system forms, such as indexing and retrieval request screens, and application forms, such as approval and data entry screens. An indexing screen, for example, allows a user to associate attributes with a document that might then be used to retrieve the document.

The Folder application software also has optional modules for managing scanning, OCR, printing, and communications functions.

8.3.1.1 Folder Manager

The Folder Manager provides the following image manipulation capabilities:

- Image display;
- Display sizing;
- Page image enlargement or reduction;

- Page image magnification;
- Reverse video (white on black or black on white);
- Image rotation in 90° increments;
- Panning (moving an image across a view screen).

The Folder Manager also includes these software tools, which users with the appropriate security approval can access:

- *Scan Manager.* This module facilitates the document[1] input process at one or more designated workstations.
- *File Cabinet.* This tool provides users with query access to the system database. Matching objects[2] are returned in a list format, from which they can be selected for retrieval.
- *In-Box.* This tool receives data objects from other points on the network. The In-Box display keeps users informed about objects that are waiting to be reviewed or processed. Users can access objects from the In-Box.
- *Terminal emulation.* Via icon selection, users open an emulator window and can choose an appropriate emulator for host-system access for PC-to-host file transfers.
- *System administration.* This software allows the system administrator to manage form, queue route, and tool assignments, as well as routing. Management includes: specifying the form views, queries, printers, and desktop tools that a user or user group might access; associating a form or overlay file with a document class; defining and changing a default route for a class of documents; assigning queries and routes for a user or user group; designating or deleting a query form; and installing foreign applications so that a non-InfoImage Folder application will be executed automatically when a foreign object is exported.

8.3.1.2 Forms Creator

Another major component of the Folder application software is the Forms Creator. Pull-down menus and fill-in screens guide system administrators in the forms creation process. The software allows administrators to set up forms that will be used on the system, such as query screens, and applications forms, such as data entry and approval screens. Form fields can even be linked to image zones, so that when an image is displayed a corresponding form is also displayed. As the user tabs through the fields on a form linked to image zones, at each field the corresponding area on the image is highlighted.

The Forms Creator allows multiple views of the same form to be created. For example, the system administrator can assign certain index fields to be visible to one worksta-

---

[1] A *document* is one or more ordered pages with associated notes, annotations, and form data. Each document belongs to a document class.

[2] *Objects* are viewable entities within the Folder Manager. Folder objects include annotations, batches, documents, folders, foreign objects, and pages.

tion operator but not to another operator. The same form can therefore look different to the two operators even though the system stores it as one document form.

If OCR is available, data can be captured from image zones and moved into appropriate form fields. Data captured via OCR can be used for automatic indexing. Another type of OCR is full-page, whereby typewritten material can be turned into ASCII data or a word processing format for storage, manipulation, or both. The form can also be linked to an interactive terminal emulation screen for bidirectional movement of data between the form and host.

The Forms Creator software allows system administrators to perform these additional tasks:

- Define image zones and set up image zones for magnification;
- Customize form views;
- Assign read-only, read-and-write, and verify qualifications and hidden characteristics to form field data for specific form views;
- Link fields to a flat file for data capture;
- Set up automatic host screen verification to ensure that the correct host screen is displayed prior to data exchange;
- Link forms to multipage, zoned-image documents;
- Set up field editing formats and default values;
- Specify copy of one field to multiple fields;
- Create user-defined field help;
- Calculate field values by arithmetic formula;
- Create table formulas, including columnar computations—sum, average, maximum, and minimum;
- Predefine pop-up value lists by field;
- Establish user exits by field, to allow users to interface with external workstation-resident programs to process data or calculate the field value;
- Create and store image overlays.

8.3.1.3 Other Folder Application Modules

Other software modules can be added to the Folder application software, including a Scan Manager, OCR Manager, OCR Implementor, Bar Code Manager, and Print Manager.

The Scan Manager resides on the workstations that have scanners. This software controls and manages input from the scanning device, the InfoImage Folder Scanner. With this software the operator can select scanner settings to ensure quality images and set up batch entry of documents.

A batch can be a collection of pages, uncommitted documents, or both. Documents are not retrievable when they are still in a batch. The user creates a batch by organizing pages into a logical grouping for processing. However, when the user scans pages and documents into the InfoImage system, the system creates an electronic batch, which exists until committal. The electronic batch ceases to exist at the end of the committal process. At this point documents can be retrieved.

At the scan workstation the operator indicates the total number of documents and pages in a batch. During scanning the system increments the numbers as well. Any discrepancy between actual and control totals is displayed to the user. At the time of scanning the user can set page attributes, including page orientation, size, and image resolution. The storage format is *tagged-image file format* (TIFF) and the compression method is CCITT Group IV.

For two-sided scanning, the operator scans all the pages on side one, then scans the pages again on side two. The system does the collation. Any discrepancy between the number of front-side pages and the number of back-side pages is displayed to the operator.

The system identifies any pages that are of unacceptable quality, listing the pages that must be rescanned, along with the reasons why. When the page is rescanned the system overwrites the rejected page with the rescanned page and updates the batch. When the entire batch is finished it is routed to the next operation. Quality checks can be performed interactively with the scan operation—the operator can view each page as it is scanned and rescan the page if necessary.

The OCR Manager is also used by the scanner-equipped workstation. This software allows operators to read and extract the contents of an image—either whole pages or zoned areas of pages. The extracted contents are converted to ASCII text. In zone mode the OCR Manager writes data from predefined zones on the image to corresponding data fields on an index form.

OCR Implementor software enables workstation operators to access captured data and use forms that contain OCR data captured by the OCR Manager.

The Bar Code Manager captures micrographics-patch and bar-code information during document entry for use in document-type recognition and document-assembly control. Documents containing the same identifier are grouped accordingly, with page separators, if necessary.

Interactive processing software modules provide the workstations with concurrent access to the InfoImage Folder system and host data applications via terminal emulation. Simultaneous views of both are available under Windows. Data exchange can even be automated between systems to further improve user productivity.

8.3.2 Director

The InfoImage Folder Director software resides on the workstations and the Unisys U6000 server. System functions are invoked by both workstation operators and the system administrator. The InfoImage Folder application calls the workstation's directory library routine, which, in turn, manages the interface to the U6000-based Director software. The Director includes menu-driven software for defining indexing parameters, queues, security, and document-class parameters.

A *document class* is a group of documents that have the same index information and use the same indexing form. A document class can have only one indexing form associated with it. For example, loan applications might constitute one document class and invoices and checks constitute two more.

The Director application service modules manage the display and distribution of all images by performing:

- Document and annotation storage and retrieval;
- Magnetic disk-based caching of images;
- Batch and single document entry services;
- Generic queue management services;
- Queueing and routing of print requests;
- Security and user validation;
- Backup and recovery procedures.

In addition, system administrator functions implement system setup, database maintenance, and system security options. With regard to security, user names and passwords are established on the Director server through the *Application Executive* (APEX). The system administrator logs on to the Director server and creates user names and passwords. When a user logs onto InfoImage Folder at a workstation, the system validates the user name and password.

The Director provides batch, document, cache, index, queue, print, security, and distribution services.

Batch services provide the mechanisms for document entry, which is a series of steps from image and information input through the committal process. A *batch* is a collection of user-grouped images and the related information that identifies how the images should be assembled into documents by indexing. Batch entry services enable the user to: create a batch; add images to a batch; assemble images into documents; index documents; validate certain conditions on batches, documents, and images; queue a batch for committal; retrieve batch contents; and delete a batch. The commit process involves moving the contents of the batch to the migration queue and moving the indexes to the index database. All pages must be accepted through the quality-check process before a batch can be committed. Once the items are accepted and moved to the queue, they can be accessed by users, and the batch is deleted from the system.

Document services manage the storage and location of images across the InfoImage Folder network. They are responsible for the movement of images between cache and optical disk and the committal and deletion of documents.

Cache services provide for storage and retrieval of images and other data on magnetic disk. The InfoImage Folder system uses four types of cache:

- *Batch cache* provides protected storage for uncommitted batches.
- *Page cache* stores retrieved document pages, which are ageable, and page images for committed documents awaiting migration to optical storage, which are locked in cache until migration.
- *Print cache* stores print requests.

- *User cache* provides permanent locked storage for system objects that contain information required by the workstation applications.

Batch images, user cache objects, and images awaiting migration are not ageable. Retrieved images and print requests are ageable, which means that the oldest (least recently used) objects can be deleted from cache as the system requires space for new entries. Batch, document, and print services use cache services as a temporary storage area. The configuration of a cache, including its maximum size, is defined during system setup.

Index services provide access to the index database and support index database-related operations, including indexing, updating, querying, and performing administrative functions. The index database consists of a set of relational database tables that manage document index records, folders, and queues.

Queue services support workflow operations, as defined by the system administrator functions. Typically, the system provides mechanisms to control access to documents and folders, server functions, forms used to access the document database, queues and inboxes, and workstation application tools and functions.

Queues are established on the server by the system administrator, who defines the fields in the queue, along with such attributes as access rights, field name, and length.

Print services provide the means for printing documents and the annotations, notations, and index information associated with documents. The two types of print service are local and remote. Local printing occurs at the workstation, remote printing occurs at another point on the LAN. Items that can be printed include batches, documents in a batch, committed document notes, and pages.

Security services provide access to the security database stored on the Director server. The security database contains all user group definitions, as well as function-access restrictions. The security levels are: user, object, session, group, and function.

When a user logs on to a workstation, security services enable the workstation to download the set of "credentials" associated with the user, which enforces access restrictions. Security services also allow the workstation application to check access restrictions locally before attempting to access server resources.

Distribution services are used when multiple U6000 Director servers are deployed on the network. As its name implies, this function distributes software across the network.

8.3.3 Database Software

The InfoImage Folder Database software provides a *relational database management system* (RDBMS) platform, which is accessed by the InfoImage Folder Director and interfaces. The RDBMS provides file management support for the index database and queue subsystem. The software operates on the Director server and is based on Oracle Corporation's Oracle RDBMS.

The Database software provides such capabilities as fast commits, deferred writes, fast data and index searches, a configurable table, and index placement across disks. Database availability is maximized with online backup and recovery by table space, manual online and offline control by table space, and index placement across disks. Space usage is minimized through such methods as compressed transaction log, compressed rollback segments, and compact storage of clustered data.

Data contention among users is eliminated through a concurrency control mechanism, which provides row-level locking. Row-level, multiversion snapshots are provided for consistent queries that do not lock simultaneous updates. The Row Lock Manager supports an unlimited number of locks. The Database software also includes an interactive utility for database administration and performance analysis.

8.3.4 Event Manager

The Event Manager is workflow software that automates daily document imaging operations by monitoring the system and directing work according to the type of documents it finds. The Event Manager works in conjunction with InfoImage Folder to create, test, and execute specific workplans. A *workplan* consists of a series of steps that perform a desired processing function. Each step is composed of one or more rules—including index data or date and time—that automate a function in the document imaging process. By capturing this information in a workplan, the Event Manager simplifies routing requirements and eliminates operational errors associated with users' "next step" decisions.

Work is routed to queues created by the system administrator. These queues reside on the Director server. Workstation users with access permission can connect to these queues. Through the queues users can assemble documents and folders into *workpacks* for simultaneous processing and automatic routing. The Event Manager provides a set of application modules that enable:

- Site-specific workplan creation;
- Graphical representation of workflow;
- Simple point and click user interface;
- Automated routing of workpacks;
- Automatic print capabilities as part of a workplan;
- Priority settings;
- Statistical and historical reporting;
- Online help;
- Supervisor authority to manage and reallocate workpacks to other queues.

The three primary modules of the Event Manager are the Editor, Interpreter, and Reporting and Administration modules.

The Editor is a Windows-based application that resides on user workstations. It contains a Workplan Builder and Workplan Simulator. With the Workplan Builder users can create and view the flow of workplan steps. Each created step is associated with one or more rules that automate a function. All the required steps can be created at once and then the corresponding rules developed, or each workplan step and associated rule can be developed before proceeding to the next step.

The workplan appears on the workstation screen as a graphical series of buttons that represent individual steps and their flow through the system. Users can click on a particular step in a workplan to obtain information about workplan rules. No programming experience is needed for workplan development. Users rely on various insert, delete, copy, and cut and paste functions to build and edit workplans. After a user develops a workplan, the next step is to test and validate it using the Workplan Simulator.

The Workplan Simulator allows users to test workplans outside of the live production environment, to ensure that plans will work before they are released for general use. The Simulator takes a specified workpack from an Event Manager start queue and runs a simulation, following the rules established in the workplan. During the simulation the user can view a graphical representation of the workplan's routing path. The user can also receive information describing a rule that was executed, the resulting system actions, and any related error conditions. After the validation process is completed, the user can modify the workplan and continue to test it until the desired results are achieved. At that time, the final version can be copied to the production database.

The system maintains two separate workplan databases: a development database and a production database. Users can only edit and test workplans in the development database. This prevents users from accidentally modifying production workplans, which are already being used in the live work environment.

The Workplan Interpreter, which resides on the Director server, executes workplans designated by the system administrator, formulating routing decisions that are based on the rules specified in the plans. Overdue workpacks can be isolated and moved from one user's in-box to another user so that processing can take place as soon as possible. Workpacks can even be deleted from queues, if necessary. After reviewing processing data, users might restructure existing workplans to eliminate situations contributing to backlogs.

Users receive objects from other users in the system via the in-box. When users open their in-boxes they automatically display the list of queues to which they have access. They select a queue to display the objects that have been sent to a user or workgroup.

In addition to maintaining a database to track workpack activities, the Workplan Interpreter also maintains performance statistics, which, in turn, provide operator and system error reporting. Users access error information via the Reporting and Administration module, which resides on a PW2 workstation and accesses either the Director server or the Interpreter statistical database. Users can produce a variety of reports about workpacks, such as work-in-progress, overdue activities, and reports of past activities. They can display report data in a report window at their workstation, print reports, or save them to disk. The type and amount of data that users can save is set by the administrative function of the Reporting and Administration module.

8.4 HARDWARE COMPONENTS

In addition to the LAN, there are several other hardware components that comprise the InfoImage Folder system. These components are: the server, magnetic and optical disk drives, workstations, communication boards, a scanner, and a printer.

8.4.1 Server

The InfoImage Folder software resides on the Unisys U6000 server and provides image services to the client workstations. The server contains the index database, locator database, and data queues that are necessary to manage image processing, storage, and distribution across an InfoImage Folder network (Figure 8.4). The server provides for magnetic disk-based cache storage of image and other data objects. It also provides for the connection and control of *optical disk storage and retrieval* (ODSR) units and optical disk drives.

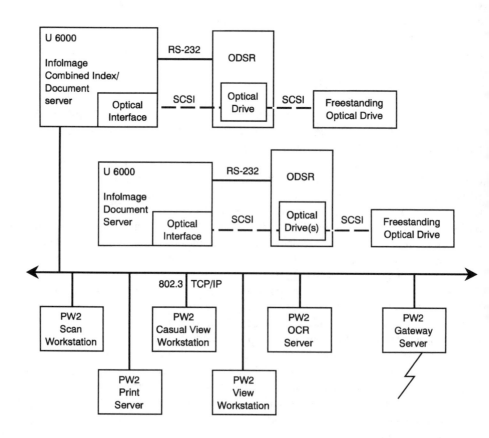

Figure 8.4 InfoImage Folder network configuration. *Source:* Unisys Corp.

An InfoImage Folder system might require more than one U6000 server. Multiple servers, each uniquely configured, can be networked together to support an organization's large system load requirements. Unisys offers two types of Director servers:

- *Combined index/document server.* This server supports both index and document services on a single U6000 server system. The optional Event Manager Workplan Interpreter executes on the combined server.
- *Document server.* Multiple UNIX server configurations use separate U6000-based document servers, which support the connection of optical disk subsystems and manage the physical storage, retrieval, and cache of documents.

8.4.2 Optical Disk Drives

Unisys provides high-density, 12-in, removable optical disk drives with its InfoImage Folder systems. The disks are WORM disks. The drives feature dual read-and-write heads for online access to both surfaces of a single 5.6 GB optical disk cartridge. The unit achieves an 80 ms average seek time, which is four to five times faster than most CD-ROM drives, but five to eight times slower than most magnetic disk drives. The sustained data transfer rate of the Unisys WORM drives is 700 KB per second.

The WORM drives come in two configurations: one for installation into an ODSR unit and the other for stand-alone use on a desktop. The stand-alone model accommodates one 12-in platter, while the jukebox version has a storage rack capacity of 107, 123, or 144 optical disk cartridges, depending on the number of internal optical drives installed. The ODSR is capable of holding up to six drives.

The ODSR unit responds to signals from the host or the jukebox itself for removal and insertion of the optical disk cartridges. A transport mechanism (robotics) selects an individual cartridge from any storage slot or disk drive or from the input/output station, and carries it to any other storage slot or disk drive or to the input/output station. The input/output station is the means through which cartridges are placed in or removed from the ODSR unit.

The ODSR unit connects to the U6000 InfoImage Folder Director server via an RS-232 cable, which controls the robotics, and a SCSI cable, which transfers the data to and from the optical disk drives inside the ODSR cabinet. The maximum time to access a cartridge is 10.5 to 12 seconds. This includes spin-down time for a cartridge currently in the drive, automated retrieval and insertion of a new cartridge, and spin-up time.

Optical disk drives, whether stand-alone or contained in an ODSR unit, connect to the Director server via a SCSI cable. Multiple drives can be daisy-chained via the SCSI cable to an optical disk interface. ODSR units connect to the Director server via an RS-232 cable and a SCSI cable. Each ODSR unit requires its own RS-232 port on the U6000. The SCSI cable connects the optical drives within the ODSR unit to the server.

8.4.3 Workstations

Unisys offers several types of InfoImage Folder workstations that are configured with different hardware and software, depending on the required functionality. All the workstations run under the MS-DOS operating system in a Microsoft Windows environment and are networked through the U6000 Director server. The following types of workstations—all Unisys PW2s—are available:

- Production view
- Casual view
- Scan
- Print server
- OCR server
- Gateway server

The production view and casual view workstations are configured to execute both the InfoImage Folder application and the image display in one set of windows concurrently, with a terminal emulation display in another window. When the workstation is directly connected to an application host communication line, the appropriate communications board is added to the configuration.

The production view workstation offers rapid, hardware-assisted image management. This is accomplished with a high-performance image kit that provides display controller and image processing functionality on one board. Using a separate board for processing-intensive tasks, such as rapid zooming, decompression, and 90° rotation of raster images, relieves the workstation's main CPU of this burden and results in accelerated image processing and manipulation. The board also controls the high-resolution, 19-in display monitor and provides CCITT Group IV image compression and image memory for fast screen graphics mapping and manipulation.

The casual view workstation provides software-driven image compression, mapping, and manipulation. No special image board is used. The workstation uses a standard VGA monitor and controller. This type of workstation suits low-volume environments, where lower screen resolution and a smaller display area (13 in) is acceptable.

The scan workstation hardware configuration is the same as the production view workstation hardware configuration, with the addition of a scanner/printer interface board. This board adds scanner control for the attached scanner and image compression functionality. When not used for scanning, the scan workstation can perform all the functions associated with a production view workstation.

A print server workstation acts as a dedicated network server for image printing. Networked users direct image print jobs to the print server through a print queue located on the U6000 Director server. The print server workstation hardware configuration is the same as the casual view workstation hardware configuration, with the addition of a scanner/printer interface board. This board controls the attached image printer and provides high-performance image decompression and formatting capabilities. The data is transferred from the print server to the printer via a high-speed video interface.

The OCR server workstation acts as a dedicated network server for OCR data capture. Networked users direct images to this workstation for OCR capture via an OCR queue located on the U6000. The OCR server consists of a PW2 workstation with a VGA monitor and an OCR board. The workstation can read digitized images, to capture full pages or zoned areas of type documents, and automatically forward the OCR data to the appropriate form or application.

When configured as a gateway server, a workstation acts as a dedicated network server for connection to and communication with an application host system. The server consists of a PW2 workstation with a communications board, as well as a VGA monitor and controller.

8.4.4 Communications Boards

Unisys offers a suite of communications, or terminal emulation, products that allow users to add image management to current applications within Unisys, DEC, UNIX, or IBM mainframe environments. These terminal emulation products facilitate image-enabled data processing through the use of DDE, which allows multiple Microsoft Windows applications, such as the InfoImage Folder and the terminal emulator screen, to exchange data.

The InfoImage Folder software offers parameter-driven setup of bidirectional data exchange between InfoImage Folder screen forms and the terminal emulation screens. This interactive data exchange provides an effective approach to multisystem integration. It allows T27, UTS, VT/UVT, or IBM 3270 sessions to be active and visible simultaneously with image view and manipulation. It also supports data file transfer from PW2 workstations to the host system and vice versa.

Host access is accomplished by direct connection of the individual workstations to the host communications line. To be directly connected each PW2 workstation must be equipped with the appropriate hardware (board) and software. With UTS, T27, and 3270 emulators[3] host access can also be achieved by dedicating a single workstation as a gateway to each type of system. User workstations connect to the gateway via Ethernet. In this arrangement the workstations and gateway server need a NetBIOS interface, which is included in the Unisys network communications software. If combined usage exceeds the host line rates of 19.2 Kbps, multiple gateways can be configured to meet user throughput requirements.

8.4.5 Scanners

The PW2-based scan workstation can be configured to support high-speed document scanners. Two scanners are available for desktop use. Scanner I handles documents up to 8.5 by 17 in. Scanner II handles documents up to 11.69 by 17 in. The scanners are controlled by the Scan Manager application, which runs on the scan workstations. The PW2 scan workstation is equipped with a scanner/printer interface board that supports physical con-

---

[3]The T27 emulator provides access to Unisys A, V, and B series mainframes; the UTS emulator provides access to Unisys 1100/2200 and System 80 hosts, via the Uniscope protocol; VT/VTS emulators provide access to DEC and UNIX host systems; and the 3270 emulator provides access to IBM mainframes, using the SNA/3270 protocol. All of the emulators support PC-to-host file transfers.

nection to the scanner, compresses images after scanning, and allows software control of scanner functions.

An optional OCR module can be added to a PW2 workstation, which enhances the InfoImage system by creating a network OCR server. In addition to allowing capture of complex text, this enhancement would enable actual page layout and structure to be preserved—without user intervention. The captured OCR data is then forwarded automatically to the appropriate application in a form it can use. Recognition speed is up to 28 characters per second. Unisys claims an accuracy rate of up to 95%, depending on font, format, pitch, and page and text alignment, as well as the resolution and clarity of the image. OCR output can be in the form of ASCII, WordPerfect, or MS-Word for Windows.

8.4.6 Printers

For printing image documents, Unisys offers its image printer, a high-duty cycle, desktop laser printer that features dual-cassette sheet feeders for standard- and legal-size paper. The printer connects to a PW2 workstation equipped with the scanner/printer interface and InfoImage Folder Print Manager software.

8.5 CONCLUSION

Unisys offers a comprehensive document imaging solution. In addition to hardware and software, the company offers a consulting service called the InfoImage Folder Professional Services Program, which includes feasibility studies, requirements definition, system and network design, systems integration, and maintenance support. (See Chapter 16 for additional information about this service and the similar services provided by other vendors.)

Chapter 9

Hewlett-Packard Advanced Image Management System

.1 INTRODUCTION

As the third largest North American computer vendor, the *Hewlett-Packard Company* (HP) is known for its minicomputers, such as the HP 3000 and HP 9000. While the rest of the computer industry has been adversely impacted by the 1990 to 1992 recession, HP has been one of the few companies to post gains—12.7% for 1991. The company's success is due in large part to continued strength in its desktop printing and multi-user UNIX systems, as well as the introduction, in 1991, of a new line of aggressively priced workstations and servers, the HP Apollo 9000 Series 700. It is also a very strong player in the market for portable test and measurement equipment.

HP is also competing with IBM and DEC in the area of network management, having announced its own integrated management platform, OpenView, in 1988. HP's approach differs from those of IBM and DEC in that it addresses other important issues, such as a standardized user interface for storing and retrieving management information. *Open Software Foundation's* (OSF) Motif provides a Windows-based user interface for management applications. OpenView Windows is a UNIX-based open GUI that other applications can interact with via published APIs.

In addition, HP's NewWave GUI for DOS-based computers pioneered many object management technologies that were adapted as standards by the Object Management Group in 1991. HP has applied its wealth of technical experience and expertise to the creation of a comprehensive development environment for its *Advanced Image Management System* (AIMS).

.2 SYSTEM OVERVIEW

HP's AIMS is a UNIX-based image management system that takes advantage of the client/server architecture (Figure 9.1). All image processing functions are performed on HP

Vectra PCs or IBM PCs and compatibles running MS-DOS and MS-Windows. The images are displayed on high-resolution monochrome or VGA monitors. Casual users of AIMS can use standard VGA monitors to view images of up to 70 dpi. Above that definition, a high-resolution monochrome monitor is required.

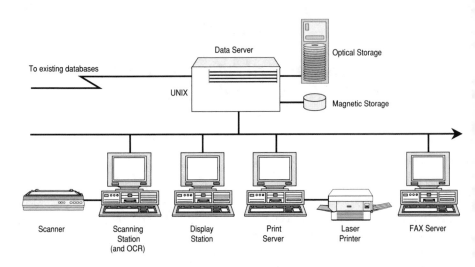

Figure 9.1 AIMS client/server architecture. *Source:* Hewlett-Packard Co.

Documents up to paper-size A3 are captured by scanners attached to designated PCs. Scanners operating at 15 seconds per page are used in distributed office environments. Higher speed scanners can be used for faster, centralized scanning. OCR can be performed on images as they are scanned in, and portions of the scanned image can be converted to ASCII text. Because AIMS supports free text searching the textual information can be used for indexing. The ASCII text can be included in word processing or desktop publishing documents. OCR requires a special card in the scanning PC.

Hardware-based compression is used on the images before they are transmitted over the LAN. Images are stored on magnetic or optical disks attached to the UNIX dataserver and decompressed upon retrieval for viewing on the monitor. Software-only compression and decompression is available for instances when high performance is less of an issue.

Laser printers providing 300 dpi output can be attached to any PC. Alternatively, dedicated PC can provide centralized print service. The dataserver controls central resources and holds the relational database in which the images and other data types are stored. SQL is used for transparent handling of large data objects. A facsimile server called HP OfficeFAX enables images in the dataserver to be faxed. Incoming faxes are automatically placed in the HP AIMS database.

Data on the HP 3000 minicomputer can be accessed via terminal emulation and linked with images via the *dynamic data exchange* (DDE) facility of MS-Windows. Be cause the linkage is performed automatically by the AIMS software it is transparent to the end user. AIMS also uses terminal emulation to integrate HP 3000, HP 9000, and IBM mainframe applications. AIMS can display information retrieved from an IBM database.

PCs running AIMS are networked together with IEEE 802.3 LAN protocols for bus-oriented networks (Ethernet and StarWAN). Through the use of an IEEE 802.3-to-IEEE 802.5 bridge, HP Vectra PCs on token-ring LANs can access AIMS and vice versa.

AIMS includes a variety of tools that enable developers to write applications. MS-Windows screens can be designed with the User Interface Builder. The User Interface Builder combines with a fourth generation language, Windows 4GL, to produce an application program that communicates with the dataserver by making SQL calls over the LAN. Windows 4GL also hides the complexities of MS-Windows, image manipulation and display, scanning, OCR, terminal emulator interfacing, and the facsimile interface. Each line of Windows 4GL replaces 10 to 20 lines of C language code.

Applications are largely independent of the UNIX machine that is used as the dataserver. For example, moving from a dataserver supporting ten users to one supporting many hundreds of users requires only a recompilation and a database move. Once developed, the application is installed on PCs, along with a low-cost set of AIMS run-time libraries.

To use the AIMS software each PC must be equipped with an *Advanced Image Processor* (AIP) card (Figure 9.2), which is a graphics coprocessor board that supports many of the AIP library functions. This card boosts the image processing capability and provides memory and high-bandwidth scanner and printer interfaces. The card consists of: a 32b processor optimized for graphics applications; compression/decompression hardware; image memory buffers that provide video RAM for scanner buffering, printer buffering, or both; conventional RAM for images and working memory; and two input/output-interface daughter boards that possess high-bandwidth interfaces for scanning and printing devices.

A software-only compression and decompression module, called Soft AIP, eliminates the need for the AIP board, but requires a 386 33-MHz computer for comparable performance.

Rather than focusing on specific user functions, the rest of this chapter describes the operational mechanisms and development environment of AIMS.

9.3 AIMS DATAMANAGER

At the heart of AIMS is HP's *relational database management system* (RDBMS), DataManager, which evolved from Informix Corp.'s database products through a joint development agreement between Plexus Software, Inc. and Informix. The AIMS DataManager (Figure 9.3) is a superset of Informix TURBO and SQL, with enhancements that permit the efficient handling of variable-length objects of up to 2 GB. This is achieved through the definition of two new data types—BYTES and TEXT—and by extensions to the SQL interface.

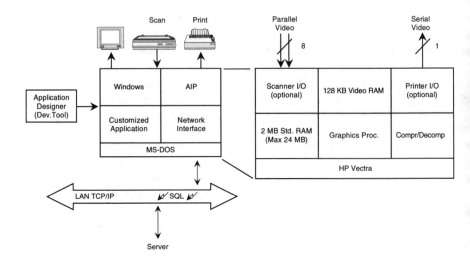

Figure 9.2 HP's Advanced Image Processor. *Source:* Hewlett-Packard Co.

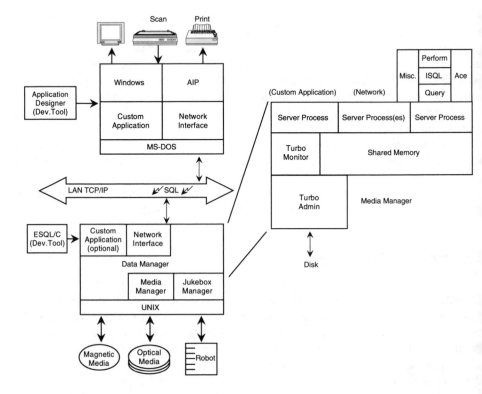

Figure 9.3 The AIMS DataManager. *Source:* Hewlett-Packard Co.

The BYTES data type was introduced to allow the efficient and flexible handling of unstructured objects, such as scanned documents, digitized voice (for annotations), and pictures. Efficiency is improved because the database does not have any knowledge of structure.

The AIMS database provides three ways of defining and handling BYTES:

- IMAGE: bit-mapped images, such as scanned documents and photos or graphics;
- ASCII: text as found in word processors and OCR-processed documents;
- BYTES: user-defined formats, such as digitized voice or sound.

The types of data BYTES refers to are listed in Table 9.1.

Table 9.1
BYTES Usage

Name	Abbreviation	Storage Format
BYTES used as image	IMAGE	TIFF
BYTES used as ASCII	ASCII	Text file
BYTES for user-defined format	BYTES	Binary file

TEXT refers to structured objects, such as programs, word processing documents, or other character-based information. The structure of these objects is used to compile an index that provides the basis for free text searches. TEXT can be stored in BYTE form if indexing is not important.

9.3.1 Free Text Search

Through the use of OCR a scanned document can be converted into TEXT. Free text search on indexed objects allows selection based upon the occurrence of words—words in proximity to each other, words in sequence, word roots, phrases, and other parameters that are commonly associated with the Boolean search capability. Like most indexing systems, provisions are also made for specifying a number of common words (a, and, the, of, etc.) to be excluded from the index in order to improve search performance.

9.3.2 Optical Storage Clustering

To handle large objects, HP has completely integrated optical storage media into AIMS. Data is stored on either WORM disks or rewritable optical disks in the order in which it is written and can not be moved afterwards. In conventional optical storage systems, closely related objects, such as two documents in the same logical folder that were stored a few months apart, are often written to different platters. HP's optical clustering mechanism stores related objects on the same optical platter. This speeds up image retrieval by eliminating the time-consuming platter changes that typically bog down input/output performance.

9.3.3 DataManager Modules

The AIMS DataManager consists of two standard modules, TURBO and Interactive SQL (ISQL), and one optional module, Embedded SQL (ESQL).

9.3.3.1 TURBO

Developed for the UNIX *online transaction processing* (OLTP) environment, TURBO is the database engine that manages image storage and retrieval at high speed, ensuring a high level of data integrity. SQL calls are accepted from different client stations and translated via a data dictionary into disk accesses. Each client is given separate TURBO server processes, which are dedicated to handling all database requests from that client.

In addition to being a database server, TURBO provides an operating environment for all database processes, which includes:

- Disk space management;
- Built-in backup and recovery mechanisms;
- A systemwide view of resource allocation, for overall performance optimization;
- A consistent interface, for easy interaction with the environment system.

Operation of the system is simplified and integrated at a single point of control, the TURBO monitor. The monitor is a full-screen, menu-driven utility that allows database and system administrators to monitor, control, and modify the operating environment, thereby simplifying system definition and initialization. Among the functions available from the TURBO monitor are status, logging, checkpoint, backup, and recovery.

In addition, the following performance enhancements are provided and can be modified via the TURBO monitor:

- Shared memory is provided between input/output and database processes to minimize disk accesses.
- Fast commits are achieved by flushing only transaction log records to disk immediately. Data is kept in shared memory and only written to disk at periodic checkpoints.
- Group commits optimize log file updates for several transactions at a time.
- Sorted writes also minimize disk access. At each checkpoint the pages in shared memory are sorted contiguously, thereby minimizing disk access.
- Performance measurements can be taken and fine tuning performed while applications are running on the systems.

Several features are included to keep the availability and integrity of the data high. For example, after a system failure automatic recovery of all databases occurs in a matter of minutes. This is achieved by restarting from a checkpoint and rolling forward according to the latest transaction log entry. Database consistency is maintained by *exclusive*, or *shared locking*, of database, table, page, or row during transactions. Applications can control the degree to which their transactions are isolated from the effect of other transactions by the setting of these row-read isolation levels:

- Dirty read, which indicates that contents are not guaranteed stable;
- Committed read, which indicates that contents are guaranteed stable;
- Cursor stability, which indicates that a row is locked during examination;
- Repeatable read, which indicates that a row is locked during transaction.

9.3.3.2 Interactive SQL

The other standard module of the AIMS DataManager is ISQL, a tool for creating and modifying database structures and designing non-Windows screen forms, menus, and report formats. Entering and retrieving information is supported by screen forms and files or interactive queries. This makes ISQL suitable for ad hoc processing of databases by both end users and programmers who need a tool for applications development and prototyping.

The SQL enhancements that support compound data types are supported by ISQL, with one caveat. Since ISQL only runs on the dataserver, with no graphics facilities, it is not possible to retrieve the image of a data object and display it on a screen. Another enhancement, the select system option, allows ISQL to access any other data server on the LAN.

A full-screen, menu-driven user interface, ISQL consists of four modules:

- ISQL Main Module, which presents and runs the main menu, with online help, and offers database select/create, table select/create, table create/modify, and system select functions;
- Formbuild form generator and *Perform* form processor, which, together with an editor, offer the facilities required to specify and execute screen queries;
- Query, which, with an integral editor, specifies and runs SQL queries, either one at a time or in sequence;
- Aceprep and *Acego*, which specify and run a report with data from a selection of tables and for which editing and management features are also available.

The complete menu structure of ISQL is provided in Figure 9.4.

9.3.3.3 Embedded SQL

ESQL allows preparation of dynamic queries and SQL database manipulation directly from customized C programs on the dataserver. In addition to supporting all the standard

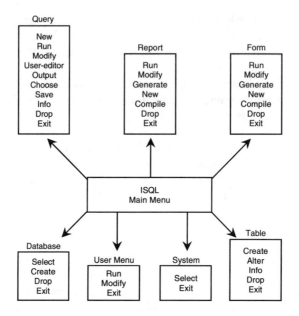

Figure 9.4 Menu structure of ISQL. *Source:* Hewlett-Packard Co.

SQL statements, ESQL provides a cursor control statement to manage multiple row output from a SELECT statement. The cursor accommodates SQL statements in procedural languages; it acts as a pointer to the current row in the virtual table, which allows the programmer to control the SELECTed data one row (record) at a time.

In most cases, the kind of database queries a user needs can be anticipated in advance. In some cases, the exact nature of a statement might not be known at compile time. *ESQL and Tools for C* (ESQL/C) provides a dynamic query facility with which ad hoc ESQL statements can be specified and executed at run time.

ESQL/C is a development tool for the C programmer, consisting of a compiler and library. The compiler is used during development only, while the library must be accessible during run time. The primary characteristics of ESQL/C include:

- Allows SQL queries from C programs and routines;
- Performs conversions and manipulations on decimal, date, and string data types;
- Uses C utility functions;
- Uses C functions from the Ace and Perform programs within ISQL.

9.4 AIMS MEDIAMANAGER

The MediaManager supports both 5.25-in and 12-in WORM and rewritable optical disks. This provides customers with more flexibility in designing systems based on their individual business requirements. Each format has its own advantages. The 12-in format suits customers who want low cost per megabyte of write-once storage, while the 5.25-in format fits best where customers need various price points and an industry-standard rewritable format.

MediaManager also manages dismountable optical devices under AIMS and controls multiple optical drives—stand-alone or in jukeboxes. Resource reservation, scheduling, and queuing are transparent to the database management. With optical storage fully integrated into SQL, there are no syntax differences to reconcile—as long as the optional SQL extensions are not used.

The data on each side of an optical platter is called a "volume," with the members comprising a volume constituting a "family." New volumes can be added as the current ones are filled. The system can handle a number of different families simultaneously. Sequential or clustered storage of images, large objects in BYTES format, or both are supported.

Applications access data through standard SQL statements and do not need to know the family or volume location to find images or manage drives or platters. However, because the data is part of the database and not an independent application, a volume configured on one AIMS system can not be read in an alien system without special provisions.

In conjunction with the AIMS JukeboxManager, the *dismountable HP AIMS MediaManager* (DIMMR) handles requests from the AIMS DataManager and controls and monitors optical media processes. It also maintains the family and volume table in the system.

The *dismountable input/output* (DIO) controls the transfer of data between shared memory and optical drives on a SCSI bus (two DIO processes per drive). The AIMS DataManager controls the data stream between shared memory and the application. Optical write-data is temporarily buffered on magnetic disks to allow the application to proceed with the next task immediately.

The *dismountable media utility* (DMU) prepares and manages optical disks for database use, accessed as family and volume. An AIMS volume contains only two partitions: *label* and *data*. The UNIX utilities are not needed for normal AIMS use because the DMU provides the necessary services.

The DMU has a screen-oriented user interface, which shows the status of all drives, including jukeboxes, as well as family and volume, reservation count, free space, and current user ID. There are 16 available commands, all listed, and online help that presents parameter and syntax information. Although screen-oriented, the commands can constitute or be part of UNIX script files.

HP offers a UNIX optical support package that consists of three parts: UNIX optical device drivers, UNIX backup utilities, and DMU commands.

The drivers are used by the AIMS MediaManager, JukeboxManager, and UNIX utilities for optical disk access. Although the drivers are customized for each interface adapter and drive combination, the format of the DMU commands is still the same for all. Bad sector reallocation is managed by the driver and is completely transparent to the user.

The backup utilities offer a variety of useful features, such as copy and compare, which can be used between platters and tape in any combination. The UNIX backup utilities apply only to WORM disks. Standard HP-UX commands provide the same features for rewritable disks.[1]

As previously noted, the DMU prepares and manages optical disks for database use. Among the utility commands are:

- Define/drop drives in the system, which causes the MediaManager's configuration table to be automatically updated;
- Shut down MediaManager, which halts all optical disk activity;
- Create an optical family and volume on a blank platter;
- Display statistics of families and volumes;
- Examine a platter for type, family, and volume;
- Mount or dismount an optical disk volume in a drive;
- Add or subtract a request for volume reservation;
- Copy one platter to another (requires a minimum of two drives);
- Compare two platters (requires a minimum of two drives);
- Dump contents of platter to tape;
- Restore or update contents of platter from tape;
- Display written sectors within a specified range.

9.5 AIMS JUKEBOXMANAGER

The JukeboxManager is an extension of the AIMS MediaManager that provides support for single and multiple optical jukebox units. It can reference platters stored outside the jukebox or jukeboxes. Operation is transparent to the user.

Optical jukeboxes rely on robotic systems, which allow a large number of optical platters stored in slots to appear on line to the computer system. An elevator unit fetches platters from storage and inserts them into the optical disk drive slot. The jukebox is controlled independently of the disk drive, and one jukebox can support several drives.

Typically, jukeboxes support 30 to 200 platters of 600 to 900 MB, contain two to 10 drives per jukebox, and complete platter exchanges within five to 25 seconds. HP's jukeboxes are available in 20-, 60- and 100-GB models and can be combined to access up to 280 GB of data. In addition, HP offers a stand-alone multifunction drive for low-cost, pilot-system development.

Platters can be moved freely in and out of the jukebox slot by the system administrator. Platters removed from a jukebox slot are classified as "on the shelf," but are still defined in the system.

The JukeboxManager consists of three modules: the DIMMR (previously described), the JukeboxManager Process, and the *Jukebox Manager Utility* (JMU). The JukeboxManager Process controls the elevator unit via an RS-232C serial port. SCSI con-

---

[1]HP-UX is based on and is compatible with USL's UNIX operating system. It complies with X/Open's XPG3, POSIX 1003.1, FIPS 151-1 and SVID2 interface specifications.

connection is also supported, with each jukebox requiring one SCSI address for the elevator unit and one for each drive in the jukebox.

The JMU is a tool for configuring and operating jukeboxes and drives. It is an extended version of the DMU utility in MediaManager, offering an expanded command set. The user interface is the same as for MediaManager. The jukebox extension allows the systems administrator to define jukeboxes, insert and remove platters, and keep track of the inventory of platters belonging to the system.

Jukebox utility commands permit the following operations to be performed:

- Define/drop jukeboxes in the system (same as DMU);
- Automatically move a platter from one slot to another;
- Physically insert a platter in the jukebox, either blank or used (from the shelf);
- Physically remove cartridges from the jukebox to the shelf;
- List all platters known to the system (i.e., all platters ever used);
- List all cartridges currently inserted in a jukebox.

Figure 9.5 shows MediaManager and JukeboxManager and their interrelationship to various other system components and utilities.

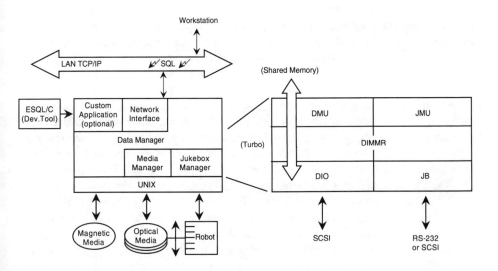

Figure 9.5 MediaManager and JukeboxManager. *Source:* Hewlett-Packard Co.

9.6 PRINT SERVER

The AIMS environment provides for local and remote print services. Files and bit-map screen dumps are provided from Windows. The AIMS Print Server is an HP Vectra equipped with a laser printer, typically an HP LaserJet III or Fujitsu. Any HP Vectra running the AIMS Print Server software (Print Spooler) and equipped with the AIP card and printer interface card can be configured to perform this task. A low-resolution monitor is sufficient for use with the Print Server.

The Print Server accepts compressed images, thereby minimizing network transmission time and bandwidth requirements. Print requests and data originate from applications running at the front end, on the AIMS client workstations, rather from the back-end server. In normal operation images are first retrieved from the server and stored on the client workstation, before being sent to the AIMS Print Server.

Print Spooler software consists of two separate Windows programs: Queue and Print. Queue acts as the printer monitor and administrator. This program can run concurrently with other programs and does not use any dedicated resources, such as the AIP card. It accepts print jobs from other workstations and routes them to the hard disk, whether Print is running or not. The Print program fetches files directly from the hard disk and sends them to the printer via the AIP card. When Print is running it allocates the AIP card permanently and dedicates it for the printing process.

9.7 FAX SERVER

The Fax Server provides a facsimile gateway for sending images held in the AIMS database. Images can be scanned, compressed, and sent over the Fax network to multiple destinations. Faxes can be routed to the AIMS database and indexed later, to the recipient, or to a LaserJet III printer. Documents sent from AIMS can include text and image. Header pages can be added automatically and include configurable text and graphics

The Fax Server is dedicated to the tasks of sending and receiving faxes and cannot be used for anything else. Scaling, compression (i.e., CCITT Group III), and decompression is performed on the Fax Server by an HP Vectra PC equipped with a fax card and LAN interface card. When configured as a Fax Server, the Vectra needs only a low-resolution graphics display monitor and a 42 MB hard disk. One Fax Server can support up to eight AIMS servers. One AIMS server can send faxes to up to 16 PC-based Fax Servers.

The administrator interface is based on MS-Windows and a run-time version is included with the Fax Server software. This enables the system administrator to print incoming faxes or monitor the outgoing queue. Sending and receiving faxes is accomplished in much the same way as with any other facsimile device.

HP offers Fax development libraries for creating AIMS applications that can be integrated with the Fax Server. Requirements include a development workstation and AIMS development software.

9.8 APPLICATIONS INTEGRATION

HP offers users the ability to integrate HP 3000 and HP 9000 applications with AIMS, as well as the ability to integrate IBM 3270 applications with AIMS.

9.8.1 HP 3000 and HP 9000 Integration

HP 3000 and HP 9000 applications can be integrated with images from an AIMS database. This is achieved by using HP AdvanceLink for MS-Windows, the Windows' DDE facility, and HP AIMS.

A typical scenario might involve a customer with an existing HP 3000 who is running an insurance application. Insurance documents can be scanned and stored as images on the AIMS DataServer. Users would then have access to the HP 3000 application via AdvanceLink, a tool for creating template files that define the information to be passed to AIMS. Indexes of images the user wants to view are automatically passed from AdvanceLink—which is also a terminal emulation package—to AIMS via DDE. The stored images are then retrieved and displayed alongside the old HP 3000 (or HP 9000) application window. This allows existing HP 3000 and HP 9000 terminal-based applications to be image-enabled without code modifications.

9.8.2 IBM 3270 Integration

IBM 3270 applications can be integrated with images from the AIMS database through the use of an image gateway and AIMS 3270 terminal emulation. Structured data from existing 3270 applications can be linked to images held in the AIMS database, which resides on an HP Series 800 Dataserver. Each PC can run up to four emulation sessions.

A typical scenario might involve an IBM mainframe user who is running an invoicing application. Via the 3270 terminal emulator, the user could access existing data stored on the mainframe. New or existing invoices could be scanned and stored on the AIMS Dataserver. The combination of 3270 and AIMS allows users to retrieve details and display the invoices associated with a particular customer on the same workstation.

Connections between HP Vectra PCs and an IBM mainframe are achieved via the image gateway. The workstations connect to the gateway via IEEE 802.3 or token-ring LANs. The gateway manages the connection and data communications to the mainframe via a token-ring or SDLC network.

9.9 CONCLUSION

HP's AIMS is among the most advanced imaging systems available. This is due in large part to its comprehensive development environment, which consists of the AIMS Applications Designer and a number of AIMS standard run-time libraries, the MS- Windows Development Kit, and a C compiler. The AIMS Standard Development Library pack includes both the AIMS Application Designer and Standard Runtime Libraries. In addition, there is full support for DDE Libraries and AIMS Fax Development Library software.

This advanced development environment facilitates the design and delivery of custom business solutions based on AIMS. On an international basis, HP works with a number of systems integrators—or "Image Partners"—who use these tools to build custom imaging systems and integrate applications across multiple platforms.

Chapter 10

DECimage EXpress

10.1 INTRODUCTION

DEC is the second largest computer maker, known for its VAX line of minicomputers and for introducing the concept of distributed computing. In fiscal year 1991 DEC posted its first operating loss in its 35-year history. In mid-1992 DEC reported a loss of $1.85 billion, most of which was a restructuring charge taken to pay for further layoffs and plant closings. Soon after, Kenneth Olsen, the company's president and CEO, announced his intention to retire.

Although the poor economy was an important factor in DEC's decline, other factors played a part as well. With the growing tendency of customers to buy "open systems," there was a widely held perception that DEC relied too much on proprietary solutions, namely its VMS operating system, and not enough on helping customers migrate to microcomputer-based LANs. This prompted potential customers to look elsewhere for their computing and communications solutions.

In addition, DEC's Pathworks-based LANs have been widely criticized for slow response time. This affected DEC's success in other areas, particularly the important niche markets for routers and wiring hubs.

Industry analysts expect DEC to eventually reorganize into market-specific business units to make the company more competitive in emerging and niche markets. Meanwhile, DEC has already taken several measures intended to improve its financial performance and change its image from that of a proprietary solutions company to that of an open systems company.

For example, in addition to moving from system-based software pricing to user-based pricing, DEC is shipping a version of its VMS operatin system that is compliant with a portable operating system interface (POSIX).[1] Further, DEC is licensing its VMS

---

[1] A derivative of OSI and UNIX, POSIX is an operating system that can be transferred from one hardware or software environment to another. Computers using the operating system can exchange information and use the information that has been exchanged.

operating system, now called Open VMS, to other vendors. It has also restructured the pricing of its DECstation 5000 series, making it one of the lowest-cost workstation lines in the industry. DEC has added a PC integration business unit to help customers with multivendor networks and it has added support for Novell's NetWare to its Pathworks LAN software products. There is also more emphasis on PCs—even to the extent of competing via mail order.

A key development that could reverse DEC's fortunes and counter its image as a vendor of proprietary solutions is its commitment to 64-bit reduced instruction set computing (RISC) chips and systems, code-named Alpha. Alpha can run twice as fast as any other RISC processor. DEC plans to offer Alpha-based systems that span the entire range of computing platforms, from palmtops to supercomputers. The systems will run on VMS and OSF/1, as well as Microsoft Corp.'s NT operating system, thus appealing to millions of existing MS-DOS and MS-Windows users. DEC has high hopes for Alpha. It might become the strategic product of the 1990s, the way VAX was in the 1980s.

10.2 DEVELOPMENT BACKGROUND

DEC's imaging solutions have evolved in several phases, with each phase building on the previous phase. Phase I was started in 1987 under the name DECimage. This phase entailed the development and implementation of a standards-based architecture designed to enable any application running on a DEC network to incorporate images in the same way that they use traditional data types, such as numbers and text.

As a result, DEC systems have already integrated the requirements for supporting imaging into their standard components and services. Specialized services, such as image acquisition, pattern recognition, and high-volume storage, are available to applications from the system. This capability can be exploited casually, as in electronic publishing, as well as in image-intensive applications, such as insurance claims processing.

The first phase focused on the development of tools and components targeted at integrating the imaging capability into DEC's mainstream architectures and products. Tool-level products, such as DECimage Application Services (DAS), integrated the imaging capability into VMS and ULTRIX[2] systems, DECwindows Motif[3], compound document architecture (CDA), and network applications support (NAS) environments.

In addition, component products were developed for display, print, and image acquisition. DECimage Character Recognition Services (DCRS) enabled applications to turn the text in the images into machine-coded, or ASCII, characters.

---

[2]ULTRIX is a DEC operating system derived from UNIX.

[3]DEC has made it easier for users to access the OSF's Motif via support of X.desktop, an industry-standard Motif desktop manager. Previously, DEC users accessed Motif via DECwindows, an arrangement that suffered from the lack of a consistent user interface. DEC bundles X.desktop with hardware running Open VMS, ULTRIX, and the OSF/1 operating system.

In 1991 DEC began Phase II of its imaging system development. DEC introduced complete imaging system and applications products that were based on a common set of networked imaging clients and servers. This second phase development strategy went by the name DECimage EXpress. Its intent was to deliver imaging capabilities to applications developers, as well as end users.

Previously, DECimage was a prepackaged offering that could not serve as a development platform. The updated version, DECimage EXpress, is a layered software product, which makes it more attractive to third parties and to customers who are attempting to develop image systems on other platforms, in addition to existing platform configurations.

Today DEC offers a highly flexible, standards-based approach to imaging, as do other vendors such as IBM and Unisys. Within the context of DEC's product line, this approach offers customers the following potential advantages:

- Modularity allows users to start small and add components incrementally as needs increase.
- Extendibility (based on NAS) offers compatibility with multiple hardware platforms and operating systems, including VMS, ULTRIX, MS-DOS, OS/2 and Macintosh.
- Integration brings the ability to manage and process images to all levels of computing and to other applications, regardless of operating system.

As these initial goals are achieved in products, architecture, and advanced development, other goals, such as explicit integrated support for additional large data types (e.g., voice, sound, and video), will be addressed. This ongoing development strategy will make multimedia imaging available in the near future. (Chapter 14 provides more detail on the concept behind multimedia imaging.)

10.3 SYSTEM OVERVIEW

DECimage EXpress is a family of packaged systems that provide image capture, indexing, storage, retrieval, display, and printing, as well as image distribution over the network. The systems are based on the VAX/VMS platform and comply with DEC's NAS software for applications integration in multivendor computing environments.

NAS is DEC's comprehensive set of open software based on industry standards. NAS enables users and applications to integrate, port, and distribute applications across a network of different computer systems, including VMS, ULTRIX, OS/2, MS-DOS, UNIX, and Macintosh.

There are three components of DECimage EXpress, which companies can select based on their current and emerging business needs:

- The client component is designed to offer an economical platform that provides the full functionality of a stand-alone system.
- The server component is designed to provide a completely integrated basic document imaging system that can be networked departmentwide or enterprisewide.

- The application development component, or APIs, provide a set of programming tools that are used to construct applications that meet unique business requirements.

DECimage EXpress is a scalable system designed to operate as a combination of specified hardware and software components (Figure 10.1). As such, it can be used to image-enable applications that run on PCs to mainframes. The applications development environment is made up of a set of routines that are used by the system administration, data storage, and document indexing subsystems to access documents within DECimage EXpress. This functionality permits the user to design solutions that address unique business problems.

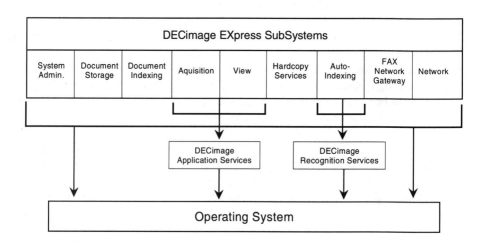

Figure 10.1 DECimage EXpress Version 2.0. *Source:* Digital Equipment Corp.

For the most part, the key features of DECimage EXpress are similar to those found in other vendors' computerized document imaging systems. In short, DECimage EXpress offers these notable features:

- Supports importing documents directly from magnetic cache or from a local scanner;
- Allows automatic preview of images during scanning or import;
- Allows automatic indexing of documents—up to five key fields—at the time of acquisition for either scanner or cache;
- Supports scanning of both multiple-page documents and multiple fixed-page-count documents, as well as single-page documents;
- Provides the ability to inspect document images for scan quality;

- Supports the replacement of a specific page of a document by rescanning and preserving the original page sequence;
- Supports cropping of document images;
- Supports up to five regions of interest to be manually or automatically indexed with each document template;
- Permits multiple documents to be appended (to form a new document), copied, deleted, or moved (to another drawer);
- Supports the retrieval of documents, using up to five index keys per drawer;
- Supports both single and dual display windows, side-by-side or top-over-bottom;
- Supports the display of bitonal images—with or without hardware assistance—as well as gray-scale and color images;
- Supports zone, rotate, pan, scroll, and image scaling, including original resolution, fit width, fit height, and fit within a window;
- Supports mailing and exporting of individual pages of a document;
- Supports bidirectional facsimile with delayed transmission capability;
- Provides for the registration and definition of:
  - All nodes to access DECimage EXpress;
  - Devices to be accessed by users;
  - Drawers to contain image documents;
  - Access to drawers by user accounts;
  - Functional privileges of user accounts, including print, index, delete, autoindex, modify, scan, fax, and system management;
- Provides a system manager utility for migrating document images to and from magnetic and optical storage, purging images from the database, and configuring the storage server.

With the introduction of DECimage EXpress 2.0 in January 1992, the following additional capabilities were added:

- Expanded connectivity. Users can have concurrent use of the document imaging system within or across departments. Users can review and act on the same document simultaneously.
- Applications development environment. Allows users to develop custom imaging applications by integrating DECimage EXpress with existing applications.
- Fax capability. By making the appropriate menu selection, the user can direct the DECimage EXpress system to send a fax of a document currently being viewed. The user can also receive a fax directly into the imaging system.
- Improved performance for the migration of images from magnetic to optical storage.

10.3.1 DECwindows Motif

Motif was developed by the OSF. It is literally the result of combining the best tools the industry has to offer. As such, Motif holds a great deal of relevance to the workstation user community in general. As a standard, Motif allows users to learn only a single interface that spans many types of computer systems. Consequently, Motif allows users to spend more time getting work done, instead of trying to figure out how to use multiple user interfaces.

DECwindows Motif combines the DECwindows programming environment, Presentation Manager from IBM, and widgets from Hewlett-Packard. Motif's Window Manager, which replaces the original Window Manager in DECwindows, permits the user to control how windows or other graphics objects operate. Motif includes LinkWorks, a hypertext service that links word processing documents, electronic mail messages, images, and other data types.

Unlike the "live links" of DEC's CDA, which import information from one application to another, LinkWorks creates a referential link. For example, the user can link a DECwindows electronic mail message to an image document created under DECimage EXpress. Many of the DECwindows Motif applications have a Link option on their main menu bar to support this service.

10.3.2 Compound Document Architecture

CDA establishes a framework for the universal exchange of data types: text, graphics, revisable spreadsheets, charts, tables, and images. This framework provides the following benefits to users:

- Promotes coexistence between standards and different document formats through consistent data representation, which is achieved with the *digital document interchange format* (DDIF);
- Facilitates the sharing of data between users across departments and networks;
- Provides single-device access to databases, images, applications, communications, and presentation graphics, and, in the future, voice and data;
- Provides data representation and exchange between different operating systems, across heterogeneous networks and hardware devices.

A practical user of CDA is the proposal group that creates a basic document with a word processor and links it to engineering drawings, data faxed from the sales force, a spreadsheet containing return-on-investment (ROI) projections, charts generated by the marketing team, and image documents containing product specifications and photographs. Figure 10.2 provides an illustration of the CDA concept.

DEC anticipates that, in addition to becoming a flagship product in its own right, DECimage EXpress will become the integration point for other vendor systems. This integration will offer users and applications the ability to access, retrieve, and deposit images and descriptive data between targeted systems.

The level of interoperability will be determined by the interfaces and standards available on other vendors' systems. However, the goal is that users on a DECimage EXpress system will have the most comprehensive access to the information on other sys-

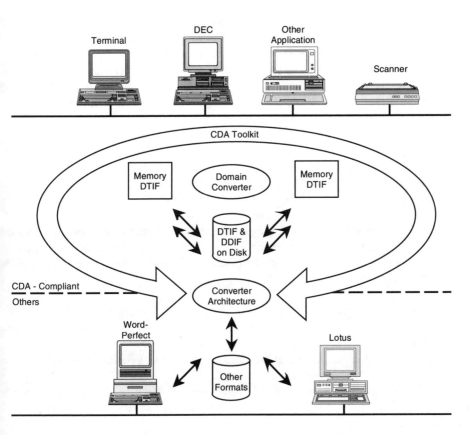

Figure 10.2 CDA application for proposal writing.

ems—even if the other systems interact with their system and each other in no other way. As such, DECimage EXpress will play an increasingly pivotal role in managing data and data flow, eventually becoming the de facto or designated standard enterprisewide.

10.3.3 Document Interchange Formats

DEC's CDA allows users to create revisable compound documents from a variety of applications across a network. The set of Base Services that accompany the CDA rely on DEC's DDIF and digital table interchange format (DTIF) to manipulate files that include text, graphics, and images.

DDIF and DTIF files, in turn, are based on abstract syntax notation one (ASN.1), an international standard (ISO Standard 8824) that defines an architecturally neutral data encoding scheme. Files based on ASN.1 are portable across multiple computer architectures.

An in-memory data structure called an aggregate is the basic unit between applica tions and the CDA access routines. The CDA access routines give application designer two modes of document transfer: incremental and document, with different levels of inter face ease and dynamic memory space (explained later). CDA Converter Architecture cre ates an environment where software can convert between multiple document formats. A variety of programs can use CDA for data access and conversion, ultimately facilitating the creation of interoperable applications.

10.3.3.1 Aggregates

Aggregates contain document data corresponding to particular areas of a given data for mat, whether DDIF or DTIF. The CDA access routines define the aggregate types needed to break the document data into manageable elements.

The aggregate type that builds the overall structure of each data format is called the root aggregate. In addition to representing the document as a whole, the root aggregate in cludes the byte stream associated with the document encoding and the context needed to manage the data path. The context includes:

- A document identifier, which distinguishes the type of document—DDIF or DTIF;
- An optional specification of user-provided memory management routines for appli cations with high-memory requirements, such as image applications;
- Processing information, such as the attributes of the file, byte stream, or aggregate.

Each aggregate contains a defined list of items that are specific to the aggregate type. Each item provides a storage cell for part of the data syntax—in DDIF or DTIF— that the aggregate builds.

10.3.3.2 Access Routines

As noted previously, the CDA's Base Services' data structures and access routines enable programmers to create, modify, read, and write compound documents. The CDA access routines apply to both DDIF and DTIF data types and are used by applications during file storage and data exchange. The CDA Document Viewers, the CDA Converter Architec ture, and compound document applications are layered on the CDA Base Services' access routines.

CDA access routines perform several tasks, such as allocating and deallocating ag gregates, storing and fetching aggregate items, and reading and writing aggregates to documents. CDA Base Services provide the interface files that define numeric equivalents for aggregate type codes, aggregate item codes, and aggregate values. Also included is the documentation for each item's data type.

At the time of document input, the CDA access routines create aggregates, store document data into the items, and return the handle of each aggregate to the application

t the time of document output, the application creates and populates aggregates before
assing them to the CDA access routines for writing.

0.3.3.3 Document Transfer Modes

'he CDA access routines provide the application designer with two modes of document
ransfer: incremental and document. The incremental mode is time-consuming to program,
ut uses less dynamic memory. Incremental mode is typically used when the attributes of
e output document format do not require the entire input document to be available in
emory to complete the conversion. The document mode offers an easy-to-use interface
nd simplifies programming, but requires that the entire document reside in memory.

0.3.3.4 CDA Converter Architecture

'he CDA Converter Architecture provides an environment for creating software that con-
erts between multiple document formats. The CDA Converter Architecture routines are
ayered on the CDA access routines.

The CDA Base Services provide support for conversion of input formats DDIF,
)TIF, and text and for output formats DDIF, DTIF, text, PostScript, and Analysis. Analy-
is is used for debugging and converts DDIF/DTIF to an ASCII representation in which
ields and values can be easily viewed. Other industry-standard formats, such as SGML,
VK1, CGM, HPGL, and Macpaint, are supported by the CDA Converter Library. Inter-
hange between the office document architecture (ISO Standard 8613-1) and CDA is pro-
ided by DEC's ODA Compound Document Architecture gateway product.

Under the CDA Converter Architecture a front-end module converts an input (on-
isk) document format to an in-memory representation, or aggregate. A back-end module
en converts the in-memory format to an output (on-disk) format. The in-memory aggre-
ate structures used for conversion of DDIF or DTIF are the same as those used for incre-
ental-mode and document-mode document transfers.

0.3.3.5 CDA Document Viewers

'he CDA Viewers read-in DDIF aggregates, interpret them in terms of pages, and then
ormat them according to layout rules embedded in the document, before displaying each
age on the screen. The CDA Viewers are callable routines and can, in turn, be used by a
igher-level application. The DECwindows Mail and VAX Notes electronic conferencing
pplications, for instance, provide this CDA document viewing capability.

0.4 CDA APPLICATIONS

s part of its CDA program, DEC offers several sample applications that deliver impor-
nt end-user services. In addition to the previously described CDA Converter Library,
ese applications include:

- DECdecision. This is an integrated decision support and data analysis package tha uses the CDA Toolkit to store DTIF files and the CDA Converter Architecture t import and export foreign file types.
- DECimage Applications Services. This package of tools and utilities provides imag support for compound document applications development. It uses the CDA Toolk to store and retrieve images in DDIF files.
- DECpaint. This is a DECwindows image editor that uses the CDA Toolkit to stor and retrieve its images in DDIF files.
- DECwindows Mail. This an electronic mail application can send and receive com pound documents. It uses the CDA Viewer to display DDIF and DTIF documents.
- DECwrite. This is a compound document editor that uses the CDA Toolkit to stor DDIF files and the CDA Converter Architecture to import and export foreign fil types.
- VAX Notes. This electronic conferencing system stores and retrieves DDIF an DTIF documents and uses the CDA Viewer for their display.

At this writing DEC offers at least 50 CDA-capable applications. Over 100 other are available from third-party software developers.

10.5 NETWORK APPLICATIONS SUPPORT

DEC's NAS software strategy provides support of multivendor installations through suite of standards-based software products. This allows users to access and share program across multiple systems.

For distributed applications to be effectively implemented there must be a transition from stand-alone operating systems to distributed operating systems. NAS can be de scribed as the "middleware" that fulfills this purpose, providing connectivity, portability and client/server computing. NAS is a powerful networking tool that is most useful in ap plications that require virtually continuous interaction at the desktop level, such as imag document processing. It enables users in any work group or department to share man types of data from different sources.

The basic principle behind NAS is to link multiple computer platforms into a cohe sive and coherent environment. Coherence is the result of standard APIs and file format that allow applications to access and manage information contained in other applications Cohesiveness is the result of sharing resources among applications independent of the sys tems on which they run.

Through NAS imaging functionality can be seamlessly integrated with NAS-compli ant applications. NAS enables applications to interact in a distributed environment that in cludes a network of computer systems and software from different vendors. In thi environment imaging applications can be shared over different hardware platforms.

NAS-based products include a version of DECwindows/Motif for Sun Microsys tems' SPARCstations and NAS Transaction Processing software that runs on UNIX, MS DOS, and the Macintosh. DEC also offers the NAS300 server package on 12 complet

'AX/VMS systems. In addition, NAS currently supports ULTRIX, OS/2, MS-DOS and
1S-Windows, Sun OS, and Macintosh OS, as well as VT, X, and 3270 terminals.

Figure 10.3 illustrates the functional aspects of DEC's NAS.

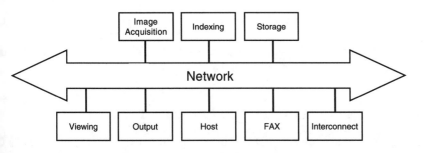

igure 10.3 Functional aspects of NAS. *Source:* Digital Equipment Corp.

0.6 DECIMAGE APPLICATION SERVICES

)AS is a set of callable routines (APIs and other programming tools) that add imaging ca-
abilities to new and existing applications, regardless of computing environment. DAS
rovides for image capture, processing, and display. DAS is language-independent and en-
bles application developers and systems integrators to handle bitonal, gray-scale, and
RGB color image data, even as they develop applications that concurrently handle image,
ext, and graphics.

The services are library-resident routines that are included with VMS DECwin-
ows/Motif. The following sets are included as part of the application services:

- Image Input Services (IIS). Functionality includes image scanner device drivers, device setup, and image data acquisition. IIS supports the MD400 and MD410 scanners offered with DECimage EXpress and allows systems integrators access to these
  two gray-scale input devices via a supported API. Remote access and sharing devices within a cluster or network are also provided.
- Image Services Library (ISL). Functionality includes image data type support, file
  input/output, image processing and manipulation, and data encoding conversion.
- Image Display Services (IDS): Provides device-independent image rendition control, image display, and X image extension (XIE) support.[4] IDS provides widget

---

[4]DECimage EXpress supports X terminals as client systems, using XIE to send compressed image data
rom an X client application to an X server.

support for Motif 1.1 and VMS DECwindows/Motif 1.0. Programming examples are included for both Motif and the X user interface (XUI). The interesting aspect of DAS is that programmers need not have specialized expertise or extensive familiarity with image-capable hardware devices. This is because basic image-specific technology is built into DAS.

DAS adheres to industry and international standards, including: X Window System, PostScript, office document interchange format (ODIF); CCITT Groups III and IV; and discrete cosine transform (DCT) compression, which is compatible with the Joint Photographic Experts Group's (JPEG) baseline standard R5 for compression.

10.7 APPLICATION DEVELOPMENT ENVIRONMENT

The DECimage EXpress Application Development Environment (DADE) is the VAX C callable programming interface, which is used to extend the DECimage EXpress system. This capability is achieved with a set of routines than can be used by the DECimage EXpress system administration, data storage, and document indexing subsystems to access documents within DECimage EXpress.

DADE is a set of over 30 APIs that include the following functions:

- Create image documents;
- Add, delete, and replace pages in documents;
- Index and move documents;
- Retrieve an image;
- Resequence pages in a document;
- Create collections of documents from lists of document identifiers.

DADE lets customers and third-party developers integrate complementary, image-capable applications systems. This means an existing Oracle application, for example, can use DECimage EXpress as an image server to extend the type and amount of information available to the end user.

Other functions users can perform with DADE include:

- Access single documents or collections of documents from the document storage subsystem;
- Perform utility functions, such as creating, deleting and retrieving a single document, or creating collections of image documents;
- Index documents and retrieve indexed documents.

As part of DEC's imaging consulting services, technical experts will integrate DECimage EXpress with the customer's existing applications using DADE.

10.8 OTHER DECIMAGE OFFERINGS

DECimage EXpress can tie into other DEC offerings, such as its ALL-IN-1 office automation software. In addition, a number of discrete components of DECimage EXpress that can be purchased separately, depending on the needs of the imaging application.

10.8.1 All-in-1 Image Software

DEC offers All-in-1 Image Software, a layered application that integrates paper-based information into its All-in-1 office automation system. This product provides users with a departmental or work group scan station, allowing users to scan, index, and store images, so that they can be retrieved, edited, and distributed within the familiar All-in-1 environment. Thus, operators using graphics-capable VTs (models 240 and up), DECwindows terminals, and PCs running MS-Windows can view, edit, and distribute images from their desktops.

10.8.2 DECimage Character Recognition Services

DECimage Character Recognition Services (DCRS) is a set of run-time services that support the recognition of text contained in scanned bitonal image files and conversion of the text into ASCII format. DCRS provides readily available OCR to large, distributed applications that need OCR to convert text within an image for routing and indexing, or for use by text-based applications.

DCRS has a library of callable services:

- Page segmentation services, which automatically separate text areas of an image from nontext areas;
- Text recognition services, which examine text regions to determine character information, font family, and font size;
- Text export services, which convert text information into ASCII, PostScript, or DIFF format for routing, indexing, and use by other applications;
- Structure access services, which allow applications to extract information, such as region boundaries or individual words, from a page structure and allow deletion of page regions that are not of interest;
- Postprocessing services, which perform such housekeeping functions as deleting buffers or structures created during the recognition process.

10.8.3 SMARTFOLDER Imaging

SMARTFOLDER Imaging is an image-capable work-system environment for folder management, document management, checklist management, FAX document integration, mainframe connectivity, and electronic mail. DEC SMARTFOLDER software, once a separate offering, is now an integral part of the DECimage EXpress system.

10.8.4 DECimage Scan Software

DECimage Scan Software is a desktop X-Windows application on VMS and ULTRIX systems that provides for the capture, manipulation, and delivery of images for use in other image applications. This application can be used with MD410, MD400, and MD300 scanners. The MD410, for example, is a SCSI-bus compatible device that is capable of scanning speeds of up to 15 pages per minute at a resolution of 200 dpi. This equates to 17,000 pages per month. The scanner also features onboard data compression.

10.8.5 DECcamera

DECcamera is a video image server that facilitates the capture of gray-scale images of three-dimensional objects. The user can capture still images from any video source and analyze, annotate and electronically send, and incorporate those digitized video images into other applications, anywhere on the network.

10.8.6 Fax Network Gateway Server

The Fax Network Gateway Server integrates facsimile transmission and reception with business applications, as well as with electronic mail. It provides economical and timely transmission of large volumes of information.

10.8.7 Storage

The DECimage EXpress system offers integrated optical WORM disk storage from 2.6 GB to 734 GB through the Perceptics Laserware optical interface. In addition, DEC offers optical storage systems through Cygnet Systems. The Cygnet Jukebox, with Laser Magnetic Storage International's double-headed optical drive, offers up to 734 GB of storage in one unit and is capable of accommodating up to 28 GB on line concurrently.

10.9 THIRD-PARTY RELATIONSHIPS

As earlier described, the openness of DEC applications encourages the participation of third-party vendors. Third-party relationships are very important to the DEC imaging strategy, just as they are in other areas, such as integrated network management (i.e., DEC's Enterprise Management Architecture [EMA]). These relationships with hardware suppliers, software developers, and systems integrators allow DEC to offer a fairly comprehensive line of imaging solutions. Some examples follow.

10.9.1 ImageNow Software

One of DEC's more recent offerings is ImageNow software, developed by Genesis Software, Inc. This software is an easy-to-install application that allows users to image-enable corporate applications without the costly, time-consuming process of rewriting code. Based on DECimage EXpress, ImageNow software provides interconnection for host system/mainframe applications of image data. There is no host system impact, nor is a rewrite of the existing applications necessary.

ImageNow software looks at two views of the data: (1) the data as it comes from the host system via the communications stream and (2) the data as it is displayed at the terminal or terminal emulation environment.

Through a learn method, ImageNow software monitors the exact point at which the user is working in the application and wants the image data applied. The learn method allows ImageNow applications to build a set of rules that are applied each time the application requests or adds an image. This method need only be applied once per application.

Running atop DECimage EXpress, ImageNow lets users who are running applications on a VAX under VMS or on an IBM mainframe under MVS access image data associated with forms-based applications that are running on Forms Management System, DECforms, CICS, or TSO. ImageNow encapsulates the original form and the images to be added. It then intercepts the images targeted for a specific transaction, to allow the application to combine the correct form with the correct images. The DECimage application manages all connections between the forms-based application and the images. This means that users can associate image documents with data records without having to modify the applications.

ImageNow allows users of an application to access a learn mode option. This option associates images with particular records, then retrieves those images. It creates an index of the associations that exist between images and forms and uses pointer files to locate the data.

DECimage application services for VMS 3.1 include DEC's X Image Extensions, which: allow compressed image data to be sent from client applications to an X display server, provide workstation support based on the DECwindows Motif environment, perform continuous tone compression, and support DEC's MD400 and MD410 gray-scale scanners.

Genesis also provides GSI Prompt Paymaster software, a contract administration system for federal, state, and local governments. This application automates the payment process, using DECimage application services and DECimage EXpress to store the individual payment source documents. The software also fits many commercial accounts payable requirements.

10.9.2 LaserView Express Software

LaserData, Inc.'s LaserView Express software is a low-end, MS-Windows-compatible package that allows PCs to access, retrieve, and display images stored in DECimage EXpress and store and print images locally. In addition, images can be exported to the Windows clipboard facility for integration with standard Windows applications, such as word processing and electronic mail.

10.9.3 Epic/Workflow Software

Computron Technologies Corp. offers Epic/Workflow software, which uses DEC's imaging technology to provide packaged workflow management solutions in document-intensive areas, such as accounts payable, insurance underwriting, and loan origination. Computron uses DECimage EXpress as an application interface platform on which to standardize its full range of imaging workflow applications.

10.9.4 PixTex Product Family

Excaliber Technologies Corp. provides VMS users with a family of image management products. PixTex software is a document imaging system that turns a DEC computer into an electronic filing cabinet for text and images.

Another offering, PixTex/EFS software, is a complete DECwindows environment for document control and electronic filing that combines a graphical user interface with the Rdb/VMS database manager and a proprietary database for RISC-based ULTRIX systems. The PixTex/EFS software provides for the acquisition, storage, and retrieval of compound documents. In addition, PixTex/EFS offers high-speed retrieval, full document control, and content-based searches. The software supports DEC's compound document architecture, document interchange format, DECnet protocols, and NAS.

PixTex/EFS System ServerPlus software is a document control product that combines a graphical user interface, the PixTex/EFS MS-Windows client, an electronic file room metaphor, and DEC's Rdb/VMS database manager for the electronic filing and retrieval of compound documents. The software enables PC users who are running Windows to access the electronic filing functions of the PixTex/EFS ServerPlus application. PixTex/EFS ServerPlus complies with DEC's CDA and NAS standards in a client/server environment.

There are many other third-party software packages that can plug into DECimage EXpress and many that meet the specific needs of niche markets, such as financial and human resources, appraisal and geographical information, court and deed administration and management, hospital information systems, and pharmaceutical and chemical industry record keeping.

10.10 CONCLUSION

For many years DEC was successful in providing an economical alternative to IBM's host-centric computing architecture. This alternative relied on a distributed computing architecture that moved information processing resources to the workgroup and departmental levels. DEC accomplished this with its proprietary VAX/VMS system, DECnet LAN, and local-area transport (LAT) server communications protocol. The company's success contributed to the widely held perception of DEC as a provider of proprietary solutions at a time when users were more interested in open systems solutions that could take advantage of products from multiple vendors.

However, DEC had been supporting industry and worldwide standards, including TCP/IP and OSI, for many years, lending validity to its claim that it had simply done a poor job of marketing this fact to prospective as well as existing customers. At least within the context of DECimage EXpress, DEC has demonstrated its commitment to open systems solutions, which has encouraged a number of third-party hardware suppliers and software developers to offer products that work in conjunction with the system.

Chapter 11

FileNet Document Imaging Systems

11.1 INTRODUCTION

In terms of customer base, FileNet Corp. is the largest image system vendor. By the end of 1991, the company had installed 500 image systems at 350 customer locations in 34 countries—more than either DEC, IBM, or Wang. The ten-year-old independent company, based in Costa Mesa, California, is among the few computer companies that posted gains in 1991 despite the stagnant economy. That year, revenues jumped 19%. At this writing, FileNet is only a $122 million company, but it holds its own against the giants of the imaging industry by the strength of its products.

FileNet's product development strategy is focused on business process automation. Its WorkFlo Business System software products, WorkForce Desktop and the WorkShop Development Environment, which were launched in 1991, elicited favorable reviews from industry analysts, consultants, and customers. In fact, FileNet has consistently received the highest customer satisfaction ratings on annual surveys by Datapro Research Group and the *Association for Information and Image Management* (AIIM).

11.2 SYSTEM OVERVIEWS

FileNet's document imaging solutions fall into two main categories: the WorkFlo Business System and FolderView. WorkFlo software improves the quality and efficiency of repetitive, procedural, and clerical business processes. FolderView, which is FileNet's latest offering, allows users to manage large numbers of documents and data in dynamic environments in which the work is less structured.

11.2.1 WorkFlo Business System

The WorkFlo Business System is a family of eight software groups that include modular application development, desktop integration, and work management functions. WorkFlo scripts control which software groups are called up to support a particular business process. The software's modularity increases the speed and efficiency of applications development. WorkFlo software modules encapsulate the underlying imaging services required for production applications. This permits organizations to focus on improving their business processes, rather than on mastering the technical underpinnings of the imaging system itself.

The document entry software group consists of modules that control document scanning, indexing, verification; concurrent host data entry and committal[1]; and the transferral of computer output to laser disk. A bar code reader and application software for automatic document indexing speed the document entry process.

The office services software group controls the FileNet system's use of the MS-Windows interface, as well as the applications that support individual services, such as word processing, spreadsheets, and graphics. With such interfaces as Microsoft's DDE and *dynamic link library* (DLL), users can integrate diverse applications in the WorkFlo Business System.

The image display and edit modules control image display features, such as scaling, rotating, and zooming; image editing features, including cut and paste and annotate; and image formats, such as TIFF, BMP, MSP, PCX, CALS, and *device-independent bitmap* (DIB).

The database modules control database query, relational database functions, file folder capabilities, and database maintenance. These modules permit file folder routing among workstations, with no limit on the quantity of documents per folder. Documents can be in multiple folders, and folders can include nonimage objects, such as data or text.

The system-managed storage modules control image cache management, document management, security, and archive capabilities. The image cache temporarily stores on magnetic disk document images that are accessed frequently during a processing cycle. Specialized software manages the resources of FileNet's OSAR optical disk library to ensure optimal performance.

The WorkFlo language modules include capabilities to execute scripts and routing. Information can be routed sequentially to multiple electronic in-baskets according to the time limits and priority levels established by the system administrator. Suspense files hold documents until all other information necessary for processing has arrived, at which time the document or file is routed to the appropriate workstation. The WorkFlo language modules also provide C language support and maintenance functions.

Local-area communications modules provide Novell NetWare support for interoperation between Novell services and FileNet imaging capabilities. The modules also provide: IBM token-ring support, for connecting distributed PC networks to FileNet solutions; Ethernet support, for local- and wide-area networks, and host-to-terminal support, through IBM 3270 and 3278 windows and DEC VT-100 and VT-220 windows. In addition, the modules provide support for a variety of bridges, routers, and gateways, which are used to link together multiple networks.

---

[1]In the parlance of document imaging, when a document is finally stored on optical disk it is said to be *committed*.

Wide-area communications modules control inbound and outbound fax services, provide IBM/SNA support, and provide remote batch delivery of images. Incoming documents sent by fax can be automatically indexed by date, time, the number of the originating fax machine, and the ID of the fax server. Document images can be routed to a single workstation on the FileNet network or to multiple workstations, according to specified distribution lists.

11.2.1.1 WorkForce Desktop

The WorkForce Desktop performs the workstation functions that operators use in imaging applications: image display and manipulation, document indexing, the archiving and re-storing of MS-DOS files, and system administration tasks. WorkForce Desktop products include Image Display for Windows, WorkFlo Runtime for Windows, and AutoForm Runtime for Windows.

Image Display for Windows equips PCs with the fundamental capabilities needed for image processing, including document display, indexing, and database query. The two run-time programs are required to initiate WorkFlo software applications and forms applications. The applications themselves were developed using the WorkFlo *System Development Kit* (SDK) and the AutoForm SDK.

With the WorkFlo SDK users can create scripts to automate, re-engineer, and manage various business processes. The scripts balance workloads, manage time limits of work-in-progress, assign and adjust priorities, identify exceptions, suspend work-in-progress, and measure productivity. System administrators and programmers use the Auto-Form SDK to develop forms for data entry, indexing, and document committal. The kit can function as a stand-alone screen generation tool or it can be used in conjunction with the WorkFlo SDK to develop WorkFlo imaging applications.

11.2.1.2 WorkShop Development Environment

The WorkShop Development Environment gives users tools to tailor applications to solve unique business requirements. With WorkShop, users can create WorkFlo scripts to automate, manage, and control the queuing and flow of images, data, and text throughout the organization. With AutoForm, users can create template-like forms for capturing, validating, and storing coded data in designated fields. This information is then accessible for use in WorkFlo scripts, as well as other Windows applications, via DDE. The information can also be interchanged with host applications via terminal emulation.

11.2.2 FolderView

FolderView software, which is installed on individual workstations, enables a much broader group of users to reap the benefits of document imaging and of WorkFlo software, in particular. FolderView features an icon-driven graphical user interface and runs under

MS-Windows and FileNet's WorkForce Desktop. A variety of navigational tools speed information access. Users can:

- Request snapshot views of folders and select a working set, based on a quick scan of their contents;
- Rearrange documents in a folder or create a new working set of documents, pulling several different folders and sorting them in any order;
- Display pages in a postage stamp format to determine, for example, whether a particular document has been filed;
- Rapidly access a specific document or page using a search mechanism called *tab*, which is analogous to a page marker.

Once folders and documents are identified, FolderView software presents the information in a manner that matches the user's personal work style. For example, the user can: customize the preferred order of folders and documents; display documents in full-page mode, various scaled options, or postage stamp format; view notes on a folder, document, or page without displaying the document; or magnify a portion of the document to make the content legible.

FolderView also makes available a range of online editing features, including functionality for: highlighting information on a page; writing a personal reminder note; marking a page for further review or follow-up; cutting, copying, and pasting selected portions of images into notes; and interfacing with Windows-based word processing packages to add text documents to a folder.

11.3 IMAGE SYSTEM COMPONENTS

FileNet offers a range of image system components, including workstations, scanners, printers, file servers, and optical disk libraries, that can be connected over Ethernet or token-ring networks and are compatible with the most widely used network operating systems.

FileNet offers no unique workstations, scanners, or printer. WorkFlo software runs on IBM PCs and on compatibles that are equipped with the MS-DOS operating system and MS-Windows graphical user interface. A UNIX workstation platform is also available. The scanners and printers conform to CCITT III and IV standards for object capture, document entry, and hard-copy output.

Where FileNet does excel in hardware is in its Series 6000 line of *image management servers* (IMS) and *optical storage and retrieval* (OSAR) libraries (Figure 11.1).

The IMS line is based on an OEM version of IBM's RS/6000 platform, which uses *reduced instruction set computing* (RISC) architecture. The server line runs the gamut from the entry-level Series 1000, which is aimed at organizations that scan less than 8,000 documents a day and store fewer than 8 million document images, to the Series 4000, which is capable of supporting 8,000 transactions per hour and, when multiple servers are used, a virtually unlimited number of document images.

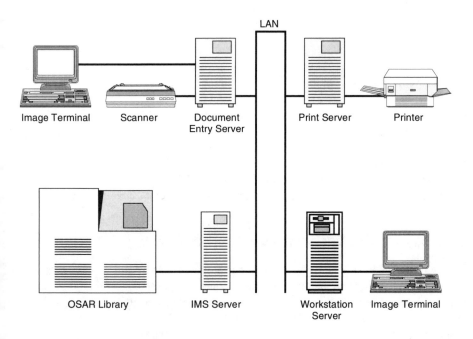

Figure 11.1 FileNet's System 4500 IMS configuration with OSAR. *Source:* FileNet Corp.

FileNet was the first company to manufacture and install disk libraries in commercial installations. OSARs offer advanced electromechanical robotics that automatically load and unload optical disks—5.25-in or 12-in—from optical disk drives. FileNet's OSAR is also offered by IBM, for use with its ImagePlus imaging systems.

The OSAR libraries can hold from 48 to 288 optical disks that have storage capacities ranging from 576,000 pages to 40.3 million pages. Up to eight OSAR libraries can be attached to a FileNet system, bringing the total storage capacity to as many as 322.4 million document images.

FileNet excels at interoperability. In addition to providing Windows applications interoperability via DDE and DLL, FileNet also offers options that facilitate information exchange through the use of IBM's *advanced program-to-program communications* (APPC), with the LU 6.2 protocol. By supporting APPC commands, WorkFlo applications can establish sessions with APPC applications on other computers. Thus WorkFlo can mask complex mainframe applications while it guides the user through a business application.

FileNet offers other interoperability features, such as file transfer capabilities that allow the interchange of business information through industry standard protocols. For example, using IBM's 3770 *remote job entry* (RJE) protocol output, reports from the mainframe can be downloaded and archived on the FileNet system for easy retrieval. This process is referred to by FileNet as *computer output to laser disk* (COLD) and replaces the often time-consuming *computer output to microfiche* (COM) process.

In multivendor LAN environments, TCP/IP's *file transfer protocol* (FTP) is a popular method of file transfer. Files are transferred over the LAN and can be processed by COLD or WorkFlo as part of the business decision process.

The FileNet *image access facility* (IAF) provides a standard interface to FileNet image management services and optical disk storage. Client libraries that provide APIs to the IAF are available for Sun Microsystems, DEC VMS, and IBM PC or compatible platforms. These libraries permit the creation of cost-effective imaging solutions and provide the means for adding image management capabilities to existing business applications.

The rest of this chapter focuses on FileNet's WorkShop Development Environment and, specifically, on the use of objects and scripts in applications development.

11.4 WORKSHOP DEVELOPMENT ENVIRONMENT

As previously noted, FileNet's WorkShop Development Environment provides the tools users need to customize applications to suit the unique requirements of their organizations. With the AutoForm package, users can create forms for capturing, validating, and storing coded data in designated fields. With the WorkFlo Script Development package, users can automate, manage, and control the queuing and flow of images, data, and text throughout the organization.

11.4.1 Forms Development

AutoForm is the means by which system administrators or programmers build forms and files. The forms and files can contain menus, fields, backgrounds, error messages, and validation tables—everything the workstation operator needs to perform specific tasks. This section focuses on the Forms Build routine and illustrates how forms are created from objects in the Windows 3.x environment.

11.4.2 Forms Build

The first step in creating a form is to access the Forms Build routine, which involves starting Windows 3.x, logging onto the FileNet system, opening the WorkShop program group, and selecting the AutoForm SDK icon from the WorkShop. At this point, the Forms Build application window is displayed (Figure 11.2). It can be moved, resized, maximized, or minimized, just like any other window.

From within a created document in the Forms Build window, the user places objects, such as a form[2], a menu, a validation table, or a menu bar. The document window within

---

[2]A basic component of a form is the form itself, which is called a *form object*. A form object can include a background image, background text, input fields, and display fields (or graphics).

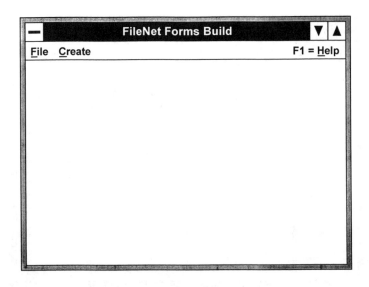

Figure 11.2 Default Forms Build window. *Source:* FileNet Corp.

the Forms Build window can be sized, scrolled, and moved, but not moved out of the Forms Build window. It can also be minimized, so that it appears as an icon. Minimizing the Forms Build window shrinks it and the document window or windows to a single icon. Restoring the Forms Build icon to a window also restores the document window or windows.

Creating (or opening) a forms file causes the Forms Build menu bar to display three new menus: Edit, View, and Window (Figure 11.3). A document window within the Forms Build window has no menu bar. Instead, the menu bar of the Forms Build window applies to the active document window. This means that the menu bar of the Forms Build window can change as the user moves from one document window to another. For example, when the user is working on a menu, the commands on the Forms Build menu bar allow the user to name the menu and do such things as define the menu items. When the user is working on a form, the commands allow the user to create fields and define field attributes.

Figure 11.4 shows a sample form window, with the default menu bar, the default pull-down menus, and the Help command. To include these attributes in the form window, the user does nothing—they are the default attributes. Alternatively, the attributes can be edited to suppress both the Form and Field menus, the Edit menu, or the Help command.

A menu bar can be attached to any number of forms; a menu can also be attached to any number of menu fields or menu bars. A menu attached to a menu field appears as a list box (Figure 11.5). A scroll bar appears when the field is too small to display all of the menu items. A menu attached to a menu bar becomes a pull-down menu on the form window's menu bar when the form is displayed through WorkFlo (Figure 11.6).

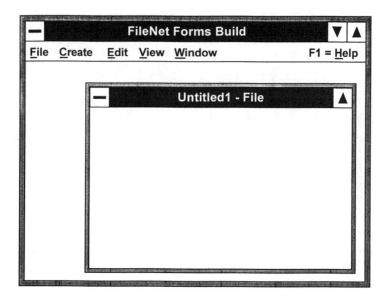

Figure 11.3 Forms Build window with menu options that appear when a forms file is opened. *Source:* FileNet Corp.

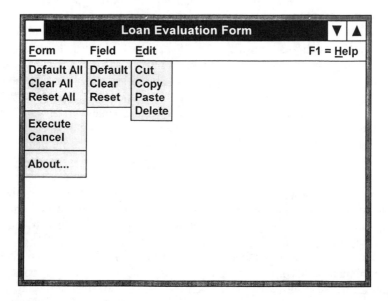

Figure 11.4 Sample form window with default menu bar, default pull-down menus, and Help command. *Source:* FileNet Corp.

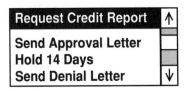

Figure 11.5 List box. *Source:* FileNet Corp.

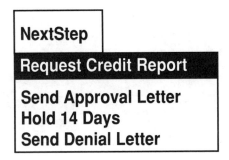

Figure 11.6 Pull-down menu. *Source:* FileNet Corp.

A validation table is an options list that contains the acceptable values for a string field. A typical validation field might include the postal abbreviations for the 50 states (AL, AK, AR, AZ, . . . WY). If the user enters a value that does not match an entry in the validation table, the value is rejected and the user is prompted to enter a new value. A validation table can be attached to any string field.

After multiple forms have been created and saved, users can open the forms by selecting the Open command from the File menu. The Open File dialog box is shown in Figure 11.7. If the forms file is not in the current directory, the user can enter a file specification in the File Name field, changing drives and directories as necessary. The user can also use wildcard characters to call up a list of forms files.

Users select objects, represented by icons, from a forms file (Figure 11.8). The Forms Build application displays one of these icons for each form object (Figure 11.9). Users select Create from the menu bar to create and name a new object (Figure 11.10). They are then prompted to name the new object (Figure 11.11). After the user names a new object, the object's document window opens so the user can define the object. When the user closes the document window, the object's icon appears in the forms file.

To view icons by object type, the user selects View from the Forms Build menu bar (Figure 11.12). By default, a forms file displays all objects. Using the commands on the View menu, the user can hide one or more types of objects.

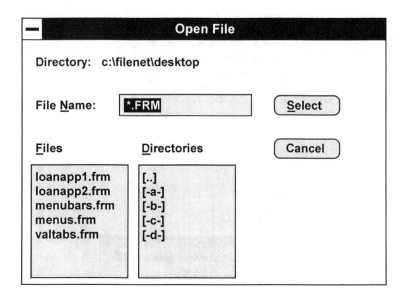

Figure 11.7 Open File dialog box. *Source:* FileNet Corp.

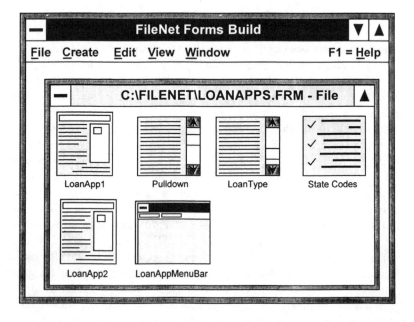

Figure 11.8 Forms file objects. *Source:* FileNet Corp.

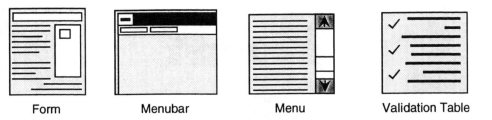

Figure 11.9 Forms file icons. *Source:* FileNet Corp.

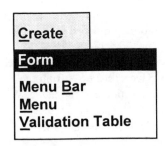

Figure 11.10 Menu options for creating an object. *Source:* FileNet Corp.

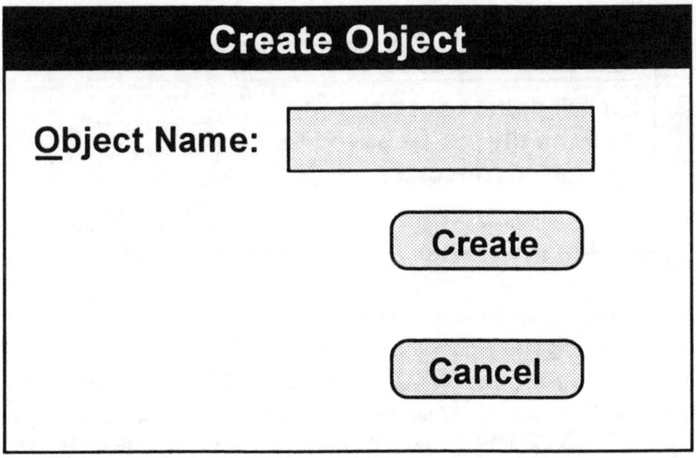

Figure 11.11 Dialog box for naming a newly created object. *Source:* FileNet Corp.

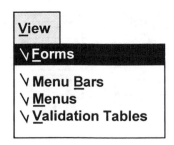

Figure 11.12 View menu. *Source:* FileNet Corp.

Saving a forms file saves changes to all open and closed objects in the file. Typically, while working on and testing a form, the user saves the forms file on the workstation's local hard disk. When the form is finished it can be transferred to each user's PC or to a FileNet server.

At the time a new form is created, it is named "Untitled" by default. When it is time to save the file, the user selects Save or Save As from the File menu. The Save command saves a forms file with its current location and file name. When Save As is selected, a dialog box appears in which the user can specify the drive, directory, file name, and extension, as needed (Figure 11.13). File names use DOS syntax.

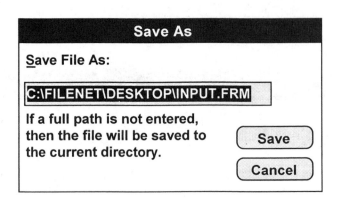

Figure 11.13 Dialog box for saving a forms file. *Source:* FileNet Corp.

To save a forms file to a FileNet server, the user selects the Save to Server command from the File menu. The user specifies the drive, directory, subdirectory, file name, and extension, as needed, using DOS syntax. To retrieve a forms file from the server the user selects the Retrieve from Server command from the File menu. A dialog box appears, prompting the user to specify the drive, directory, file name, and extension (Figure 11.14).

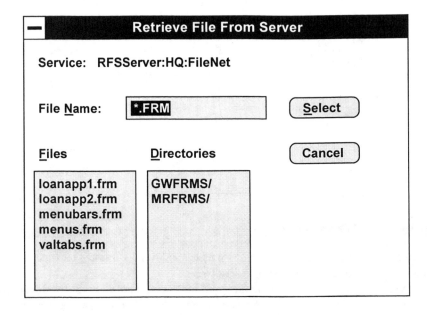

Figure 11.14 Dialog box for retrieving a forms file from the server. *Source:* FileNet Corp.

11.4.3 Script Development

In addition to AutoForms, FileNet's WorkShop Development Environment includes the WorkFlo Script Development package, which allows users to automate, manage, and control the queuing and flow of images, data, and text.

Basically, a *script* is a set of instructions, or calls, that can be activated upon command. The instructions consist of functional statements that automate various tasks, such as storing documents on optical disk, retrieving disks for processing, moving data from one application to another, and routing information from workstation to workstation. A series of scripts work together to complete the tasks assigned to the system, with each script performing one or more steps of the task. The advantage of scripts over native-mode programs is that the various steps of a task can be put into the order that best fits the application, which gives the user greater control over the operation.

The WorkFlo script language makes use of subsystem calls, which access the software on the servers to request such functions as document scanning, indexing, retrieval, and display. All calls access the root server for security checking before being passed to the other servers. A WorkFlo call causes a *remote procedure call* (RPC) to be executed. Figure 11.15 shows the flow of a remote call after a script has initiated a subsystem call.

What follows is a script example that implements DDE between applications. Using DDE for the example accomplishes two objectives: (1) it describes how DDE works and (2) it illustrates how scripts are structured.

WorkFlo script executes:

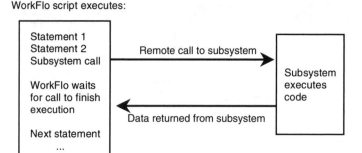

Figure 11.15 Functional aspects of a subsystem call. *Source:* FileNet Corp.

11.4.4 Dynamic Data Exchange

DDE is a protocol that applications running under Windows 3.x use to exchange data. The exchange process can be automated with scripts.

FileNet describes DDE as a bulletin board for posting messages. Software packages act as either DDE clients or servers. Servers monitor the bulletin board for commands to execute and for items to accept or supply data to. Clients post and receive messages, but by themselves do not perform services. To conduct a "conversation"—the exchange of data and commands—both the server and the client must be executing at the same time.

A DDE conversation is conducted through a series of subsystem calls. A DDE *Open call* opens a session. The call must specify both the application and the topic for the DDE conversation and must retrieve the handle established for the conversation. The first DDE server to respond to the application and topic is accepted. All other conversations are terminated. After exchanging all necessary data, the module closes the DDE session with the DDE *Close* call, which frees the handle. The DDE Open and DDE Close syntax is as follows:

```
call "DDE Open"
    set(F_Application :=application_name
       ,F_Topic :=topic_name
    get(DDE_handle :=F_DDEHandle );

call "DDE Close"
    set(F_DDEHandle :=DDE_handle );
```

In the example above, "application_name" is the string containing the name of the application the user wants to communicate with, "topic_name" is the string containing the topic for communication, and "DDE_handle" is the type of handle in the module that is stored for a particular DDE session.

What follows is an example of how the syntax is used to open a session with DispImg, FileNet's display software. The application name is "FileNet Display." It has two topics: FileNet Display (the same name as the application) and System. In the following two examples, the first script initiates a conversation on the FileNet Display topic and the second script ends that conversation and frees the handle.

```
DDE_handle : handle; - - Handle for DDE conversation
...
call "DDE Open"
   set(F_Application :="FileNet Display"
      ,F_Topic :="FileNet Display")
   get(DDE_handle :=F_DDEHandle);

call "DDE Close"
   set(F_DDEHandle := DDE_handle);
```

The DDE *Request* call requests data from a DDE server. The call returns data for any item that the server has knowledge of. For example, the user might want to know the value of a field in a spreadsheet. The syntax is as follows:

```
call "DDE Request"
   set(F_DDEHandle :=DDE_handle
      ,F_Item :=item
   get(F_RequestData :=data);
   get(F_RequestData ;=data);
```

In the syntax above, the "DDE_handle" is the type of handle in the module that is stored for a particular DDE session. The "item" is the string containing the name of the item the user wants data about, and "data" is the string containing the communicated data.

The following are two examples of how this syntax is used. The first example shows how a WorkFlo script would request a display clipboard. (A clipboard name is a one-character string such as A or B.) The second example shows how a WorkFlo script would find out the current page type. A page type might be IMAGE, TEXT, FORM, MIXED, OTHER, or NONE.

```
DDE_handle     : handle; - - Handle for DDE conversation
ClipboardName : string; - - Name of clipboard
error             : number; - - Error returned by call
...
error :=call "DDE Request"
   set(F_DDEHandle := DDE_handle
      ,F_Item := "Name"
   get(ClipboardName := F_RequestData );
```

```
DDE_handle    : handle; - - Handle for DDE conversation
PgType        : string; - - Type of page
error         : number; - - Error returned by call
...
error :=call "DDE Request"
   set(F_DDEHandle := DDE_handle
      ,F_Item := "PageType"
   get(PgType := F_RequestData );
```

The DDE *Poke* call sends data to a DDE server. This call allows the user to send data about a particular item to the DDE server. For example, a user would use the Poke call to fill in a field on a spreadsheet. The syntax is as follows:

```
call "DDE Poke"
   set(F_DDEHandle :=DDE_handle
      ,F_Item :=item
      ,F_PokeData :=data );
```

In the following example of how Poke call syntax is used, a WorkFlo script is being used to fill in the third column in the third row of a loan origination application spreadsheet.

```
spreadsheet_h : handle; - - Handle for DDE conversation
loanamt       : number; - - Amount of loan
error         : number; - - Error returned by call
...
error := call "DDE Poke"
   set(F_DDEHandle := spreadsheet_h
      ,F_Item := "R3C3:R3C3"
      ,F_PokeData := loanamt);
```

The DDE *Execute* call sends commands to a DDE server. For example, the WorkFlo script language can send commands to DispImg, the display software, to do things with an image, such as rotate or scale it. The syntax is as follows:

```
call "DDE Execute"
   set(F_DDEHandle :=DDE_handle
      ,F_ExecuteCommand :=command );
```

In the following example, a WorkFlo script sends a command string to the FileNet Display application that requests the next page of a document and scrolls the image to the left.

```
DDE_handle      : handle; - - Handle for DDE conversation
error           : number; - - Error returned by call
...
error  :=call "DDE Execute"
    set(F_DDEHandle := DDE_handle
        ,F_ExecuteCommand :=
            "[NEXT PAGE][SCROLL LEFT]" );
```

In all of these examples, the scripts include comment lines that start with two hyphens. Commenting saves the WorkFlo programmer debugging and maintenance time by identifying the purpose of the statements. A debugger routine is used to test and edit the scripts. The programmer enters debugger mode by selecting the WorkFlo icon from the WorkForce Desktop. More than one script can be tested simultaneously.

Typically, all WorkFlo tested scripts and completed forms, as well as FileNet software for Windows, are stored on a LAN server. Having everything stored in one place makes upgrades and new installations much simpler to perform.

11.5 SUPPORT SERVICES

FileNet claims an average system uptime of over 99%. This average is made possible by its Sentinel program, which includes an automated remote diagnostics and maintenance service that continuously monitors FileNet systems at customer sites. Corrective measures are taken at the first hint of trouble, before a system can go down.

When a customer opts for this service, special modules are installed in the FileNet image management system to monitor performance. With the Sentinel modules always on line, the system is continuously checked for errors and potential errors and monitored for resource use. Statistics are gathered and sent to FileNet's *Technical Assistance Center* (TAC), where technicians examine the data. If any errors have occurred or have the potential to occur, the situation is addressed immediately. Customers receive system performance reports and reviews on a quarterly basis.

FileNet's TAC specialists and system support engineers also have access to a special support laboratory that contains dedicated systems they can use to simulate the customer environment when they are investigating intermittent or complex support issues. The information gathered in the lab is used by TAC to speed up the problem resolution process for all customers.

Other technical support services provided by FileNet include software maintenance updates, preventive maintenance, and engineering changes. Of note is a relatively new offering by called ProNet, which is a suite of professional services that provides consulting, disaster recovery planning, and assistance with WorkFlo applications development.

11.6 CONCLUSION

FileNet appears to have made all the right moves in competing successfully against the established industry giants. Its nearest competitor in the imaging systems market is IBM—the WorkFlo software works on any IBM PC or compatible workstation and over token-ring and Ethernet LANs. In addition to offering a UNIX version of WorkFlo and supporting IBM's APPC with LU 6.2 protocol, FileNet has licensed IBM's RS/6000 platform for its own line of IMS servers and, in the process, has potentially diminished IBM's performance edge.

FileNet also holds a competitive advantage over Wang Laboratories. Although Wang is a pioneer in the area of document imaging and staked its future on office automation and imaging technologies, its chronically poor financial condition has contributed to its inability to compete. In mid-August of 1992, Wang filed for Chapter 11 bankruptcy, clouding its immediate future in these emerging markets.

PART IV

WIDE-AREA NETWORKING

Chapter 12

Considerations for Imaging Over WANs

12.1 INTRODUCTION

When a WAN connects geographically separate LANs (Figure 12.1), the benefits of imaging can be extended throughout the entire enterprise. All that is required are the appropriate transmission facilities and network interconnection devices to physically link separate LANs.

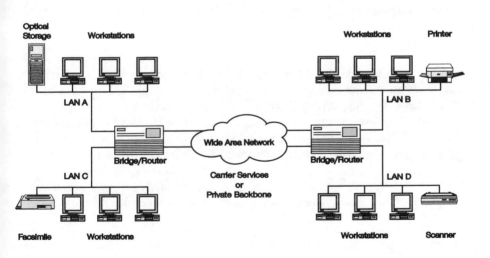

Figure 12.1 Extending the image application to remote locations via the WAN.

12.2 TRANSMISSION FACILITIES

To transfer image files to remote corporate locations, carrier-provided services or private backbone facilities can be used to interconnect LANs. Because of the huge size of image files and the need to support myriad other applications, however, not just any carrier service or backbone facility will suffice, even if the image files are compressed before transmission.

12.2.1 Dial-Up and Analog Leased Lines

Conventional switches, such as AT&T's 5ESS and Northern Telecom's DMS series, which are used in about 90% of local central offices, are currently limited to switching bandwidth in 64 Kbps increments.[1] Thus, they are suitable only for switching voice and low-speed data—not image traffic between high-speed LANs operating at up to 20 Mbps. In addition to creating intolerable transmission bottlenecks, dial-up and analog leased lines are also commonly affected by voice frequency impairments that can corrupt data. This means modem transmission is limited to 19.2 Kbps and, with sophisticated data compression algorithms, 38.4 Kbps.[2]

To minimize the effects of line impairments on analog leased lines, extra-cost line conditioning can be requested from the carrier. But there are no performance guarantees with line conditioning; the carrier promises higher quality lines on a "best effort" basis. The low-speed and uncertain line quality of dial-up and analog leased lines renders them suspect for carrying any type of LAN traffic, let alone image traffic.

12.2.2 Packet-Switched Services

Packet-switched networks thrived in the 1970s and 1980s as a way for asynchronous terminals to access remote computers over noisy dial-up and analog leased lines. CCITT X.25 standards were the driving force behind the acceptance of packet-switching networks. But carrier-provided packet data services based on the CCITT X.25 standard are limited to 56 Kbps, mostly because of the X.25 protocol's overhead burden, which, among other things, provides error checking and correction at every network node to ensure error-free transmission.

If a receiving node detects a transmission error, it requests a retransmission from the sending node. While this is valuable for point-of-sale applications that require the accurate

---

[1]This situation is changing, at least with AT&T's 5ESS local central office switches. At this writing, AT&T is installing upgrades to 5ESS switches that will allow transmissions to be switched at rates higher than 64 Kbps.

[2]An emerging CCITT standard called *V.fast* permits modem transmissions at *fractional T1* (FT1) speeds. Asynchronous transmission at 115.2 Kbps without compression has already been demonstrated, raising the possibility of high-speed image transfers over the public dial-up network.

transmission of credit card and other financial information, it is a cumbersome and unnecessary process when imaging traffic is being transmitted between LANs. Therefore, consideration must be given to more reliable digital services, starting with *digital data services* (DDS).

12.2.3 Digital Data Services

DDS, the first digital service for private-line communications, was introduced by AT&T in the mid-1970s. It offers a range of speeds from 2.4 Kbps to 56 Kbps. Being a digital service, DDS does not require a modem, but rather a digital termination device called a *digital service unit* (DSU). The appeal of DDS for data is the higher quality of digital versus analog transmission. Until FT1 was introduced in the late 1980s, DDS at 56 Kbps was one way to connect LANs via remote bridges. However, the 56 Kbps line rate proved to be a serious bottleneck to Ethernet and token-ring LANs that operate 178 to 285 times faster. (The same applies to switched 56K service.) DDS (and switched 56K service) are not very practical for handling large image file transfers on a continuous basis.

DDS is also a relatively expensive service, due to its reliance on a network of hubs called *serving wire centers* (SWCs). Since there are a limited number of hubs in each state and all traffic switching occurs at these hubs, getting traffic to its destination typically involves a lot of back-hauling. This increases the mileage between end-points and, consequently, inflates the charges for DDS lines. And, since DDS is implemented over a separate overlay network, there is no upgrade path to higher-speed services, such as FT1.

The demand for DDS will diminish as the popularity of FT1 continues to grow. The fact that AT&T plans to enhance FT1 with management and diagnostic capabilities has fueled industry speculation that AT&T might be phasing out DDS.

12.2.4 Fractional T1

FT1 entails the provision and use of incremental bandwidth between 56 Kbps and 768 Kbps, without payment for an entire T1 facility. Instead of paying for a full T1 line, FT1 allows users to order only the amount of bandwidth needed to support the image application. This saves the user the expense of leasing a full T1 line for partial use, while easing the WAN bottleneck between LANs, which is a problem with DDS and X.25 at 56 Kbps. Since FT1 is widely available among interexchange carriers, there is less of a back-haul problem to contend with than with DDS. And, since it is derived from a T1 facility, FT1 offers high reliability and availability.

It is important to remember is that FT1 is an offering of the interexchange carriers. At this writing, only New England Telephone and Pacific Bell offer tariffed FT1 access, while some telephone companies offer FT1 access on an individual case basis. For the most part, users must still pay T1 charges on the access portion of the circuit, even though they might need only one-quarter or one-half of the bandwidth to support image applications between interconnected LANs.

12.2.5 Integrated Services Digital Network

Primary rate (23B+D) *integrated services digital network* (ISDN) is another internetworking option that can support image applications. ISDN is a carrier-provided switched digital service that is billed on a time and distance basis, just like an ordinary phone call. ISDN channels are available in bandwidth increments of 56/64 Kbps, 384 Kbps and 1.536 Mbps.

The billing method can be an advantage or a liability, depending on how many hours a month the ISDN channels are used. Used continuously, ISDN channels in the United States are considerably more expensive than the bandwidth equivalents offered over dedicated leased lines (FT1/T1), which entail fixed monthly charges (determined by distance), no matter how long the line is used. But, if ISDN channels are used only 20 hours a month, ISDN can be more economical than paying for full-time leased lines.

Although ISDN is not yet widely available—due in large part to its different implementations among local-exchange and interexchange carriers—this is about to change. The industry has made great strides in implementing a standard version of ISDN that ensures interconnectivity between serving areas and between different types of central office switches and customer premises equipment. This effort is known as *National ISDN* and is expected to be completed in 1994.

12.2.6 Dedicated T1 Lines

T1 digital lines are an ideal medium for interconnecting LANs from point to point. They offer excellent reliability and availability, in addition to acceptable bandwidth capacity. An increasing number of bridges and routers offer T1 interfaces to facilitate LAN-to-WAN connectivity.

However, with imaging applications already putting a strain on today's Ethernet and token-ring LANs, running image applications over T1 lines might not be an adequate long term strategy. Instead, complementary LAN interconnection strategies are called for, such as frame relay over T1, which provides a more efficient use of the available bandwidth.

12.2.7 Frame Relay

An outgrowth of ISDN, *frame relay* is a bearer service that has become a high-performance alternative to X.25 packet-switched networks for LAN interconnection. The technical concept behind frame relay is simple: eliminate unnecessary protocol processing and overhead to increase network throughput. Error correction and flow control already exist at the upper layers of most modern computer communication protocol stacks, and thus can be relegated to the "edges" of the network, rather than performed at every node within the network, as in X.25. Frame relay eliminates 75% of the protocol overhead of X.25, including error correction.

Frame relay operates over T1 lines, using the available bandwidth more efficiently. One of the selling points of frame relay is *bandwidth on demand*, which entails an application momentarily seizing the entire amount of available bandwidth and, upon completion of its duty cycle, relinquishing it to other voice and data applications.

Another way that frame relay makes more efficient use of the available bandwidth is through its burst mode of transmission. The burst mode makes it possible for an application running over a 384 Kbps FT1 line, for example, to momentarily transmit information at the full T1 rate, provided that there is enough free bandwidth available on the network.

A potential problem with frame relay networks is congestion control, which can be caused by the speed of the application being much higher than the frame relay backbone. A LAN operating at 10 Mbps, for instance, can easily overwhelm a frame relay link operating at the T1 speed of 1.544 Mbps. And, at any given time, several users might want to access the full transmission bandwidth of the T1 simultaneously.

An overload condition might also occur when too many customers are exceeding their *committed information rate* (CIR) and grabbing more bandwidth than they are really entitled to. While this presents no problem if the carrier's network can absorb the extra load, severe congestion problems can result when everyone routinely exceeds their CIR.

The network must have a means of detecting such situations and initiating procedures to prevent overload conditions. Although the frame relay standards provide various mechanisms for congestion control, to date few carriers and equipment vendors support them.

Most carriers try to prevent congestion occurring in the first place by making excess bandwidth available to frame relay users. When frame relay is run over private T1 lines, however, this solution is only available if the network is overconfigured with extra bandwidth. But the cost of extra facilities negates the efficiencies and cost savings promised by frame relay.

Alternatives to frame relay and T1 fall into the category of broadband services. There are three transitional services to broadband: *fractional T3* (FT3), T3, and *switched multimegabit data service* (SMDS). The services are transitional, operating in the 1.544 Mbps to 45 Mbps range and providing a jump-off point to *broadband ISDN* (BISDN), which will be provided over the emerging *synchronous optical network* (SONET) in conjunction with *asynchronous transfer mode* (ATM) switching.

12.2.8 T3

T3 service is typically offered over fiber facilities. The applications touted by T3 advocates include: LAN interconnection; multiple T1 line replacement; and high-speed backbones that integrate voice, data, video, and image traffic.

There is no stampede to embrace T3, because it uses proprietary optics. For this reason, T3 service entails constructing ICB access lines from the customer premises to the carrier's serving office. Special construction costs at each end differ widely from region to region, from a low of about $8,000 to a high of about $150,000. Since these costs are almost never factored into the crossover comparisons with T1, the true cost of T3 makes it difficult for even the largest companies to justify.

In the absence of optical standards for T3, proprietary interfaces have proliferated, which, in turn, restrict the ability of users to mix and match different manufacturer's equipment end to end. T3 services, like AT&T's T45, require that the customer negotiate the type of optical interfaces that will be placed in the various serving offices of the interexchange carriers.

12.2.9 Fractional T3

Some carriers are capitalizing on the appeal of FT1 by extending the "fractional" concept to T3. Under this concept, the user can order bandwidth in T1 increments up to the full T3 rate of 44.736 Mbps. This service is designed for users who need more than the 1.544 Mbps offered by T1, but less than the full bandwidth offered by T3, to support the interconnection of Ethernet or token-ring LANs. This enables corporate locations to share such high-bandwidth applications as document imaging, CAD/CAM, and bulk file transfers between hosts. A bridge is used to connect each LAN to the public network. From the user's point of view, the public network appears as an extension of the LAN.

Current FT3 offerings are not intended as a migration path to more advanced broadband services, such as broadband ISDN, which will be based on SONET and ATM technologies. Among the carriers offering FT3 is US West. By using only one type of advanced multiplexer to implement FT3, the company has avoided the "mix-and-match" equipment problem associated with proprietary T3.

12.2.10 Switched Multimegabit Data Services

SMDS is a public, high-speed, packet-switched transport service for connecting LANs, host computers, image databases, and other high-speed applications.

SMDS is offered by the *regional Bell operating companies* (RBOCs) as a *metropolitan-area network* (MAN) service. Supporting T1 and T3 access, SMDS employs a packet-switched, dual counter-rotating ring architecture. The two unclosed rings each transmit data in only one direction. If one ring fails, the other handles packet transmission. This protection mechanism safeguards users' data against loss caused by a network fault.

An SMDS customer has private access to an SMDS switch for up to 16 devices per access link. The devices are connected in a bus arrangement similar to an Ethernet LAN. SMDS access can be customized to suit the individual bandwidth needs of subscribers. By means of access classes, limits can be enforced on the level of sustained information transfer and on the burstiness of the transfer. In the case of T3, the access classes are 4, 10, 16, 25 and 34 Mbps. For T3 access paths, an *ingress access class* can be applied to the information flow from the CPE to the MAN switching system, and an *egress access class* can be applied to information flowing from the MAN switching system to the CPE. Subscribers can select both types of access classes. For T1 access paths, the same 1.536 Mbps access class is applied to both directions of information flow.

Currently, subscribers access SMDS via dedicated T1 access lines, with or without frame relay. On each access line, the required customer premises equipment consists of a router with an SMDS interface and *a channel service unit/data service unit* (CSU/DSU) with an SMDS interface. The router/bridge works in concert with the CSU/DSU. The router handles the protocol processing and passes the information to the CSU/DSU for lower-level protocol processing and transmission to the SMDS network. This process works in reverse at the receiving end.

The *data exchange interface* (DXI) provides standardized connectivity between the two devices. A *local management interface* (LMI) permits the CSU/DSU to pass performance information to the router so it can be sent to a *simple network management protocol-* (SNMP) based management workstation.

At this writing, vendors are just starting to introduce fully compliant (DXI-LMI) products for SMDS access. These vendors include ADC Kentrox, Digital Link Corp., Cisco Systems, and Wellfleet. Products that adhere to the DXI-LMI specifications will be interoperable.

SMDS will provide an effective and economical means of moving images among corporate LANs within a metropolitan area. In the future, SONET will link these MANs nationwide at gigabit speeds, permitting image traffic to be conveyed beyond the confines of the metropolitan area.

12.2.11 Broadband ISDN

By the time narrowband ISDN emerged from the laboratory in the late 1980s and began to be deployed in the real-time business environment, it was already apparent that ISDN's B (64 Kbps) channels would be inadequate to support emerging high-speed data applications. Specifically, users wanted to interconnect LANs and achieve high-resolution image and video—capabilities that require considerably more bandwidth. Consequently, ISDN came under increasing attack for being "too little, too late."

But standards bodies recognized early on that the requirement for high-capacity channels within the framework of ISDN could be satisfied sometime in the future under a service concept called *broadband ISDN* (BISDN). BISDN increases the channel capacity to 600 Mbps and beyond for multimedia high-speed connectivity and bandwidth on demand. But BISDN requires a transport network of tremendous capacity. With no such network in place, interest in BISDN waned in favor of other broadband technologies and services, such as FDDI and SMDS, which were projected for near-term deployment.

SONET was originally conceived to provide carriers with a standard optical transmission medium for interoffice trunking. With private network users expressing interest in T3 for their backbones, the SONET concept was extended to include the local loop and is currently being extended further to include the customer premises.

It soon became apparent that the standardized, high-capacity, intelligent transport medium offered by SONET provided the infrastructure that would make BISDN a reality much sooner than originally thought. Projected for deployment in the mid-1990s, BISDN offers users higher throughput, reliable performance, and standard interfaces.

Because SONET's development parallels that of BISDN, many design aspects were worked into it to accommodate future BISDN services worldwide. Although this compatibility might only be at the physical level, even that is a major achievement. Taking advantage of the availability and capacity of optical fiber—of which over 2 million miles are already installed in the U.S. alone—SONET brings to BISDN the ability to reliably transport enormous quantities of information. Access to the broadband network will be offered over a set of interfaces at 155 Mbps and 622 Mbps, using high-speed, fixed-length packet switching offered by ATM. Not coincidentally, these rates correspond to speeds that have been standardized for SONET fiber-optic systems.

The BISDN networking fabric will include ATM for switching and SONET for transmission. As the demand for broadband services increases throughout the 1990s, new switching systems employing photonic switching fabrics will enter the network, perhaps with enough capacity to support every conceivable type of service—old and new.

Vendors are already offering SONET-compliant CPE with interfaces to the public network. With SONET progressing rapidly, we will see limited implementations of BISDN in a couple of years, starting with high-speed LAN interconnection that supports picture-quality video and image applications.

12.3 LAN INTERCONNECTION DEVICES

The devices that facilitate the interconnection of LANs over WAN facilities fall into four categories: repeaters, bridges, routers, and gateways. *Repeaters,* which are the simplest and cheapest of the devices, extend the range of LANs and other network facilities by boosting signal strength and reshaping distorted signals. *Gateways,* which are the most complex and expensive of the devices, provide interoperability between applications by performing processing-intensive protocol conversions.

In the middle of this "complexity spectrum" are bridges and routers. At the risk of oversimplification, traditional *bridges* implement basic data-level links between LANs that use identical protocols; traditional *routers,* on the other hand, can be programmed to handle multiple network protocols, thereby supporting diverse types of LANs and host systems over the same WAN facility. Some vendors bundle the functionality of both devices into the same unit, permitting concurrent bridging and routing. Of the two types of devices, there is more confusion about which bridging method is appropriate for any given LAN environment.

12.3.1 Bridging Methods

There are several bridging methods: source-route bridging, which is preferred by IBM; transparent bridging, which is a basic method of LAN interconnection supported by most bridge makers; and *source-route transparent* (SRT) bridging, which is a relatively new standard that allows source routing and transparent bridging to be used together on the same network.

12.3.1.1 Source-Route Bridging

Source-route bridging is a method of internetworking token-ring LANs that uses a process called *route discovery* to find the optimal path for communications between end stations. The route between end stations is discovered through the use of *explorer packets,* which are sent between the source and destination end stations. When the explorer packet reaches its destination, the end station responds by issuing a packet containing the routing information. If multiple routes are available, this packet is sent back to the source over all the routes. The originating station selects the best route based on the fewest hops to the destination station.

One of the problems with source routing is that it creates a significant amount of overhead in mesh networks, which can bog down network performance. The amount of overhead increases as more stations and links are added to the network.

Since the end stations are involved in route selection, they might not have up-to-date knowledge of the best path, especially if the path is temporarily congested. Because they are not able to implement adaptive routing, source-routing bridges cannot dynamically reroute traffic around failed links. To reroute traffic, a new route discovery sequence must be initiated. Source-routing bridges also cannot balance the traffic load in response to congestion.

12.3.1.2 Transparent Bridging

Transparent bridging originated in the Ethernet environment. It enables stations, regardless of location, to communicate as if they were on the same LAN. In a process called *filtering* the bridge looks at the destination address to see if it is listed in the table of source addresses. If it is not, the packet is sent over the bridge to the next LAN. If a match is found, the bridge simply ignores the packet.

In a process called *learning* the bridge looks at all the packets originating on the LAN to build and update its table of source addresses. A table is maintained for each LAN connected to the bridge. The tables are updated when new packets are detected or when addresses "expire" after a specified time without use.

If a packet contains an address that has not yet been learned, it is sent out over all active links. The best path is determined by an industry-standard spanning-tree algorithm that incorporates such factors as the number of hops from the designated root bridge and the speed of the links. If there are any redundant paths, they are put into standby mode and used only in the event of primary link failure.

12.3.1.3 Source-Route Transparent Bridging

The *source-route transparent* (SRT) bridging method combines source routing and transparent bridging, permitting the data of both to be passed over the same network.

With SRT, the *routing information* (RI) field indicator is used to distinguish between frames that are using source routing and frames that are using transparent bridging. Transparent bridges, including those supporting Ethernet, do not alter the routing indicator. Source-routing bridges do change the routing indicator, setting it to one. By inspecting the routing indicator, the SRT-compliant device can determine whether the frame requires transparent bridging or source routing.

By supporting both bridging methods, SRT-compliant devices eliminate the need for multiple types of internetworking equipment and separate network facilities, and thus can result in considerable cost savings. In this era of budget trimming and staff cutbacks, these considerations loom large for most companies. In several key areas, SRT enhances the capabilities of source routing and transparent bridging.

Transparent bridging employs the simplest method of forwarding packets and is able to learn other locations based on newly encountered addresses. In source-route bridging, the originating device sends out explorer packets to discover the route between source and destination end stations. SRT not only supports both methods, it also uses less route discovery overhead than source routing, because by this method both the source and destination end stations can discover the route simultaneously.

Source routing does not provide automatic reroutes around congested or failed links and makes no provision for load balancing. Unless provided by proprietary methods, transparent bridging does not make use of idle standby paths during normal operation or offer load balancing in the event of congestion. SRT uses standby paths dynamically in the event of primary link failure. And, since SRT makes use of idle standby paths, it also offers more efficient utilization of available bandwidth.

In addition to supporting 4 Mbps and 16 Mbps token-ring LANs, SRT-compliant devices can consolidate Ethernet and token ring over the same WAN facilities.

Although SRT does not translate packets between end stations that use source routing and transparent bridging, its support of both provides the necessary internetworking platform for future interoperability between applications that will perform such translations. Current translation schemes used by internetworking vendors are proprietary and tend to negate the benefits of open systems by requiring the user to rely on the products of a single vendor.

Even with these advantages, however, SRT-compliant bridges do not solve the problem of consolidating IBM's *systems network architecture* (SNA) and token-ring traffic over the same network. This is an important concern among many corporations that want to carry forward their considerable investments in fully functional SNA equipment for imaging applications, and, at the same time, take advantage of token-ring LANs for automated workflow operations. The optimal solution lies in choosing an SRT-compliant internetworking device that also supports a capability known as *synchronous data link control* (SDLC) passthrough.

12.3.1.4 SDLC Passthrough

Since little of the installed base of SNA equipment has been upgraded to support token-ring connectivity, the capability to support SDLC traffic is a very significant feature of today's internetworking devices. Before SDLC support, expensive adapters were required to attach such devices as 3174 cluster controllers to a token-ring LAN. Alternatively, the two traffic types had to be separately routed over the WAN—not a very good way to support imaging applications. The latter solution entailed an overhead burden and cost of two separate networks—just because older SNA equipment could not be attached to the LAN simply and economically.

With internetworking devices that support SDLC traffic, users are finally able to consolidate parallel networks into a single multiprotocol backbone. One benefit of this arrangement is that it encompasses the SNA environment without any modification to the installed base of cluster controllers and front-end processors. Thus, SDLC passthrough is also useful for integrating different generations of equipment that might be supporting image applications.

Combining SDLC serial traffic from SNA devices with LAN traffic—and supporting such commonly used non-SNA protocols as NetBIOS, TCP/IP, and IPX/SPX—can greatly reduce communication costs.

SDLC passthrough also provides an economical migration path for older SNA cluster controllers and front-end processors to token-ring, peer-to-peer networking. Cluster controller/FEP performance is improved by speeding up the communication lines from the slow 4.8 and 9.6 Kbps serial lines employed by SNA to WAN link speeds of 64 Kbps and higher.

Reliability is also improved, because the SDLC data stream is encapsulated within the token-ring frame format for routing across the WAN. This allows the advantageous use of redundant routes not available under SNA. If a line fails, image traffic can be rerouted in an average of three seconds—well within the time-out threshold of SNA sessions.

12.3.2 Routers

Whereas bridges are transparent to network protocols and are used mostly for point-to-point links between LANs, routers can be used to build huge, complex internetworks. In the process, routers offer the highest degree of redundancy and fault tolerance, conducting congestion control in conjunction with end nodes, to ensure that packets traversing large internets do not experience critical errors that can time-out host sessions.

Routers generally offer more embedded intelligence and, consequently, more sophisticated network management and traffic control capabilities than bridges. Bridges deliver packets of data on a "best effort" basis, which can result in lost data, unless the host computer protocol provides protection. In contrast, a router has the potential for flow control and more comprehensive error protection.

Whereas a bridge only checks the source and destination address and some of the control information in the frame of a packet, to see if it is bound for another network (filtering), a router does much more. A router keeps a map of the entire network and uses the map to examine the status of the different paths, so it can determine the best way to get the packet to its destination.

Because they forward packets based on a routing table that indicates the best path between two stations, routers make the most efficient use of multiple paths. Routers devise their own routing tables, which adapt quickly to changes in network traffic, thereby balancing the data load. Routers can also detect changes in the network and avoid congested or inoperative links.

When a packet arrives at the router, it is held in queue until the router finishes handling the previous packet. Then, the router scans the destination address and looks the address up in its routing table. The routing table lists the various nodes on the network, as well as the paths between the nodes. If there is more than one path to a particular node, the router selects the shortest path first. If the packet is too large for the destination node to accept, the router segments it into several smaller packets.

Routers are very good at bypassing link failures and congested nodes, which is critical for applications that cannot tolerate unnecessary delays or prolonged outages. Bypass is facilitated by the ability of routers to share route information with each other. Bridges cannot do this because they rely on a simple filtering mechanism. When one bridge gets overloaded, the others never find out about it, and packets might be dropped. Unless the end station is intelligent enough to request that dropped packets be retransmitted, they can be lost.

Because routers are protocol-specific, they are typically equipped to handle a dozen or more protocols, which adds to their cost. High-end multiprotocol routers can cost as much as $75,000, compared to $6,000 to $30,000 for most bridges.

12.4 BANDWIDTH ON DEMAND

New data services are being introduced by carriers at a rapid pace. High-speed switched digital services, such as switched 384 Kbps and switched 1.536 Mbps, are already available, as is switched T3 service at 44.736 Mbps, while frame relay and SMDS are just taking off. ISDN, having suffered from nonstandardized carrier implementations, is undergoing standardization for a phased rollout that will extend into 1994. These new services are of critical significance to private network users. Not only do they promise considerable cost savings over private network solutions, but the private network must now be positioned with appropriate products to fully support such public network services. Anything less would result in the private network becoming an obstacle that locks the corporation out of future economies and efficiencies, potentially damaging its competitive position.

An increasing variety of traffic, the mix of which can change dramatically over a short time, poses a special challenge to network planners. Private networks must handle a constantly changing blend of voice, data, video, and image traffic. Complicating things is the fact that traffic is increasingly being driven by the end user rather than the network planner, resulting in wholly unexpected traffic patterns, bandwidth needs, and performance requirements. While the interexchange carriers are trying to address these needs with a variety of switched digital services, the RBHCs have not been keeping up with equivalent access services.

Inverse multiplexing provides an economical way to access the switched digital services of the interexchange carriers by providing bandwidth on demand. In essence, users "dial up" the appropriate increment of bandwidth needed to support a given application and pay for the number of local access channels only when they are set up to transmit voice, data, image, or video traffic. Upon completion of the transmission, the channels are taken down. This obviates the need for private leased lines to support temporary applications.

Under the bandwidth-on-demand concept, extra bandwidth can be obtained from the public network whenever it is required by a specific application. In addition to supporting image transfers, the bandwidth can be used to accommodate peak traffic periods and to reroute traffic from failed private lines. Advantages of this approach to ordering bandwidth include: the bandwidth is available immediately, without the delay inherent in ordering new lines; the user pays only for the bandwidth used, according to time and distance; and the need for standby links, which users are billed for whether the links are fully used or not, is eliminated.

12.4.1 Inverse Multiplexing

Inverse multiplexing enhances a firm's use of wide-area bandwidth. The devices, which reside at the customer premises, gather data from a bandwidth-intensive application. The information is then divided into multiple 56 Kbps, 64 Kbps or 384 Kbps channels, to support aggregate transmission rates of up to 3 Mbps. The multiplexers synchronize the information across the channels and transmit it to a similar device at the remote location via switched public network services. At the remote location the data is remultiplexed into a single data stream (Figure 12.2).

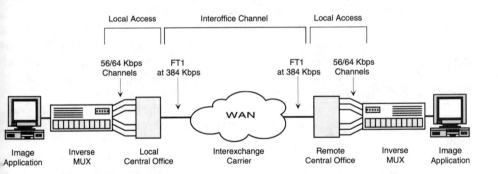

Figure 12.2 Network access via inverse multiplexing.

Tariffs for the widely available 56- and 64-Kbps digital services offered by the public carriers have come down dramatically in the last year as US Sprint, MCI, and AT&T continue to jockey for competitive position. In most cases, it now costs no more to place a data call over switched 56 Kbps service than to place a 9.6 Kbps modem call over analog facilities. Aggregating 56- and 64-Kbps channels to support such applications as video-conferencing, imaging, and high-speed data networking is clearly more economical than paying the monthly cost of extra lines By aggregating switched digital bandwidth into a higher-speed channel, the user pays for the connection only while it exists.

12.4.2 LAN Interconnection

Inverse multiplexers support a variety of applications that require bandwidth in the range of 56 Kbps to 768 Kbps. Among the applications most supported by inverse multiplexers is LAN interconnection. Instead of using private T1 lines for LAN-to-LAN connections, the inverse multiplexer can build the required increment of switched bandwidth to handle traffic from bridges or routers.

While bridges and routers can be interconnected over the public switched network via network access equipment—such as first generation inverse multiplexers, modems and ISDN terminal adapters—first, a user or LAN administrator must manually plug the router into the network device and set up the call. Cisco Systems, a leading manufacturer of routers, and Ascend Communications have developed a new call control procedure to facilitate this process. The specification, which might become an industry standard, defines call control procedures for high-speed dial-up transmissions using switched digital services for LAN interconnection.

The call control procedures defined in this specification are based on the international CCITT V.25 bis recommendation, to which Cisco and Ascend have added open extensions. The specification describes the synchronous protocol used to establish connection between the DTE, such as a Cisco router, and *data communications equipment* (DCE), such as the Ascend multiband bandwidth-on-demand controller. V.25 bis allows the router to tell the controller where and when to send traffic and over what path. With this intelligence, the router can create new or alternate paths for redundancy or transmit at less expensive times of the day. For example, corporate branches in the United States and Japan might be open for only two concurrent hours a day, making it difficult to justify the expense of a dedicated connection between them. With V.25 bis, each site could store up its image files and then pass all the traffic in that two-hour window.

The specification is supported by most synchronous modems on the market today Calls can be made over E1, T1, FT1, ISDN PRI (*primary rate*) and ISDN BRI (*basic rate*) facilities.

The specification brings true dial-on-demand routing to the LAN/WAN internetworking environment. In doing so, the dialing specification has a number of immediate applications:

- Switched back-up internet connections for T1/E1 or FT1 leased/private lines;
- Switched overflow internet connections to supplement leased/private lines during periods of heavy traffic flow;
- Switched internet connections for remote offices with intermittent, bursty, high bandwidth data transmission requirements;
- Switched internet connections for fault-tolerant disaster recovery.

The Cisco and Ascend dialing specification allows routers to establish circuit-switched connections, as over an ISDN service, between remote sites when bandwidth is actually needed. This means intelligent internetworking routers can control switched digital calls at up to 3 Mbps, sensing when a line is needed or when a line is about to be saturated and requires additional bandwidth.

3Com Corporation's NETBuilder line of bridges and routers, for example, is certified for use with Ascend's multiband controller, greatly enhancing 3Com's support of switched digital networks for LAN interconnection. Connectivity for NETBuilder bridges and routers and the Ascend multiband controller is available via a standard V.35 or RS-449 interface. The network can be configured for a logical circuit with bandwidth ranging from 56 Kbps to 4 Mbps, in increments of 56 Kbps, 64 Kbps, or 384 Kbps. Using the multiband controller, network managers can assign bandwidth to NETBuilder's WAN ports automatically, manually, or on a scheduled basis.

12.5 CONCLUSION

Running imaging applications between LANs over the WAN via carrier-provided services, dedicated facilities, or both extends the benefits of imaging across the entire enterprise. Doing this requires appropriate transmission facilities and LAN interconnection devices.

The carrier-provided services that are most appropriate for imaging applications are frame relay and switched multimegabit data services; they have been developed specifically for high-speed LAN interconnection. Initially, both services are provided at the T1 rate, but eventually T3 will be supported, allowing LAN interconnection at 10 Mbps, 16 Mbps, and 20 Mbps.

The choice of LAN interconnection devices is basically a choice between bridges and routers. Both devices can be optioned for access to frame relay and SMDS. However, the proper choice of bridges from among the several available types can meet the interconnectivity needs of users more economically than multiprotocol routers. A relatively new type of device, the inverse multiplexer, can work in conjunction with bridges and routers to provide switched bandwidth in the desired increments to support ad hoc LAN interconnection for image transfers. Using an inverse multiplexer can be an economical alternative to using dedicated facilities for only occasional image transfers.

PART V

RELATED INTEGRATION AREAS

Chapter 13

Videoconferencing and Image Transfer

13.1 INTRODUCTION

Videoconferencing is often thought of as a method of linking people together over long distances for the purpose of holding a meeting. But, actually, videoconferencing has progressed to include the transfer of document images, presentation graphics, and "talking heads." Image, text, and graphics from a variety of sources can be multiplexed over the same video circuit to permit a new level of interactivity among conference participants.

The roots of videoconferencing can be traced to AT&T's demonstration of the Picturephone Meeting Service at the New York World's Fair in 1964. Although attendees found the concept intriguing, the Picturephone could not be turned into a commercial success because the digital compression technology and high-speed digital communications infrastructures necessary for widespread videoconferencing implementation were nonexistent.

Only during the past few years has videoconferencing become accepted among corporate managers as a strategically significant communications tool. The growing popularity of videoconferencing can be attributed, in part, to the increasing number of transmission options that have become available. These transmission options, which include fiber-optic, FT1, and ISDN facilities, as well as satellite links via inexpensive, rapidly deployable *very small aperture terminals* (VSATs) have improved video communications and greatly reduced costs.

Advances in digital compression technology for video signal transmission have also contributed to renewed interest in videoconferencing. The image quality of a transmitted signal is largely a function of application: whereas one-way commercial television broadcasting requires high resolution, the resolution requirement for videophone is very modest, because the rate of picture change is relatively low. The video transmission data rate for interactive systems—systems that require both transmit and receive capabilities—such as videophone and videoconferencing systems must be limited so that the signal can be conveyed over ubiquitously available media. Digital compression technology, which is partly achieved by removing both interframe and intraframe redundancies, can effectively compress these video signals by a ratio of as high as 6250 to 1.

A *coder/decoder* (codec) device reduces high-bandwidth video signals to the T1 rate of 1.544 Mbps and, even further, to sub-T1 rates as low as 56 Kbps (Figure 13.1). Because the cost of these facilities—as well as the cost of satellite links—is continually being reduced as a result of the nationwide expansion of fiber-optic networks, videoconferencing has suddenly become affordable for virtually any company that has a use for it.

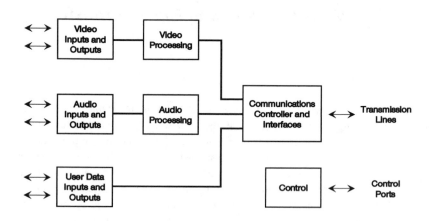

Figure 13.1 Block diagram of video codec functionality.

The video codec performs real-time processing of analog voice and video into a digital signal that is then decoded back into analog voice and video at the receiving end. There are four steps to this process:

1. Preprocessing. The codec removes high-frequency noise.
2. Encoding. Each block of the picture, ranging from 8 by 8 to 16 by 16 pixels in size, is digitized.
3. Decoding. The digital signal is turned back into the picture it represents.
4. Postprocessing. Noise is removed.

The increasing popularity of videoconferencing can also be attributed to the innovations associated with the technology. Only a few years ago, establishing a videoconference entailed building a dedicated, custom studio and hiring separate contractors to install audio, video, and other auxiliary equipment, such as facsimile and graphics devices. Such an undertaking cost companies as much as $500,000. Today, however, videoconferencing vendors offer rollout systems that include all the necessary equipment for a videoconference and cost far less.

Compression Labs, for example, offers the Gallery 2000 portable videoconferencing system for approximately $30,000. The system includes: a single-chip camera with focus, tilt, and pan capabilities; three microphones; an audio system with an integral echo canceller; and two 25-in monitors. The firm's high-quality Rembrandt 56 codec costs an additional $56,000, however.

13.2 APPLICATIONS

Businesses can benefit from videoconferencing in a variety of ways. Cutting travel costs, although important, is not the only motivation for implementing videoconferencing systems. Busy corporate executives who must administer nationwide operations know only too well that the time constraints imposed by travel also limit their managerial effectiveness. Instead of consuming valuable time with the logistics of travel for face-to-face meetings at individual locations, executives can take advantage of videoconferencing systems to conduct general meetings and individual sessions with appropriate personnel. By minimizing business travel, executives can make better use of their time and other organizational resources. In the process, the quality and the timeliness of decision making can be greatly improved.

Businesses can also take advantage of the opportunities for education offered by videoconferencing. Many college campuses across the country offer continuing education programs to businesses that are willing to pick up the modest cost of a VSAT or microwave link. This offering allows employees to continue their education during the work day without having to take time off to commute to a campus. And, the interactive communication provided via videoconferencing systems allows a give-and-take between students and instructors that closely emulates a traditional classroom environment.

In the retail environment, videoconferencing technology can broadcast information on merchandise and new products to dispersed store locations. The timely delivery of this information enables store managers to be more responsive to the marketplace and reduces the costs associated with carrying unwanted inventory. As a result of this process, retailers can eliminate the need for costly discount sales to dispose of obsolete merchandise.

The convergence of videoconferencing and imaging is illustrated by a unique application developed by Harrah's Hotels & Casinos in Nevada. To improve guest registration procedures, the hotel allows guests to place a videoconference call at a kiosk located at the airport. Guests can check in from the airport, while they wait for baggage or transportation, thus saving time when they arrive at the hotel. The system uses basic rate ISDN (2B+D) for information transfer, and 45 Mbps fiber-optic facilities for switched, full-motion video. At Harrah's guest center kiosk, an ISDN phone (terminal adapter) provides voice communication with the reservations agent via the ISDN line. The kiosk also includes a touch-screen video monitor from which various accommodations and services can be selected, as well as a credit card reader and a receipt printer. A second ISDN line serves the kiosk camera's pan/tilt controller, which is operated remotely by the reservations agent. A fiber-optic line serves the reservation agent's full-motion video monitor. At the reservation center, the agent uses a computer to capture a single-frame video image of the guest for transmission to the hotel front desk. There, the image is output from a laser printer along with the registration information. When the guest arrives at the hotel front desk, the clerk verifies the guest's identity before handing over the room keys.

Whether used for product introductions, sales promotions, employee training, management messages, or collaborative projects between widely dispersed corporate locations, videoconferencing is increasingly viewed not as a prestige technology, but as a practical and immediately useful tool that can yield competitive advantages.

13.3 IMAGE TRANSFER CAPABILITIES

To effectively conduct business meetings with videoconferencing, it is often necessary to employ tools normally used to convey information in person—charts, memos, correspondence, files, and spreadsheets. These documents are typically produced on desktop PCs with a variety of sophisticated applications software and are then carried to the videoconference room, where they are used somewhat haphazardly. Either the remote location can view the material clearly and understand it, or they cannot—it all depends on the quality of the image and the size of the item displayed before the camera. Presentation need not be this uncertain, however; new integration strategies are merging office machines and videoconferencing systems.

Manufacturers of video codecs are experiencing increased demand for the integration of PC applications with videoconferencing equipment. VideoTelecom Corp., for example, has made integration the core element of its product offerings. The company ships its MediaMax video system in the expanded chassis of an IBM PC/AT. This integration lets users bring the computational power and image display capabilities of the PC into the videoconference.

VideoTelecom is not the only company that sees the trend toward greater computer integration. Videoconferencing pioneer Compression Labs has an OEM agreement with DataBeam Corp. to market that company's Data-Beam CT 500 interactive document-conferencing system along with its own codecs. The CT 500 transmits full-page documents, computer graphics, and photographs during a videoconference and allows meeting participants at each site to view, modify, and annotate those images.

Other codec manufacturers are adding similar capabilities to their videoconferencing systems, allowing attendees to get more value out of these electronic meetings. Optel Communications, for example, offers its VideoWriter software to video codec manufacturers. This software allows videoconference participants to display, transmit, and share scanned documents, PC-generated text, and graphics on videoconferencing room monitors. The system is compatible with either NTSC or RGB monitors.

Optel's VT 100 software allows annotation, PC-to-PC screen sharing, and electronic blackboarding. The annotation feature generates an overlay for any image displayed or shared between sites, including motion video. The PC-to-PC screen sharing allows users at each end to share and interact through the same PC application, such as a spreadsheet package. For electronic blackboarding, the VideoWriter comes with a 6 by 9-in writing tablet that allows "chalk talks" between participating sites.

Video capture and video editing boards for the IBM PC and compatibles, as well as the Apple Macintosh II, can turn videoconferences into video-graphic systems. Northern Telecom and Workstation Technologies have teamed up to produce an Apple NuBus card that adds black-and-white video in a window to a Mac II. The board, which can produce up to 15 frames per second of video, can display black-and-white video along with all the graphics, text, and CAD capabilities of the Mac.

With the release of Apple's QuickTime display video capability, video codec manufacturers are looking at migrating their video compression technology to the MAC. CLI's Cameo Personal Video System, for example, uses a companion module and Macintosh software to convert an Apple IIc or higher system into a videoconferencing system running over ISDN at 128 Kbps.

Users of DOS-based computers have had a wide selection of still and motion video boards available since the mid-1980s. One of the best known of these products is the Targa image capture board from Truevision. Truevision has since expanded its product line to include such products for the Macintosh.

Intel-Princeton is also quite active in developing desktop video systems. Along with PictureTel and IBM, the company has produced a line of chips and expansion boards that will convert ordinary PCs into multimedia computers and, eventually, into videoconferencing systems. Intel's *digital video interactive* (DVI) product line lets users play back compressed video in real time under Windows, OS/2, or MS-DOS. The present DVI technology, which requires very high data rates, is suitable for LANs and CD-ROM players.

Sun Microsystems offers a still-frame video system called VideoPix for its desktop SPARCstation. VideoPix allows users to capture, manipulate, store, and send color or black-and-white images across a UNIX network. Images can be captured from a wide variety of video sources. Users can crop, resize, remove motion blur from, and adjust both brightness and contrast of images. An OpenLook graphical interface by Sun and AT&T features pull-down menus and point-and-click mouse controls, which allow drag and drop images. VideoPix also includes software libraries for developers to integrate video image capture into applications.

Cogent Systems uses VideoPix for an automated fingerprint ID system called LifeID, which is aimed at police departments for use in the identification of suspected criminals. By attaching a small, specialized video camera to the system's still-frame capture board, users can perform a live scan of a human finger. The gray-scale image is then processed, stored in a master file, and compared against a database of thousands of fingerprints. If a video camera is attached to SPARCstation, a digital color photo of the person can also be captured and stored.

VideoPix installs in a single-width SBus slot on desktop SPARCstations and SBus-equipped SPARCservers running OpenWindows 2.0. The board contains standard RCA and S-Video jacks that can be connected to input devices such as a video still camera, camcorder, TV, video disc player, or VCR.

Now that videoconferencing has become an accepted technology for corporate use, it will not be long before participants discover the need for integrated graphics and document transfer capabilities as well. The conference room can even be wired into the corporate LAN so that text, document images, and graphics can be pulled off the network and projected onto the conference room screen.

Desktop videoconferencing featuring integrated voice, video, and data communications is possible with the fiber distributed data interface (FDDI) standard (Figure 13.2). FDDI, which operates at up to 100 Mbps, is the most efficient way to handle high-speed data traffic. It can be used in enterprisewide and metropolitan networks, is well suited to heavy network traffic with video frames from 20 to 80 KB, and offers asynchronous service that gives a tight delay boundary under extremely high loads. Since few workstations can handle the large amounts of data required to support audio and video capabilities, data must be reduced by skipping video frames or pixels, rendering the video, or employing prototype compression chips.

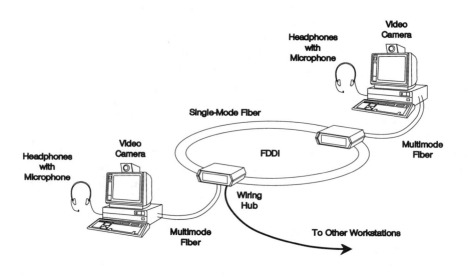

Figure 13.2 Videoconferencing over an FDDI LAN.

DEC has developed a desktop videoconferencing prototype that uses standard protocols to move video and audio messages over an FDDI network. Eventually, DEC expects videoconferencing to merge with other multimedia applications. For example, a conference of software developers might choose to play back or splice in a previously recorded program bug or dysfunction for the conference members to view. They also might record a portion of the videoconference and send it via electronic mail to someone who could not participate. The emergence of such "desktop movies," created by the user and shared with other members over a network, could advance users' capabilities over what they have today, to the same extent that desktop publishing advanced user functionality over simple text editors.

13.4 WIDE-AREA VIDEO TRANSMISSION

Videoconferencing sessions can be transmitted via a variety of media, including copper-based high-speed digital facilities, such as T1, satellite and microwave, and fiber-optic networks.

Satellite transmission has been a traditional and reliable method for videoconferencing. However, improvements in codec technology, the widespread availability of high-quality digital facilities, and the declining cost of services might signal a shift toward fiber and ISDN as the preferred means of implementing videoconferencing.

13.4.1 Very Small Aperture Terminals

Videoconferencing via satellite and using VSATs, is a well-established, reliable transmission technology for private networks. VSAT systems, introduced in 1981, integrate transmission and switching functions to provide preassigned and on-demand links for both point-to-point and broadcast applications.

The components associated with a VSAT earth station include the antenna, which is typically a parabolic reflector (dish) with a 0.3 to 2.4-meter diameter; and a *radio frequency* (RF) power unit that supplies 1 to 5 watts of power to support communication at up to 1.544 Mbps over the C band or Ku band (the two bands most commonly used for VSAT transmission). VSAT earth stations are linked, via satellite, to the *master earth station* (MES), which performs routing and management functions.

The MES can be operated by a single, large company from its headquarters site or shared among several small companies subscribing to a facility operated by a service provider. Figure 13.3 illustrates a typical VSAT network configuration.

VSAT networks can be configured for point-to-point, point-to-multipoint, or interactive VSAT broadcast. In point-to-point systems, VSATs located at each communication site transmit voice, data, and video information directly through the satellite to one another, without requiring a hub. In contrast, point-to-multipoint VSAT networks involve a centralized hub earth station that broadcasts video, voice, and packetized data, in any combination, to a selected group of remote receive-only VSATs. Interactive VSAT networks are a variation of point-to-point and point-to-multipoint network types in which two-way interactive, or "intelligent," VSATs communicate either through a hub in a star configuration or among themselves through the hub in a mesh arrangement.

In addition to video codecs, VSATs can be interfaced with virtually any standard synchronous data source, including host computers, CAD/CAM equipment, and multiplexers. Most VSATs support transmission speeds of up to 56 Kbps, and some also support the full range of leased-line transmission speeds, including T1 and E1, which operate at 1.544 Mbps and 2.048 Mbps, respectively. In addition, some VSAT vendors offer customized networks that support nonstandard or FT1 rates, such as 384 Kbps and 512 Kbps, to accommodate the specific videoconferencing needs of individual customers.

In many business applications VSATs offer significant advantages over conventional terrestrial networks. Advances in technology are creating smaller, more powerful, and economical satellite dishes that offer considerable efficiency, convenience, and flexi-

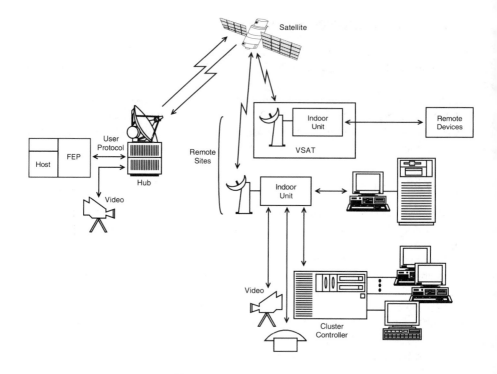

Figure 13.3 Typical satellite/VSAT network configuration.

bility over terrestrial private leased lines—including fiber-optic transmission systems. VSATs can help companies overcome the burden of local-access charges, which—in view of dramatic rate reductions on interexchange services—constitute an increasingly disproportionate share of total circuit costs. By moving from private leased lines to VSATs businesses can bypass local telephone companies entirely and stabilize their monthly transmission expenses.

VSAT networks also offer easier network expansion than terrestrial networks. Instead of coordinating system upgrades, additions, and changes with multiple telephone companies and interexchange carriers, VSAT users can add capacity to a network in a matter of minutes by simply allocating additional transponder bandwidth. With proper planning, additional VSAT locations can be brought on line within a single business day.

A potentially serious drawback to using VSATs for interactive videoconferencing applications is the problem of delay. While the round-trip half-second or more delay is not a problem for broadcast videoconferencing applications, it can be an annoying—if not intolerable—condition for interactive conversations. The round-trip delay is considerably shorter over terrestrial facilities, increasing the likelihood that fiber will become the transmission medium of choice for wide-area videoconferencing in the near future.

A final consideration for VSAT videoconferencing systems is the issue of security. Just as they do with data and voice transmissions, businesses and government agencies must often take steps to protect video signals from unauthorized reception. Video transmissions can be protected via extra-cost scrambling and encryption options.

Most vendors use an algorithm based on the *digital encryption standard* (DES) to encrypt audio. DES is the most thoroughly tested cryptographic algorithm available. It was developed by IBM and adopted in 1977 as a federal standard by the U.S. National Bureau of Standards. The U.S. National Bureau of Standards, renamed the *National Institute of Standards and Technology* (NIST), is a unit of the Department of Commerce. Groups such as the American Bankers Association, the *American National Standards Institute* (ANSI), and the *National Security Agency* (NSA) still endorse the DES.

DES-based encryption software uses an algorithm that encodes 64-bit blocks of data and uses a 56-bit key. The length of the key imposes a difficult decoding barrier to would-be intruders because 72 quadrillion (72,000,000,000,000,000) keys are possible. Because DES requires so much bandwidth, a variety of other proprietary encryption algorithms are also available. But the level of cryptographic security these other algorithms provide varies widely and none have been tested as rigorously as the DES.

13.4.2 Microwave

While VSATs might prove to be an economical solution for videoconferencing between geographically disbursed locations, terrestrial digital microwave technology is better suited for short-haul video transmissions involving distances of 10 to 40 miles (Figure 13.4). For longer distances, repeaters must be added, which can greatly inflate start-up costs. By using the high end of the radio frequency spectrum, microwave provides enormous transmission capacity that can interface directly with terrestrial digital facilities, including T1 (1.544 Mbps), T2 (6.312 Mbps), and T3 (44.736 Mbps).

Advances in microelectronics technology have greatly reduced the cost of microwave transmission systems in recent years, making microwave suitable for supporting video applications—especially instructional video that is broadcast within a fairly limited geographical range. Whereas many organizations typically combine voice, data, and video over a single high-speed backbone network, in some circumstances it is advantageous to off-load video from the backbone and put it onto a dedicated facility, such as microwave.

One such situation involves statewide school systems that operate educational video networks. Some of these networks include as many as 15 nodes, each offering several channels of video. Separating video from voice and data greatly simplifies the management of these networks and can facilitate the expansion of both the video and voice and data networks, since upgrades can be made to one network without impacting the other.

13.4.3 Fiber Optics

Fiber-optic transmission systems use light at ultra-high frequencies for the bulk transportation of voice, data, image, and video communications over hair-thin strands of plastic or

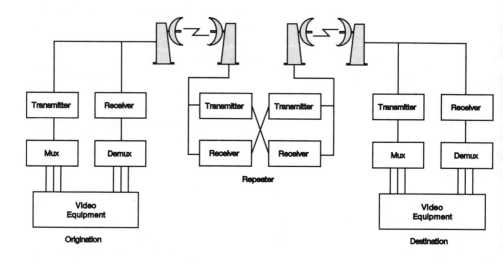

Figure 13.4 Microwave transmission for videoconferencing.

glass. The laser components at each end of a fiber-optic link enable the use of very high frequencies for encoding and decoding information into binary form (pulse/no pulse). This translates to a data transmission speed of 565 Mbps over optical fiber, versus only 1.544 Mbps for T1 over copper-based digital facilities and 19.2 Kbps over copper-based analog facilities.

Optical fiber is the most advanced transmission medium currently available; it provides bandwidth capacity and digital capabilities once offered only by satellites. The nationwide deployment of fiber by interexchange carriers makes it an economical alternative to VSAT and microwave technologies for both domestic and international videoconferencing. Transoceanic links, such as TAT-8 (and other fiber links to follow), offer an abundance of fiber bandwidth between the United States and Europe—as well as (anticipated) lower transmission costs, which are prompting some corporations to reconsider the implementation of videoconferencing technology, previously considered too costly.

Sony Corporation of America and *Williams Telecommunications Group* (WilTel) offer a portable videoconferencing system that uses fiber-based switched T3 facilities. The service, called ViaTV, offers broadcast quality video and audio, and is competitively priced with systems that use T1 or lower bandwidth circuits. WilTel provides the fiber facilities and Sony's Conference and Satellite Systems Division provides the videoconferencing equipment.

As existing fiber facilities become retrofitted for SONET compliance, transmission speeds of up to 2.488 Gbps will become the norm. SONET will ultimately permit speeds of up to 13 Gbps. At its lowest level of functionality, SONET provides a standard fiber-optic interface; but SONET promises to bring about tremendous changes in communications, including eventually replacing the current asynchronous T3 network. By employing end-to-end SONET equipment, the same fiber cable that currently supports the asynchronous network will offer a one-thousand-fold increase in transmission capacity. In the not-too-distant future, fiber-optic technology will broadcast video signals through the public network as easily and routinely as voice signals.

With such a high-capacity communications infrastructure in place, videoconferencing will be possible via equipment that is not unlike AT&T's original Picturephone Meeting Service—only on a grand scale. And, as fiber continues its migration to the residential environment, *high-definition television* (HDTV) transmission will also be made available to consumers.

13.4.4 Integrated Services Digital Network

The long-term objectives of ISDN are to implement a common standard for the provision of carrier services that will minimize operating costs while maximizing the performance and reliability of the network and to provide a network platform from which new information services can be launched in a more efficient and expeditious manner.

The gradual process of ISDN implementation is the result of a massive, coordinated effort on the part of carriers and equipment vendors, with the user community providing input on potential applications, including the transport of compressed video. As such, ISDN has potentially dramatic implications for videoconferencing.

Although there are desktop videoconferencing and videophone systems that operate at 64 Kbps on the market, they generally do not provide the same image quality as higher-speed ISDN systems. Because ISDN provides for narrowband channels at 384 Kbps (H0) and 1.536 Mbps (H11), the network makes high-quality videoconferencing available through the circuit-switched network. Now that AT&T has filed tariffs for the H0 channel (i.e., switched 384K service) and H11 channel (i.e., switched 1536K service), users will be able to realize the full potential of ISDN-based videoconferencing.

Videoconferencing through the use of switched bandwidth, rather than dedicated leased-line facilities, offers several compelling advantages. With switched bandwidth, implementing videoconferencing on a demand basis can be as easy as making an ordinary telephone call; advance notice to the carrier for extra bandwidth is not required. In addition, videoconferencing can be implemented on short notice, without the need for making special scheduling arrangements with session participants in widely dispersed locations.

Videoconferencing under ISDN is also more economical, with charges based on the amount of bandwidth used, according to a time- and distance-sensitive rate schedule. In contrast, the subscriber pays a distance-sensitive fixed monthly charge for leased facilities, no matter how much—or how little—bandwidth is used. Because videoconferencing, unlike voice and data communications, is not typically a continuous requirement, using ISDN for videoconferencing can be an economical transmission arrangement, particularly for occasional video users.

Videoconferencing under ISDN also offers greater potential for connectivity than leased facilities. ISDN-based videoconferences can include participants external to the corporate network, provided that the external parties have ISDN links and compatible videoconferencing systems.

With the availability of ISDN's 384 Kbps-H0 channel, which is equivalent to AT&T's switched 384K service, the cost for a one-hour videoconference is one-third the cost for the same service using AT&T's *ACCUNET reserved digital service* (ARDS) at 384 Kbps. A coast-to-coast videoconference with ISDN's H0 channel costs only $75.00 per hour, versus $225 per hour over ARDS.

Call-setup time under ISDN is only a few seconds—just like for an ordinary phone call. After the initial 30 seconds, the billing is in 6-second increments. And when the session is over, the users just "hang up." Conversely, a 384 Kbps ARDS "call" must be reserved at least 24 hours in advance (except for an emergency, but then an emergency setup charge is tacked on). ARDS billing is in 30-minute increments. This means that a 35-minute session costs the same as a session lasting an entire hour. Furthermore, a hefty penalty is incurred if the reserved service is cancelled within 24 hours of its scheduled start time, or if the connection is discontinued before its reserved time is up.

More often than not, the videoconferencing equipment is remote from the multiplexer location. If the distance is more than 60 feet, assuming a CCITT V.35 interface, a pair of 384-Kbps line drivers are necessary. This requirement can be met with *digital service units* (DSUs) designed to provide FT1 service.

As shown in Figure 13.5, the videoconferencing equipment is interconnected via a 384-Kbps channel of the ISDN-equipped T1 multiplexer. One DSU can be collocated with the multiplexer. The multiplexer's videoconference channel is cabled to a 384 Kbps V.35 channel port of the DSU (external timing is selected for the port).

The companion DSU is located in the meeting room with the video equipment. The two DSUs can be up to 6,000 feet apart when two 22-gauge twisted pairs are used. Plugging in the video equipment to the DSU's 384 Kbps-V.35 channel port completes the installation.

Videoconferencing promises to be a commercially successful application for ISDN. It also ushers in another interesting video application for ISDN: freeze-frame image transfer. Eastman Kodak Company, for example, offers a still-video transceiver capable of transmitting a full-frame color image over a single B channel. Although the device, called the SV9610, can transmit images over standard voice-grade lines at rates ranging from 2.4 Kbps to 14.4 Kbps, its use over ISDN lines offers tremendous improvements in transmission speed and quality. Via ISDN, the SV9610 has a transmission speed of only 12 seconds, versus 45 seconds over ordinary phone lines. In addition, picture quality is greatly enhanced by ISDN's end-to-end digital connectivity.

13.4.5 Local-Access Channels

Videoconferencing poses a special challenge to network planners because it is a temporary application that uses a significant amount of bandwidth. While FT1 and ISDN PRI are available on the long-haul portion of the public network from interexchange carriers, the RBHCs have not been keeping up by providing equivalent access services.

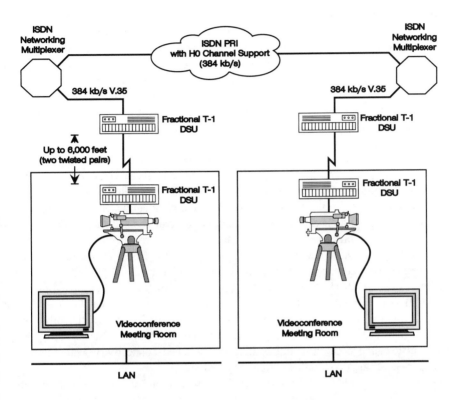

Figure 13.5 SDN configuration for videoconferencing.

Inverse multiplexing provides an economical way to access the switched digital services of the interexchange carriers by providing bandwidth on demand. In essence, users "dial up" the appropriate increment of bandwidth to support the video conference and pay for the number of local access channels only for the time they are used. Upon completion of the video conference, the channels are taken down. This obviates the need for private leased lines to support videoconferencing and associated applications, such as image transfer.

For example, if it is determined that 768 Kbps of bandwidth is all that is required to support a videoconference of acceptable picture quality, the inverse multiplexer is used to call up 14 56-Kbps local-access channels. This number of channels provides the bandwidth necessary to support the videoconference, with slightly more to spare. If, in the middle of the videoconference, the participants decide to review a vendor case file, they can use the inverse multiplexer to call up two additional 56-Kbps channels to accommodate the transfer of the image documents. Next, an image workstation on the LAN establishes a connection to the inverse multiplexer. The case file is retrieved from the image server on the LAN and displayed on the workstation's monitor. This output is sent simultaneously to the remote location, via the inverse multiplexer, and to the local videoconference room, where it occupies its own window on the meeting display. The inverse multiplexer synchronizes the information across the channels and transmits it, via switched public network services, to a similar device at the remote location. There, the data is remultiplexed into a single data stream. By aggregating switched digital bandwidth into a higher-speed channel, the user pays for the connection only while it exists. After the contract is reviewed, the inverse multiplexer takes down the two channels it had set up to support the image application. When the videoconference is over, the inverse multiplexer takes down the original 14 channels.

US West provides a bandwidth-on-demand video service called MediaConferencing. The service bundles Ascend inverse multiplexers, VideoTelecom video codecs, and US West switched digital services. Since high-quality videoconferencing commonly requires data speeds of 336 Kbps or 384 Kbps, which is the bandwidth equivalent of six aggregated 56-Kbps or 64-Kbps switched channels, Ascend's multiband controller provides an economical way of implementing the service. Ascend and VideoTelecom can even support broadcast-quality videoconferencing at speeds as high as 768 Kbps. This speed represents only one-half of the total bandwidth available over a full T1 line.

The Ascend hardware is used to dial up either multiple-switched 56 Kbps or 64 Kbps digital connections. In addition to videoconferencing, users can also exchange graphic information or scanned document images on a second screen, a capability made possible by VideoTelecom's equipment. LAN internetworking and disaster recovery applications also can benefit from the high-speed switched connectivity available to US West customers through Ascend's multiband controller.

An innovative video hub from Teleos Communications combines a wiring hub, a switch, and multiple inverse multiplexers into a single device, eliminating the need to buy separate boxes to send videoconferencing signals over the WAN. The cost savings are especially apparent in videoconferencing transmissions that use a *multiport control unit* (MCU), which is a video "bridge" that links multiple remote codecs. The Teleos Videohub costs between $3,000 and $5,000 per port, compared to the typical per-port price of $7,000 to $12,000 for an inverse multiplexer.

The Videohub also connects sites that use different data services—or even different carriers. The Videohub supports videoconferences between sites that use Nx56/64 Kbps (FT1) and switched 384-Kbps or switched T1 services and allows connections among sites that use services from AT&T and MCI. This capability was not possible previously because, normally, the two carriers' networks do not interoperate (Figure 13.6).

The Videohub also cuts down on cabling at sites that have more than one codec or that move a roll-about codec from room to room in a building. Rather than requiring dedicated cabling, the Videohub plugs directly into the building's unshielded twisted-pair wiring. And, having all video communications supported and managed by the hub can provide an added benefit of supporting videoconferences between multiple codec sites in a campus environment.

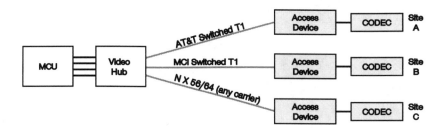

Figure 13.6 Videohub application.

13.5 CONCLUSION

Videoconferencing is finally taking its place as a strategically significant corporate communications tool. Improvements in technology and the introduction of new digital services for wide-area videoconferencing are contributing to corporate demand, which, in turn, will fuel competition and further innovation.

Chapter 14

Multimedia Imaging

14.1 INTRODUCTION

Multimedia is the integration of text, image, audio, and video within a single application program or online session. Until recently, the concept was viewed as exotic and futuristic. This view changed in 1991 with the falling prices of desktop computers and audio-visual subsystems, the availability of better multimedia authoring tools, and agreement on industry standards. The entrance of IBM and Apple into the market did as much to legitimize multimedia as it did to accelerate its development. A joint product development effort between IBM and Apple includes multimedia products, which will encourage further development of cross-platform applications. Also fueling the growth of the fledgling multimedia industry are continual advances in compression technologies and the availability of new broadband transmission services.

The integration of formerly separate applications has already found practical uses in education and business. In a training application program, for example, a CD-ROM contains all the information necessary (approximately 600 MB) to teach an installer how to set up and operate a new product for a customer. Through a combination of text, audio, and full-motion video, the installer can read the relevant technical documentation, view a demonstration of the setup procedures, and listen to a warning about possible electrical hazards—and all the material is accessed from the same program. When the installer completes a module of instruction, a built-in test facility can determine the installer's level of proficiency and provide suggestions for review.

This scenario is not meant to imply that multimedia is the exclusive domain of stand-alone computers. In the application described above, the user need not have a CD-ROM or any other video storage device to access the training program. An alternative method of information delivery entails accessing the program stored on a local or remote LAN server. The multimedia server might be a jukebox containing a dozen or more CD-ROM disks, each offering a different course of instruction.

Multimedia communication systems hold the promise of providing better support for widely distributed workgroups by facilitating complex communication such as problem solving, negotiating, planning, and design. In this regard, multimedia is becoming a useful add-on capability to videoconferencing systems.

Such multimedia conferencing systems consist of video and PC monitors, remote controls, speakers, software, cameras, and microphones. The systems are based on the concept of multimedia presentations, differing only in the fact that video, audio, documents, and computer data are passed between two or more geographically separated locations. A single screen can be partitioned into several windows that display text, graphics and the individual participants. Some systems offer a real-time drawing capability, permitting users to diagram difficult concepts. Special bridging arrangements with the carrier enable three or more locations to interactively participate in a multimedia conference.

With prototype multimedia conferencing systems, participants can annotate snap shots and hand-drawn sketches with synchronized pointing, drawing, and writing. A graphical desktop displays miniature versions of the images. From the desktop, users can select images to be enlarged, grouped, mailed, printed, and copied. They can also record a portion of the videoconference and send it via electronic mail to someone who could not participate.

The concept of "video mail" can advance further, allowing users to incorporate video messages with data, graphics, and images. With the same compression techniques used for videoconferencing, this "media mail" can be sent in encoded form to a dedicated messaging server for distribution to speaker-equipped PCs. The messages can be stored on hard disk for playback or downloaded to floppy disks for manual distribution.

A multimedia system entails the integration of multiple technologies: computer television, and telephone. Out of this consolidation, multimedia supports the functionality of each, but has the potential for many new applications. Processing, storage, communication, and high-resolution display capabilities are required in any multimedia information system. High-speed network interconnection among user workstations and geographically dispersed databases are required to manipulate and retrieve the unique data types. The multimedia architecture is summarized in Figure 14.1.

14.2 WORKSTATION REQUIREMENTS

Although the vast installed base of PCs does not offer integrated text, audio, speech, video, and data communications, these capabilities can be added to handle the demands of multimedia.

The CPU should be at least an Intel 80386SX or compatible. Anything less is too slow to permit the potential of multimedia to be realized and might even discourage the user from approaching multimedia applications. A color VGA monitor is a virtual requirement for multimedia, as are add-in boards for sound, graphics, animation, and data compression. Internal or external CD-ROM drives are available and are required to run prepackaged multimedia titles.

Business users value such multimedia capabilities as voice annotation and video mail. These, too, can be added to most PCs, Macintoshes, and UNIX-based workstations via special boards. There are even multifunction boards that combine document imaging

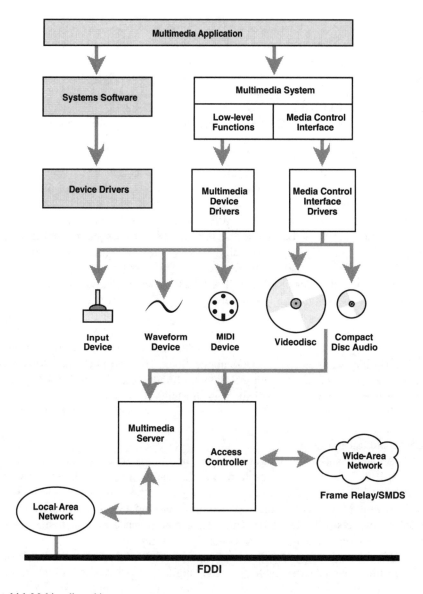

Figure 14.1 Multimedia architecture.

high-resolution color, data compression, and Windows acceleration onto one card—and at less cost than multiple boards.

In early 1992, the first multimedia-ready PCs became available from such companies as CompuAdd and Tandy. The PCs featured internal CD-ROM drives, audio interfaces, and sound cards. At about the same time, IBM announced its intention to offer, by

1994, a full line of notebook and desktop PCs equipped with audio and video capabilities as standard features. The computers will have three key functions integrated onto the motherboard: a video controller, compression processor, and digital signal processor. IBM's plans also include multimedia RISC workstations and a multimedia server capable of distributing digitally stored video over a token-ring LAN. In the short term, IBM will provide multimedia capabilities through an extension to OS/2 2.0 called *Multimedia Presentation Manager* (MMPM). MMPM includes digital audio signal compression and playback and, later, will provide digital video support. Eventually, IBM will make MMPM a standard feature of OS/2.

Another major company that supports multimedia is Sun Microsystems. Sun has built some multimedia capabilities into its workstations. Through its subsidiary, *Sun Microsystems Computer Corp.* (SMCC), the company provides—at no extra cost—a microphone and built-in speaker with every SPARCstation.[1] These additions allow users to play, record, and receive audio over a network via the SPARCstation's multimedia mail application. Sun's Audio Tool software allows users to rewind, play, and record electronic mail for use in multimedia mail and in over 30 third-party applications.

Mobius Computer Corp. offers a SPARC-based series of multimedia workstations for mixed-media applications on UNIX networks. The firm's Mirage IPS operates at 15.8 *million instructions per second* (MIPS) and comes with a 17-in flat-screen display that provides 1,152 by 900 dpi resolution. The unit is compatible with Sun OS and Solaris operating systems. Although the product comes with Solaris, an optional module provides DOS compatibility so users can run DOS applications. The Clarity Rapport Mixed Media software package, which comes with the system, provides a user interface for multimedia applications that is comparable to PC and Macintosh interfaces.

Macintosh users have several ways of bringing multimedia to their desktops, including Apple's new QuickTime operating system extensions and third-party add-in boards for still-image and full-motion video.

QuickTime lets users incorporate dynamic, or time-based, data into a wide variety of documents. It defines a new movie-file format that can be cut, copied, and pasted in the same way as text or graphic objects and played back without the use of additional hardware or software. Movies can be incorporated into word processing documents, while add-in modules let users animate charts. QuickTime can enhance presentation software, in essence converting it into a multimedia authoring environment.

DEC is still in the early stages of implementing multimedia and will initially support such applications over Ethernet LANs, using the digital video hardware of Fluent, Inc. The company's SQL multimedia software supports compound documents, customizable binary large-object files, ASCII text, tables, and images.

Over the next few years there will be a steady stream of announcements from computer manufacturers and third-party application developers in support of multimedia. It is

---

[1] SPARC is an acronym for *scalable processor architecture*, which is a proprietary offering of Sun Microsystems that is also licensed to other computer manufacturers. Because of its open architecture, SPARC has become a de facto industry standard for UNIX-based platforms.

only a matter of time before multimedia becomes a standard feature of most PCs, operating systems, and application programs.

14.3 COMPRESSION METHODS

To support audio and video, a workstation must handle large amounts of data easily. For example, as an uncompressed stream of bytes, a 10-minute video clip can easily reach 20 GB. About 5 MB more is needed for voice-grade audio to accompany the video clip. Few workstations on the market today can routinely handle such large data sets.

Consider that an uncompressed *National Television System Committee* (NTSC) composite signal, such as the one received on home television sets, is represented digitally as 640 by 480 by 30 true-color (RGB) frames per second. This picture represents almost 28 MB of pixel data per second for NTSC. For *high-definition television* (HDTV), an emerging NTSC replacement, this figure is almost 20 times as large. Handling such amounts of data on a workstation is a problem that still awaits a solution from developers of sophisticated multimedia applications.

The most obvious solution is to reduce the amount of data. Common methods for reducing video information, known as *size reduction*, include skipping video frames and skipping pixels within frames. The amount of data can also be reduced by rendering the video. One way to do this is to convert true-color video into black-and-white video to achieve a 4 to 1 reduction in the amount of data. Another way to reduce the amount of data is to convert true color into 8-bit pseudo color.

Audio compression typically employs *pulse code modulation* (PCM), which reduces the number of bits required to represent a sample of stereo-quality sound. These data reductions require codec logic of the kind commonly used to send digitally encoded voice over high-speed T1 lines.

Compression chips are available that employ a variety of data reduction techniques. Several compression algorithms are contending for use in workstations. One is the ISO's *Joint Photographic Experts Group* (JPEG).

14.3.1 Joint Photographic Experts Group

JPEG was designed for compressing continuous-tone (photographic-quality) monochrome and color still images. It is based on an algorithm that, based on a *discrete cosine transformer (DCT)*, eliminates redundant image information by dividing the image into small blocks. The higher the compression ratio, the more information is deleted and, therefore, the more image detail (and quality) is lost. JPEG can be used to compress images at ratios of up to 25 to 1 without a noticeable loss of image quality. Thus, a 25-MB image can be cut to less than 1 MB. Higher compression rates are possible with JPEG, but beyond 25 to 1 the loss of image quality starts to become noticeable.

JPEG is symmetrical; that is, all things being equal, the same amount of computing power is used to compress an image as to decompress it. Compression and decompression times are about the same when the functions are performed by software. With hardware-assisted JPEG compression, however, there is a significant performance boost on the compression side.

JPEG can also be used to compress video. It treats each frame as a separate image and compresses each frame individually through a process called *intraframe coding*. This means a user can randomly access any individual frame within the compressed video. But, even with compression ratios of 25 to 1, a few seconds of compressed 24-bit color video, with a resolution of 640 by 480 pixels, requires a large hard disk for storage. The data transfer rate required to play back that compressed video is faster than CD-ROMs (which run at 1.2 Mbps to 1.5 Mbps) can handle.

14.3.2 Motion Picture Experts Group

Another compression algorithm being considered for standardization by the ISO is the *Motion Picture Experts Group* (MPEG). MPEG was designed specifically for video. Like the JPEG algorithm, MPEG is DCT-based. Along with intraframe coding for removing redundancies within a frame, MPEG employs interframe coding, which eliminates redundant information between frames. In a video sequence, for instance, an actor might only turn his head; the background stays the same. MPEG recognizes that the background is redundant and does not need to be stored for each frame. This scheme, however, prevents easy access to individual frames within a compressed MPEG video.

With MPEG, there is an interframe about every 15 frames (every half second). If a multimedia application required access to an individual frame, it would have to reconstruct or interpolate the data using several frames. This means that there can really be no random access to individual frames. This sacrifice, however, allows for higher lossless compression rates than with JPEG-compressed video.

MPEG can compress video at rates of up to 50 to 1, high enough to allow the compressed video to be decompressed at a data transfer rate of about 1.5 Mbps, which is compatible with CD-ROM drives. MPEG allows random access to video data and the synchronization of video and audio tracks by multimedia workstations.

Unlike JPEG, MPEG takes an asymmetrical approach to compression; that is, more computing power is required to compress full-motion video and audio than to decompress it. Multimedia applications that require video to be compressed only once and decompressed over and over again include training, publishing, and games that are available on CD-ROMs.

14.3.3 Px64

Still another compression algorithm, known as Px64, has been standardized by the CCITT. This algorithm, also known as H.261, is used in videoconferencing systems. It specifies a uniform method for encoding and decoding video signals and permits the signals to be transmitted at a variety of data rates, from 64 Kbps to 2.048 Mbps, in increments of 64 Kbps. The higher the data rate, the better the picture quality. The standard also specifies such characteristics as videoconferencing software algorithm requirements and screen resolution parameters.

Since adoption of the H.261 standard, significant advances have been made in compression technology. To accommodate these changes, the H.261 standard allows for algorithm negotiation during call setup. Algorithm negotiation enables vendors to design their codec systems to adhere to the standard, as well as to their own proprietary compression algorithms.

When a call is placed the transmitting device determines which compression algorithm the receiving device is using. If the receiving device supports the standard, the transmitting device automatically selects the Px64 algorithm. If both codecs use the same proprietary algorithm, however, the proprietary algorithm can be used to ensure the highest picture quality.

In addition to running both proprietary and standard compression algorithms, some codecs can support additional data types including text, graphics, and document images, which can be displayed in conjunction with the videoconference. There are a variety of ways this can be accomplished, such as by splitting the screen to display videoconference participants on one side and document images on the other side. Or, the screen can be partitioned into multiple windows to display any mix of text, graphics, document images, and video.

14.3.4 Digital Video Interactive

Intel was the first company to offer a motion-video compression solution for the PC: *digital video interactive* (DVI). The real significance of DVI is that it prompted multimedia developers to consider the PC as a viable platform for their applications.

With DVI, multimedia applications can be developed and played back in digital form and sent across networks or stored in any random-access device. DVI allows users to capture full-motion video at 30 frames per second. Captured data can be stored on hard disk or CD-ROM and played back on a microcomputer. DVI products also enable users to capture video and audio from such sources as laser discs, TV broadcasts, and video cameras for use in Microsoft Windows- or OS/2-based applications.

Intel offers other compression methods, including *real-time video* (RTV) and *production-level video* (PLV). RTV is a symmetrical online compression scheme that is used to capture and edit VHS-quality video. The standard frame size is 128 by 240, which can be bumped up to 256 by 480 during decompression. Initially, the software performs motion compensation by comparing adjacent frames. If the differences are small, it subtracts one from the other; if the differences are large, it might decide to use the current frame as a reference. *Vector quantization*, which is the process of finding frequently occurring pixel clusters and encoding them, is used to compress the reference frames themselves. The audio information is compressed, using *adaptive differential pulse code modulation* (ADPCM) and interleaved with the video data.

PLV entails the user submitting to Intel a video on 1-in tape. Intel applies higher-powered computers and devotes more time to optimizing quality and compression. Although RTV and PLV use essentially the same compression methods, PLV permits different-size pixel blocks to be tried when optimizing motion compensation.

14.3.5 Fractal Compression

There continues to be a lot of innovation in the area of data compression. With *fractal compression*, for example, the repetitive patterns of an image are identified and matched. Two patterns are considered the same as long as one can be stretched, squeezed, or rotated to look like the other. The process continues until the image is the size specified by the user. This process is computationally intensive, with compression taking longer than decompression (asymmetrical). But compression rates of 100 to 1 can be achieved with little or no noticeable loss of image quality.

Another advantage of fractal compression is scalability. Because patterns, rather than pixels, are viewed as the fundamental blocks of image construction, the process of fractal compression can double the size of an image by mathematically scaling the pattern, instead of just inserting extra pixels. Fractal compression is also less expensive to implement than JPEG.

14.4 REAL-WORLD BUSINESS APPLICATIONS

Although education and training are viewed as ideal applications for multimedia, pontificating industry analysts are still awaiting the emergence of the so-called "killer application" that will implant multimedia firmly into the corporate consciousness. However, since 1990 companies like IBM and Unisys have been quietly and successfully hammering away at the market with interactive, self-service multimedia terminals, called *kiosks*, that provide a variety of automated services.

14.4.1 Multimedia Kiosks

The prolonged recession has caused the market for automated services to open up and grow at a fairly rapid pace. Businesses forced to trim budgets and scale back personnel view automated services as a way to meet the informational needs of customers, as well as contain workloads and minimize pressure on remaining staff. Government agencies, too, are turning to automated services to cope with budget deficits and maintain current service levels. The multimedia kiosks offer a high degree of user interactivity, allowing organizations of all kinds to meet these and other important needs. IBM and Unisys, along with a number of other firms, are pursuing a variety of application areas, including retail, financial, insurance, air travel, utilities, and government.

The multimedia terminals combine video capabilities and touch-screen technology in ergonomic, kiosk packaging. Bundled into a kiosk are such components as a credit card reader, optical disk, printer, loudspeaker, and a proximity detector, which automatically starts the application when someone comes within a few feet of the system. A customer-designed run-time program presents information in text, graphic, or video formats for photo-quality images or full-motion video displays.

In a typical financial application, for example, a bank sets up a kiosk in a convenient lobby location or other public access point to allow customers to see if they qualify for a car loan and how they might manage the payments over three, four, or five years. Rather than take up a bank officer's time, customers can approach the kiosk and, based on inputs they would provide, score themselves on various factors that lead to loan qualification. Also available are the current interest rates and payment schedules. Customers can then approach a bank officer for the loan application or comparison-shop elsewhere.

Many banks are using kiosks for issuing statements and for allowing customers to make account inquiries. A bank cannot provide these types of services with an *automatic teller machine* (ATM) because the dozen or so people standing in line will not tolerate waiting that long. The kiosk is most effectively used for advertising purposes and for issuing detailed information to users. The application is meant to hold people long enough to do an effective job of selling—typically 3 to 5 minutes—and in the process, supply the user with all the information requested.

Kiosks fulfilled this mission well during the 1992 Winter Olympics, issuing information in many different languages. For example, Unisys kiosks were placed at strategic locations in Albertville and surrounding villages. Visitors pressed the flag of their country to call up currency exchange rates, transportation schedules, customs regulations, and other useful information, which was displayed in their native languages.

IBM provided kiosks at the U.S. Olympic trials for kayak and canoe racing, which were held in mid-1992 on the Savage River in Maryland. Users were able to retrieve a variety of data, such as information about the rules, the scoring system, the racers, competitive techniques, and hotel accommodations in the vicinity.

14.4.2 Other Uses for Kiosks

Kiosks can be placed virtually anywhere to serve the informational needs of users. For example, Air France uses kiosks at the Charles de Gaulle Airport to issue airline tickets. At that kiosk, travellers pass their credit cards through the magnetic-stripe reader to pay for tickets. Tickets and boarding passes are issued via the integral printer. With tickets and boarding passes in hand, passengers can board the plane immediately.

The State of New Mexico's Tourism Department places kiosks not only at airports in that state, but also at the airports of surrounding states, to entice tourists into visiting New Mexico. Travellers at airports as far away as Arizona, California, Colorado, and Texas can call up video presentations of New Mexico's state parks, recreation areas, historical sites, and natural wonders. Of course, the real objective of this kind of advertising is to stimulate the state's economy by infusing it with the dollars tourists bring in.

Kiosks are also an ideal way to serve the physically challenged—in compliance with the Federal Disabilities Act. The small footprint of most kiosks permits its placement in locations where space is already at a premium, but those locations, though small, do permit wheelchair traffic.

14.4.3 Kiosks Yesterday and Today

Kiosks were introduced in the mid-1980s for a variety of applications, but they failed to catch on as a viable way for businesses to disseminate information about their products and services. Times have changed, however, and businesses are becoming more sophisticated in their development of applications for the kiosk. In days past, applications would deluge users with facts that were not necessarily relevant to their informational needs. There was very little interaction that let users specify the kind of information they wanted. And there were no provisions for graphics, let alone video, to hold the users' attention.

Today multimedia is being used not only to attract users to the kiosk, but once the users are there, to keep their attention until the entire message can be delivered. There is also more opportunity for user interaction, which is important for providing entertainment, as well as for getting the message across. Instead of showering the user with data, businesses are getting right to the point with their kiosk applications. Businesses are also taking the time to educate potential users on the value of kiosks—in both convenience and service—before they install the kiosks.

Another reason businesses are putting more effort into and thus having more success with kiosks today has to do with their growing appreciation of self-service. Businesses are experiencing reductions in staff, due to economic concerns, yet they still need to convey information about their products and services in a consistent manner. Since kiosks provide a solution to both problems, businesses have more incentive to make them work—so much so that units from several vendors are now a common fixture in hotels, airports, convention centers, shopping malls, stores, travel stops, and hospitals.

Government agencies are also experiencing economic concerns. For example, while the demand for services continues to rise, just about every motor vehicle department in the country is hamstrung by budget cuts and staff reductions. This is forcing motor vehicle departments to look at ways to streamline workflow and automate such routine services as license renewal and vehicle registration. By automating and decentralizing services, kiosks greatly reduce cost per transaction and the tension level of overworked personnel who previously faced long lines of angry and frustrated people.

The answer for the motor vehicle department lies in locating kiosks at shopping malls and other public access points. This placement allows users to select "renewal" from the terminal display, pay the renewal fee with a credit card, and walk away with a temporary license in a matter of minutes. The motor vehicle department's mainframe can collect information from the kiosks at the end of the day for processing. A permanent license can be mailed to drivers within ten days.

Other government applications that lend themselves to the use of multimedia kiosks include applications that handle court information, receive payment of fines via credit card, and provide procedural and directory information.

14.4.4 Applications Development

Kiosks can be built from off-the-shelf components. Using a PC for the platform, applications can be developed on PCs and then ported over to the kiosk. This type of development eliminates online mainframe compiling and makes the time it takes to develop applications much shorter than if a high-level language like COBOL is used. This time savings allow developers to devote more of the time they would otherwise spend compiling lines of code, debugging programs, and performing other maintenance tasks developing new applications.

Instead of using high-level programming languages, applications developers can use multimedia authoring tools that rely on scripts or objects. A *script* is a set of plain-English commands; an *object* is a symbol or icon that represents an action or a line of executable code. Learning to use scripts and objects does not require programming expertise; thus, customers can develop their own applications without vendor support.

However, although no knowledge of high-level languages is required and no compilation is involved, the application developer should understand DOS utilities and be able to use off-the-shelf paint packages, such as CorelDraw, Micrografx Designer, or Paint-Brush, to design the screens for the application. The software toolkit provided by the kiosk vendor usually includes the latest version of DOS, Microsoft Windows, run-time customizers, a security initialization program, diagnostic utilities, device drivers, graphics, editors, and a video library. The toolkit and some telephone support are usually enough to get most businesses started on developing their own multimedia applications.

Companies like IBM and Unisys offer customers assistance in developing kiosk applications. The process typically begins with the preparation of a *storyboard*. A storyboard is a script of the transactions that will eventually appear on the display screen. If the application involves video, the marketing support team typically work with a third-party production unit, which performs the actual filming and postproduction work. The pressing of laser disks is typically done by companies with specialized production capabilities, such as 3M, Pioneer, or third-party CD-ROM publishers.

Often custom video work is not necessary. Stock footage is available from any number of small firms that specialize in supplying generic footage. Or the customer can supply video from television advertisements or training courses for integration into the kiosk application.

Customers often use outside suppliers who can bring specific skills and expertise to the development of niche applications. These are usually *value-added resellers* (VARs) who already service niche markets with the vendor's hardware. Alternatively, the kiosk vendor can generate the complete application, including network integration, and offer it to the customer as a package.

14.4.5 Network Integration

Kiosks can coexist in just about any type of host environment, including IBM 3270, SNA/SDLC, and UNIX. The platform can be networked in the X.25 as well as the TCP/IP environment, or run over Ethernet and token-ring LANs.

Remote diagnostics can be implemented over dial-up lines via RS-232C interfaces. A dial-up connection can be used to gather alarms that report when, for example, the printer is out of paper, there is no touch-screen activity, or the PC is down. Kiosks can also be equipped with integral diagnostic functions that tell an on-site engineer or operator when components are not functioning properly.

Retrieving accumulated information input by users is a function of the application. Typically, a dial-up connection transfers all accumulated information stored on the unit's hard disk for further processing by the host (Figure 14.2). Alternatively, the application can be designed to sort information into separate files based on inputs from users. That distribution can allow the host to be more selective in its retrieval request. For example, a file might contain the number of users who made a specific touch selection during the course of the day. This touch selection might indicate a product preference or a request for specific information by mail.

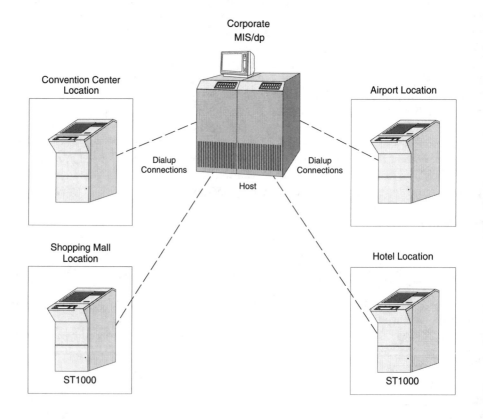

Figure 14.2 Unisys multimedia kiosks in a distributed environment.

When equipped with a leased-line modem, the kiosk can accessed by a host computer or network control center via polling over a multidrop leased line. Accumulated information from each unit can be retrieved automatically upon request by the host or network management system.

14.5 MULTIMEDIA WITH E-MAIL

There are several efforts underway to permit the transfer of multimedia and compound documents between users of *electronic mail* (e-mail) systems. Protocol extensions that allow users to exchange multimedia files via Internet mail protocols have been approved by the *Internet Activities Board* (IAB), which is the group that plans and implements enhancements to the *Internet*. Internet is a global entity that consists of over 5,000 networks and connects hundreds of thousands of hosts in 36 countries.

The extensions, known as RFC 822, enable the Internet mail protocol, *simple mail transfer protocol* (SMTP), to carry sound, graphics, scanned images, and application program files.

Application programs are becoming available that allow PC users to combine several types of files for transmission over corporate LANs via e-mail. In these programs, after the user creates a message, a standard Windows list prompts the user to select other files for integration into the message. The files can contain audio, graphics, images, and video clips. This allows, for example, the recipient of a message to view a spreadsheet while listening to an explanation of the assumptions underlying the data.

14.6 MULTIMEDIA AND HYPERTEXT

Hypertext is a search and retrieval method by which any type of information (i.e., object) is indexed, and threads are created to have one item lead to another. Hypertext allows users to jump from one topic to another, based on their immediate informational needs. By keying in on highlighted words and phrases, for example, users can access detailed explanations in a pop-up window. This feature allows users to look up terms or access related information quickly without having to leave the main text. A link might take users to other files or databases containing more information on a topic of interest. Tables and diagrams can be accessed in the same manner, as can scanned images, audio messages, and video clips.

A common application of the combined use of hypertext links and multimedia is the tour guide. Users can view museum tours or vacation spots stored on video tape or optical disk. At a point of interest, viewers can stop the tape or disk and select options from a pop-up menu that allows them to leave the main tour to pursue another avenue of interest. For example, they might call up a text explanation of a historical fact or statistic and then examine the item in more detail by pointing with a mouse to highlighted words.

14.7 MULTIMEDIA AUTHORING TOOLS

A number of tools are available for developing multimedia applications. Some require knowledge of high-level programming languages, while others rely on the Windows graphical user interface, which permits users to build effective presentations without requiring programming expertise.

For years media professionals have used authoring software to create educational, sales, and training programs, though effective use of the software usually entailed a long learning curve, and the programs themselves could only be run on a narrow set of supported hardware. These problems have largely been solved by Microsoft's Multimedia Extensions to Windows, which installs on top of Windows 3.x.

The Multimedia Extensions product addresses a critical need of multimedia applications developers for hardware compatibility. It provides a standard platform on which developers can create and run multimedia applications that use the hardware of many different vendors. Since it uses a *media control interface* (MCI)—a protocol layer that provides a buffer between Windows and the hardware—Multimedia Extensions is also flexible enough to accommodate new hardware types as they become available.

Multimedia capabilities are showing up in mainstream application programs, most notably, in presentation graphics packages. For example, Software Publishing Corp.'s Harvard Graphics for Windows takes advantage of Multimedia Extensions to allow users to add audio and animation files to presentations. Other products, such as Madison Avenue from Eclipse Technologies and Curtain Call from Zuma Group, provide tools for adding sound effects and voice narration to presentation graphics. All three products are useful for developing low-cost demonstration disks, exhibition displays, and training modules.

Another type of Windows-based product is MediaOrganizer from Lenel Systems International. MediaOrganizer allows users to organize, index, and retrieve multimedia data in text, still-image, animation, digital- and analog-audio, and full-motion video formats. Images can be displayed in multiple, scalable windows on the same screen. Users can name multimedia objects and insert descriptions to use for retrieval; this identification permits several types of database searches, including Boolean, wild card, and synonym.

14.8 MULTIMEDIA STANDARDS

Many vendors view multimedia as an important feature to include in products or combine with other applications, such as videoconferencing. Even when used well, multimedia is still only a wrapper that makes information easier to assimilate. For this reason, multimedia has found immediate acceptance in the fields of training and education. However, its use elsewhere is still ambiguous. Nevertheless, an aggressive industry marketing campaign was launched in late 1991 to herald the arrival of multimedia personal computing.

The Multimedia PC Marketing Council, founded in 1991 as a subsidiary of the Software Publishing Association, includes such companies as CompuAdd, Creative Labs, Fujitsu, Headland Technology/Video Seven, Microsoft, NCR, NEC Technologies, Olivetti, Philips Consumer Electronics, Tandy, and Zenith Data Systems. An early objective of the council was to agree on a standard for multimedia computing that allows existing PCs to be easily upgraded with a CD-ROM drive, sound board, and the software required for multimedia. Initially, the council chose the Intel 80286 as the minimum microprocessor configuration, but after strong opposition from industry, the 20Mz 80386SX microprocessor became the accepted basic platform. The council also developed a trademarked MPC (*multimedia personal computer*) logo to be affixed to products that adhere to the standard.

For developers, MPC represents a minimum standard for building multimedia capabilities into existing applications. For users, MPC provides some guidelines for constructing PCs or upgrading existing ones to support these applications. An MPC-capable system includes a CD-ROM drive that provides 600MB of storage and supports high-quality CD audio as well. Digital audio support is also specified by the MPC standard, allowing audio data to be recorded and played back to and from the computer's hard disk. An onboard synthesizer provides a polyphonic music playback capability, while the *musical instrument digital interface* (MIDI) allows the user to drive an external electronic musical instrument. The MPC specification supports the playback of animation through a movie file format. It also provides enhanced support for the display of bit-mapped graphics, and an interface to a timer that is used for event synchronization. The MPC logo on software means that it will be compatible with hardware carrying the same symbol.

There are two other multimedia logos: MPG (*Multimedia Publishers Group)* and MPC (the acronym for *Multimedia Products Corp.*, an MPG member company). Table 14.1 summarizes the characteristics associated with each logo.

Table 14.1
Multimedia Logos and Characteristics

	MPC	*MPG*	*MPC*
Organization	Multimedia Personal Computer	Multimedia Publishers Group	Multimedia Products Corporation
Organization's Goal	Promote a plug-and-play hardware and software standard	Make CD-ROM products understandable and affordable to consumers	Produce educational CD-ROM titles for children
Minimum Platform	80386SX, 2 MB of RAM, VGA, fast CD-ROM drive, sound board and either Windows 3.0 with Multimedia Extensions or 3.1	Titles run on one or more platforms: DOS, MPC, or Macintosh	DOS-based PC with 640K of RAM, VGA, a CD-ROM drive with speakers or headphones, and a mouse; Macintosh versions also available
Behind the Logo	Multimedia PC Marketing Council	Advanced Strategies Corporation	A private firm
Members	System, upgrade-kit, and software firms	CD-ROM software publishers	NA
Address	730 M St., N.W. Suite 700 Washington, DC 20036	60 Cutter Mill Rd. Suite 502 Great Neck, NY 11021	300 Airport Executive Park Spring Valley, NY 10977
Telephone	202-331-1801	516-482-0088	914-426-0400

Source: PC Computing

14.9 CONCLUSION

Although still in its infancy, the multimedia market is dynamic and innovative. A break-through development can quickly cut multimedia loose from it current niche confinement and release it into the streets of mainstream business applications.

In addition to standards for such functions as video compression and digital signal processing, the development of high-speed networks based on such technologies as ATM, FDDI, and SONET will ease the transition of multimedia from being merely an add-on capability that sits on top of existing applications to being an integral part of sophisticated applications that greatly facilitate the dissemination, acquisition, and assimilation of information through the effective consolidation of multiple media types.

PART VI

PLANNING AND SERVICES

Chapter 15

Planning and Implementation Issues

15.1 INTRODUCTION

The first document imaging solutions were aimed at big companies with intensive document-handling requirements. Typically, these high-end solutions were based on turnkey mainframe or minicomputer systems and were very expensive. With improvements in technology, imaging systems are becoming more affordable and available at a range of levels, from host-based to stand-alone. PC LAN-based imaging systems are gaining in popularity, as they attract more and more businesses with promises of productivity improvements and cost savings.

It is not hard to understand why businesses have become captivated by imaging. Over the years huge investments have been made in office technologies, yet there have been little or no measurable increases in productivity. One theory holds that productivity gains have remained elusive largely because of the huge quantity of paper these technologies continue to generate. Imaging is the first technology to address the paper problem. Imaging not only minimizes the amount of new paper generated, it also improves paper management.

If properly deployed, the benefits of imaging systems include better document control and reduced processing time, storage space, and clerical support. These benefits lead logically to improved customer service, which is of strategic importance to most businesses.

Business do not need to process millions of transactions annually to make an imaging solution worthwhile. If a department or workgroup spends 20% of its time handling paper documents, a document imaging system might be justified. Another justification for an imaging system involves the value a business places on the timeliness of transaction processing. For example, if an invoice is not paid on time, a discount might be lost or penalty interest might accrue. Whenever a monetary value can be associated with a document, or there is legal exposure, an imaging system can be justified.

When considering an imaging system and calculating the return on investment, companies should factor in the cost of human intervention. For example, the cost of processing an invoice might be $0.15 if it can go through an established, routine process. But, if a document is missing information, the processing cost can jump by 50 times, or $7.50 per item. Invoices that require exceptional treatment can account for a disproportionate share of the total processing cost, perhaps as much as 75%. And the return on investment will take much longer than if all items were processed under ideal circumstances.

15.2 ORGANIZATIONAL ISSUES

Few companies have the advantage of implementing an imaging system without considering an entrenched base of potential users. In fact, most imaging systems will be run by the same employees that used the outmoded practices and procedures being replaced. Implementation is best undertaken with a team approach that gives all parties a chance to buy into the new system. Consider including in the planning process *management information system* (MIS) personnel and senior management, as well as representatives from records management and the various business units.

Department managers are often forced into defensive postures because adopting new ways of doing things usually means that they must give up resources—in the form of budget and staff, power and prestige, or control of various operations. Perhaps as important, they see themselves as having to sacrifice an operating philosophy that they have invested considerable time and effort to construct and maintain throughout their tenure. To suddenly have to put their methods aside for a system they might perceive as just another management fad can be a bitter pill to swallow.

With microcomputers now well entrenched in corporate offices, individuals, workgroups and departments have become acutely aware of the benefits of controlling information resources and the need for data and document coordination. By becoming informationally self-sufficient via imaging systems and the ability to share resources via LANs, they can better control their own work. They can, for instance, increase the quality and timeliness of their decision making, execute transactions faster, and become more responsive to internal and external constituencies.

In many cases, imaging has the potential of moving accountability to the lowest common point in the organization—where many end users think it properly belongs. This scenario also has the potential of peeling back the layer of bureaucracy that has traditionally stood between users and centralized information resources.

Instituting change from paper-based to image-based systems can be perceived as very threatening to those who are most affected by it. Adopting an imaging system might involve redistributing responsibilities and, consequently, power and influence. Therefore, the "soft" issues of feelings and perceptions must be addressed first, to assure success with the "hard" issues involving the technical requirements of image system implementation.

The best way to defuse the emotional and political time bombs that might jeopardize the success of imaging is to include all affected parties in the planning process. The planning process should be participative and should start with an articulation of the organizational goals and anticipated costs and benefits that the move to imaging is intended to achieve. This stage of the planning process is also intended to address the most critical concern of the participants: "How will I be affected?" Once the organizational goals are known, they become the new parameters within which the participants can shape their futures.

This participative approach not only facilitates cooperation, it has the effect of spreading ownership of the solution among all participants. Instead of a solution dictated by top management, which often engenders resistance through emotional responses and political maneuvering, the participative approach provides all those involved with a stake in the outcome of the project. With success come the rewards associated with a stable work environment and shared vision of the future; with failure, come the liabilities associated with a tumultuous work environment and uncertainty about the future. Although participative planning takes more time, its effects are often more immediate and long lasting than imposed solutions, which are frequently resisted and short-lived.

If managers resist change, however, this does not necessarily mean that they are protecting their own turf against encroachment. It might mean that the operations they control are really not suitable for image technology.

15.3 PLANNING CONSIDERATIONS

Document imaging has caught the attention of business executives and technical professionals in many organizations. It appeals to management because it offers opportunities to improve customer service while reducing operating costs. It appeals to technical professionals because it incorporates many areas of technology in an innovative and productive way. However, implementation requires proper planning to ensure that these expectations are realized.

15.3.1 Indexing Versus Workflow

Developing an imaging system is not a simple task. Among the issues that must be considered is whether the imaging system will be used primarily for document indexing or workflow automation.

In indexing, the application primarily supports the storage and retrieval, or indexing, of large quantities of images. Indexing requires strong data management capabilities, but is usually fairly straightforward to implement, especially in a stand-alone system. In many cases, indexing systems can be set up using off-the-shelf software and hardware.

Many imaging applications, such as loan origination or insurance underwriting, require that documents flow through a work process. These workflow applications are more difficult to implement than indexing applications, but vendors like FileNet, IBM, and Unisys offer tools for this type of application development.

15.3.2 Understanding Processing Requirements

The success of document imaging often hinges on the extent to which business processes and workflows can be understood. There are several ways to go about this. The most obvious way is to learn how people do their jobs and solicit their input on ways the process can be improved. If there are procedural problems, they must be hashed out among all participants early on so workflows can be properly scripted for automation.

It is recommended that various departmental processes be mapped out and scripted well ahead of image system implementation. Among the problems that often come to light are processes that result in duplication of effort, employees working at cross-purposes, and situations that produce unnecessary paperwork and filing requirements.

The key planning effort that must be performed prior to imaging system implementation is an evaluation of document processing needs. At minimum, the following tasks should be performed:

1. List all documents that are currently being processed by the business;
2. Determine how many of each type of document arrives at each business location on a daily, weekly, monthly and yearly basis;
3. Find out who provides the data in the documents, how the data is used, and what information systems or applications currently use the data provided in the documents;
4. Establish what information is most frequently used in a retrieved document;
5. Determine appropriate index fields for each document;
6. Prepare a flowchart for each type of document, identifying the path it follows when it is received in the office, the stops it makes, what happens at each stop, and what alternative paths exist.
7. List the possible exceptions associated with each type of document and note the procedures for resolving them.

Most companies have a tendency to change frequently in both structure and function. In fact, this tendency is looked upon as good because it keeps the organization in step with changing customer needs and market directions. To ensure its effective implementation, imaging also requires this kind of self-examination. After all, automating an inefficient process only wastes corporate resources.

The best applications for imaging technology are those for which:

- Business function is widely understood and the need for improvement, in terms of quality and timeliness, is clear;
- The workflows lend themselves to automation;
- The time spent in paper handling can be dramatically reduced;
- A significant positive return on investment is likely;
- Early implementation mistakes will not jeopardize mission-critical functions or place the company at risk.

If the goal of imaging is only to overlay the technology on the existing organization, the benefits of investing in the technology will be minimal. There are several levels of technology implementation that merit consideration, categorized by increasing levels of process reorganization:

- *Pilot projects.* These are projects that are set up for limited use at a single location. The projects have little value because instead of fostering commitment, they tend to promote a "wait-and-see" attitude that more often than not guarantees failure.
- *Internal integration.* By helping to move information between processes, this method can yield significant benefits. However, if existing processes are not made more efficient first, long-term gains will be limited and return on investment prolonged.
- *Process redesign.* This is a method by which an entire organization or discrete departmental process is restructured to take advantage of imaging technology. Although this method can produce noteworthy improvements in efficiency, it can also be difficult and time-consuming to execute.
- *Network engineering.* This method extends the reorganization process to locations outside the company's main location. This activity can produce enterprisewide benefits, but is also difficult to implement.

To properly implement a technology at the right level of process reorganization requires that companies understand their business processes. This is not as easy as it sounds; it involves a commitment of staff, effort, and time. Matters are further complicated by corporate managers who have a stake in preserving the status quo. To overcome these obstacles, it might be more effective to have a consultant evaluate various business processes and workflows or to use the professional services of an imaging system vendor. That way, a more objective and accurate assessment can be rendered, which, in turn, ensures that investment in corporate resources are targeted wisely.

Alternatively, an evaluation of business processes and workflows can be performed internally, either with third-party assistance or follow-up review to validate (or invalidate) the conclusions. The high cost of imaging system implementation warrants these extended measures.

15.3.3 Levels of Implementation

One of the major decisions that has to be addressed early on is whether to implement imaging at the PC level, in conjunction with LANs, or at the minicomputer or mainframe level. Economics favor the former, since this solution takes advantage of the installed base of PCs. It also provides more implementation flexibility and scalability than either the minicomputer or mainframe solutions. All that is required—at incremental cost—are the right software and peripherals. However, with cooperative processing, a company can use its mainframe or minicomputer for image databases and add LAN-based server functions.

With proprietary imaging systems, the vendor typically provides a host gateway that runs on the imaging server. With LAN-based systems, on the other hand, the host gateway can be implemented through a communications server or at the PC. A LAN-based host gateway, therefore, provides a more flexible, higher-performance solution.

LANs are particularly well suited for workflow image applications because they are able to support the transfer of images between all nodes—workstations, scanners, storage devices, and printers. LANs also allow for greater flexibility in host access because users have a variety of gateways and terminal emulators to choose from. LANs can give remote users access to both the document image index and the images themselves. Usually, remote users are able to review the documents in the image index and select images for retrieval by facsimile transmission. Thus, any office with a modem-equipped PC or fax machine is a potential imaging location, even though it might not be locally attached.

LANs also provide more opportunities for performance tuning. Using LAN management systems, analysis tools, and utilities, managers can measure performance accurately and take immediate steps to make improvements, such as segmenting the network into subnets, caching images, using compression, and adding higher-performance peripherals. Because performance demands can vary on a daily basis, the ability to respond quickly constitutes a key benefit of LAN-based imaging systems over mainframe-based systems.

Performance on the main imaging network can be maintained by putting resource-intensive services, such as scanning, printing, and faxing, on *subnetworks*. These subnetworks, or subnets, can be selectively isolated from the rest of the network with bridges or routers. A subnet would allow a large accounts payable department, for example, to scan 10,000 invoices a day without bogging down the main network. The scanned images would be stored on disk and registered in the image system index via a batch process. Similarly, when a large number of documents must be printed, the data can be dumped off to a subnet for printing, instead of tying up the main network.

Performance can also be improved by caching, or *prefetching,* images. Prefetching involves moving images from optical media, where they are permanently stored, to magnetic media and provides a faster access time for workflow operations. Caching is implemented based on an understanding of which images are likely to be required next. This technique is effective in workflow applications in which there are queues of images to be worked on. The vendors' storage management utilities are used to implement image caching.

The storage media also affects image system performance. Generally, magnetic storage offers much higher performance than optical drives.[1] However, optical disks are used as permanent image storage repositories because of their high capacity. With LAN-based servers, which can provide tens of gigabytes of online storage, the selection of storage media should be based on the cost-benefits of the storage alternatives and not necessarily on technical feasibility.

---

[1] The performance gap between magnetic disk drives and optical disk drives is rapidly closing. For example, Pinnacle Micro's PMO-650 rewritable optical drive has a 19-millisecond access time, which is the same as most magnetic disk drives. The gap between price-per-megabyte of storage is not closing as fast. For example, the PMO-650 costs approximately $4,000, whereas the average cost of a 660 MB magnetic disk drive is approximately $1,600.

Data compression algorithms, such as V.42 bis and MNP 5, have long been a part of modem communications over dial-up and analog leased lines. In recent years, vendors have been adding data compression to bridges and routers as well, to improve throughput between LANs. Now there is file transfer software that implements data compression across operating systems, allowing images to be compressed under IBM's MVS, for example, and decompressed under MS-DOS. Although IBM offers compression products, they run on only one operating system at a time; that is, they do not permit files to be compressed on an MVS mainframe and decompressed on MS-DOS PS/2s.

15.3.4 Role of Operating System

Another area of concern involves the degree to which the imaging software is integrated with the *network operating system* (NOS). The integration can have a significant impact on the performance of critical imaging functions, such as scanner and printer drivers, optical subsystem drivers, and database interfaces.

The NOS controls server operation and essentially provides the framework for communications over the entire LAN. The operating system comprises many modules, which are responsible for recognizing users, associating their identities with access privileges, and routing requests. The system, of necessity, determines the server configuration, including the microprocessor type, the amount of accessible memory, and hard disk storage.

Many of the components of imaging systems, such as scanners, printers, and monitors, have been developed for other applications, such as desktop publishing. Fortunately, imaging vendors recognized long ago that they needed to have standard drivers in their systems for these components, and they have largely given up on trying to market proprietary components, unless existing standards do not fit the bill.

Most LAN-based imaging systems use NetBIOS, a transport-layer programming interface, to communicate between the client workstations and image servers over the network. At the NetBIOS level, there is no distinction between the server and client. The two types of computers communicate by sending small messages called *datagrams*.

Since NetBIOS is a high-level specification, the imaging system that uses it will operate similarly across different network operating systems. On the other hand, it typically operates more slowly than an imaging system that uses native network protocols, such as NetWare's SPX/IPX and Banyan's VINES IP.

Be aware that not all imaging vendors support NetBIOS or native LAN protocols. Hewlett-Packard, for example, offers UNIX-based systems that support TCP/IP. Fortunately, Microsoft and Novell have developed driver standards that allow multiple protocols to operate on the same LAN and use the same *network interface card* (NIC) to communicate with an attached workstation.

15.3.5 Topology Considerations

Most office technologies are brought in to solve specific business problems, which means that, usually, adoption of a technology begins in the department that has the particular need. If the solution is successful and it can be applied elsewhere, the technology tends to spread to other departments. The same is true of imaging.

Since the great bulk of paper that enters departments or workgroups never leaves, when planning image systems, it is recommended that a departmental topology be designed with emphasis on workflow, rather than on a central repository that will be accessed by all departments. Performance diminishes when too many users try to access the relatively limited number of mainframe ports. Workflow operations depend on instant access to stored images, which is best achieved by LAN-based image systems or dedicated host-based systems.

15.3.6 Impact on Existing Networks

When planning an image system, organizations must assess how system deployment will impact existing networks, both LANs and WANs. Because data files are very large, careful planning is necessary to avoid impeding the flow of traffic. Therefore, the cost and method of adding extra bandwidth must be considered. Organizations can improve the flow of traffic on LANs by employing one of these methods:

- Take advantage of ubiquitous twisted-pair wiring to add more bandwidth. If need be, fiber backbones can connect local LANs within a building or campus environment.
- Segment existing LANs so that image traffic is separated from other applications. Segmenting overgrown LANs into smaller subnets with bridges and routers can improve overall network performance and facilitate management.
- Make use of data compression to minimize the traffic that must traverse the LAN. Because of their size, image files lend themselves to high compression ratios.

Organizations that want to integrate standard data and images on the same Ethernet must address several issues, among them, packet size. IEEE 802.3 networks operate on a contention medium-access protocol called *carrier-sense multiple access with collision detection* (CSMA/CD). A station that has packets to send must first check to see if the transmission medium is available. If transmission is possible, the station transmits a packet. The maximum packet size for the IEEE 802.3 standard is 1500 bytes. Larger packet sizes allow an 802.3 network to approach the theoretical maximum throughput of the network, which is 10 Mbps. This is because larger packet sizes decrease the likelihood of an information-destroying packet collision.

It is possible to implement networks with packet sizes that exceed the 802.3 standard and thus improve image transmission performance on LANs. But implementing nonstandard packet sizes has several ramifications. Because larger packet sizes violate the 802.3 standard, steps must be taken to ensure that this violation does not negatively impact other network hardware and software, which have been designed to the standard. This can be accomplished by ensuring that network interface boards on all network stations have enough buffer memory to support nonstandard packets. However, such interface boards are usually more expensive. If adjacent networks are not configured to support larger packet sizes, internetworking can become more complex. It becomes complex because a packet-restructuring function must exist at network interface points and, because this requires increased processing, network performance can degrade.

Another factor to consider in image system implementation are performance bottlenecks. Although the source of bottlenecks can be any one of the many system components, in an imaging system, the input/output devices are usually the culprits. For example, a jukebox's robotics and disk spin-up and spin-down time can constitute a serious bottleneck. The situation worsens when a few large documents that are stored across multiple optical platters are requested at the same time.

There are several ways to alleviate bottlenecks. The first entails prefetching the images using workflow software, which allows the system to batch-retrieve images overnight. A second solution involves employing an optical-storage manager that writes to a single optical disk all the images that belong to one folder. This organization prevents folders from being fragmented over multiple optical disks as they grow. A third way to avoid bottlenecks is to implement a hierarchical data-storage scheme. This scheme involves understanding the use and life cycle of a document. When a document is in the active part of its life cycle, it can be stored on magnetic storage, which has fast retrieval capabilities. When the document becomes inactive, it can be automatically moved to optical media in a jukebox. When the document is archived, it can be moved to an archive medium, such as helical scan tape. A document should be able to move back and forth through this hierarchy.

The different protocols used on LANs and WANs also affect the transport of images. Although the communication protocol selected should not have a significant impact on the LAN, the network layer and transport layer protocols of the OSI reference model significantly affect internetworking transmissions over a WAN. It is therefore advisable to avoid protocols that feature a high degree of error-checking overhead and acknowledgments and to seek instead protocols that feature multiple-packet receipt acknowledgment.

Image system planning is quite difficult when there are other types of data flowing on the network, so it is necessary to consider whether a dedicated imaging network or a shared network is better. The main issues are the predictability of the traffic pattern and the performance required. Transmitting mixed data types across a network does not necessarily cause problems, but performance optimization becomes a requirement, and this might entail some compromises.

Although due consideration should be given to mixed usage of the network, image-intensive production environments, such as a claims-processing application, will likely require dedicated networks. In this and other instances in which applications require a dedicated network for imaging-related tasks network parameters can be tuned to optimize performance for predictable traffic patterns.

Once device input/output and network speeds advance to the point at which frame-size optimization decreases in importance, multimedia data—such as images, data, voice, and text—will traverse the network without degradation. To be on the safe side, a pilot image network can be segmented from the production network and used to test all of these assumptions.

The question of whether the CSMA/CD access method of Ethernet or the predicted delay of token ring seriously affect an imaging system applies to implementing nonimaging systems as well. Different traffic types can theoretically make a difference in the effectiveness of a contention, media-access protocol like CSMA/CD. Deterministic protocols, like token ring, provide a more predictable worst-case response time for instances in which many stations have information to send. But in low traffic situations, deterministic protocols also impart a fixed-delay overhead.

Contention, media-access protocols provide immediate access to the transmission medium when there are few stations with information to send or when a station infrequently sends information. The performance of a contention, media-access protocol degrades significantly if there are many stations attempting to generate traffic.

The bottom line is the location of bottlenecks in a distributed imaging system. Even though token-ring networks demonstrate more effective throughput at high-usage rates, most imaging systems are not able to load the network to the level at which bottlenecks become an issue.

Organizations can employ these methods to improve the flow of traffic on WANs:

- For image traffic, take advantage of new high-capacity digital services, such as Frame Relay and SMDS, which run over T1 and T3 facilities.
- Use ISDN's high-capacity channels (384 Kbps and 1.536 Mbps) for dial-up bandwidth. This option can relieve congestion during peak traffic periods. The user pays only for the amount of bandwidth used and the period it is used, just like an ordinary phone call.
- Use compression-equipped bridges and routers to minimize traffic on the WAN. For example, 4 to 1 compression applied to a 384 Kbps FT1 line yields the throughput of a T1 line, but at much less cost.
- Use routers that have the capability to automatically reroute traffic around failed links and balance the traffic load across multiple paths.
- Make use of traffic-reduction techniques, such as "large packet," in conjunction with burst-mode technologies, to minimize acknowledgment messages that can waste bandwidth.

The last item, the use of traffic reduction techniques, deserves elaboration. Novell's IPX protocol, for example, breaks down the data into 512-byte packets for transmission over the WAN and normally requires acknowledgment of each packet. Thus, traffic can build up on the links very quickly. Using a router that employs "large packet" technology can greatly reduce the amount of traffic on the links by bundling together 512-byte packets into a single 4096-byte packet. With fewer packets traversing the link, there are fewer acknowledgments. With fewer acknowledgments, there is less delay. Novell's "packet burst" technology complements the large packet solution by allowing more packets to be sent out with one acknowledgment—like shipping a freight train of information instead of just a freight car.

5.3.7 Applications Integration

Dynamic data exchange (DDE) and *dynamic link libraries* (DLLs) provide the means to exchange information between applications, which is essential for integrating imaging with nonimaging applications. DDE is a mechanism for exchanging data between applications displayed in different windows. It uses the Windows messaging system and clipboard facility to implement interprocess communication. DLLs, on the other hand, are standard libraries that are linked to an application at run time. In document imaging, a developer can directly image-enable a business application by using an image vendor's DLLs to perform such functions as retrieving the image ID from storage, returning the image to the workstation, decompressing the image, and displaying the image in a window.

DDE and DLLs are also useful for exchanging information between imaging system and host-based applications. DDE can be used to exchange information between a Windows-based terminal emulator and an imaging application, including keystrokes, function keys, and data written to the screen from the host. Once this data is available to the imaging system, it can be incorporated into workflow processing. Alternatively, an image application can make DLL calls to send or receive information from the emulation session.

Imaging system tables are maintained by widely supported relational databases, such as those offered by Oracle and Informix. The use of these standard SQL-based databases allows data processing applications to become tightly coupled with imaging systems, because developers can use the SQL database's native tools to access the image system's tables. In some cases, client/server tools, such as Oracle's SQL*Forms, can be used to integrate imaging with other applications. In addition, an application can be easily integrated with an imaging system if the same database used by the imaging system is used to develop an application. The key element needed to image-enable a typical data processing system is an index that links the entities in the database with the corresponding images.

If the imaging application requires integration with existing applications, information must be exchanged between the two systems and the integrity of the cross-references between them must be maintained. Integrating imaging with an existing application is easier if the image vendor stores the image index in an SQL database. That way, the same database engine can be used to develop the nonimage elements of the application. If such a standardized database engine is not available, in addition to having to learn two data management environments, the user must be concerned about implementing fault recovery for two dissimilar environments. The bottom line is that operating costs easily double when the applications must span two data management environments.

For those who want to develop an integrated imaging system, the key concern is how well the imaging system's development tools fit organizational requirements. Addressing this concern requires an assessment of the development tools the organization currently uses; the components of the development environment that allow application testing and debugging are critical to successful imaging implementations.

Essentially, there are two types of development tools: script-based and object-based. *Script-based tools* offer high-level support for indexing and workflow processes. Large, complex imaging systems, such as those offered by Wang and FileNet, were built with script-based tools. Many smaller vendors of document imaging systems (and multimedia systems) also use script-based languages.

Object-based tools are very popular in the Windows client/server environment because generally they do not require the same level of programming expertise as script-based development tools. The "objects" are discrete modules of code and data that have distinct functions. They can be used to customize existing applications or modified separately to speed applications development. The use of objects also reduces production costs and simplifies maintenance. Object technology promotes application code reusability, interoperability, and portability, in turn, improving the overall reliability of distributed programs.

Object-oriented tools can build sophisticated imaging systems, especially if the imaging vendor provides well-documented APIs to access image system functions. IBM and Wang are two companies that publish their APIs. A competitive strength of IBM's Image-Plus product family is the availability of powerful APIs, which facilitate the development of specific applications from standard programming languages. This was not always the case, however. IBM had to be pressured into making more APIs available. With Version 2 of ImagePlus, IBM offered only 15 APIs. Now, as IBM adds functionality to the mainline ImagePlus product, it will provide more APIs. More than 100 APIs are currently available with ImagePlus/2, allowing developers to fully integrate image processing with existing business applications.

15.4 SUPPORT ISSUES

There are a variety of support issues that organizations must attend to when they are deciding to implement a document imaging system. Among them are systems reliability, systems integration, and training.

15.4.1 System Reliability

Companies that commit business-critical documents to imaging technology must give thought to keeping these systems and networks reliable and stable. Specifically, they must think about how these systems and the networks they run on can be protected against failure. The possible solutions include but are not limited to:

- Uninterruptible power supplies (UPS);
- Redundant components and subsystems;
- Alternate routes between corporate locations on the WAN and bypass circuitry between LAN hubs and major subsystems;
- Local service and support from vendors, to minimize system downtime.

Organizations must determine which protective measures are already available and to what extent they can be applied to the imaging system. If new protective measures are needed, such considerations must be included in the planning process and factored into the purchase price of the imaging system.

15.4.2 Systems Integration

When an imaging system is designed from scratch and is composed of products from different vendors, the task becomes one of tying together these diverse components to provide users with transparent access to every element on the network. But rarely do inhouse staff have the depth and breadth of expertise to accomplish this formidable task alone. Systems integrators can help.

The use of systems integrators can be justified on the grounds of:

- Specialized industry knowledge, awareness of technology trends, and experiences gained from a broad customer base;
- Knowledge of specific protocols, interfaces, and cabling requirements;
- Reputation for doing quality work within a limited time frame;
- Ability to transfer knowledge to existing systems staff so they can take over responsibility for ongoing management, administration, and control;
- The need for an outside party to act as a catalyst in implementing change and to validate (or fine-tune) inhouse plans.

A systems integrator brings objectivity to the task of tying together diverse products and systems to build a seamless, unified network. To accomplish this, different physical connections and incompatible protocols must be reconciled. The systems integrator uses hardware and software expertise to perform the necessary customization.

Qualified systems integrators have in place a stable support infrastructure that is capable of handling a high degree of ambiguity and complexity, as well as any technical challenge that might get in the way of the integration effort. In addition to financial stability, this support infrastructure includes staff representing a variety of technical and management disciplines, computerized project management tools, and strategic relationships with carriers, vendors, and specialized service firms.

Integration firms provide a number of discrete services. It is worth remembering, however, that no single firm can provide all of these services, which is why they frequently team up to propose a total solution. Services that integration firms or teams provide include:

- *Design and development.* This service includes: network design; facilities engineering; equipment installation and customization; hardware, software, and network integration; acceptance testing; and network management.
- *Consulting.* Consulting services include business planning, systems/network architecture design, technology assessment, feasibility study, RFP development, vendor

evaluation and product selection, quality assurance, security auditing, disaster recovery planning, and project management.

- *Systems implementation.* Implementation services involve procurement, documentation development, configuration management, contract management, and program management.
- *Facilities management.* Services cover operations, technical support, hot-line services, change management, and trouble ticket administration.
- *Systems re-engineering.* Services include maintenance, systems and network optimization, remote monitoring and diagnostics, and automated design tools.
- *Training.* Systems integrators provide hands-on user training, technical and management courses, executive briefings, and industry trends seminars.

15.4.3 Training

Because an imaging system can be quite complex, especially when configured for workflow applications, extensive operator and supervisor training might be required. Reputable imaging system vendors offer a full line of instruction about their products and technology, dedicated training staffs, and training facilities.

The nature and scope of a vendor's training offerings can usually be ascertained by reviewing copies of the training materials before committing to a specific imaging system vendor. The materials should provide clear and comprehensive learning objectives, be supported by well-organized lesson structures and descriptions, and be able to function as reference material after the training sessions. If the vendor does not provide this kind of depth in its training package, the customer might be getting less out of the capital investment than anticipated at the time of purchase.

It is always a good idea to ask about the experience and qualifications of the trainers. The vendor should not simply send technicians to provide training; generally, technicians lack a user's point of view and rarely make good instructors, unless they have been specifically trained for that responsibility.

Many times formal classroom training at the vendor's facilities is not sufficient, especially if the imaging system requires a high degree of customization. In this case, the vendor (or systems integrator) should be willing and capable of offering on-site training at the customer's location. It is advisable to identify the extra costs, if any, of training for employees hired after the original training period, as well as the cost of any follow-up training that might be needed to fine-tune user skills.

15.5 CONCLUSION

Despite the large investments companies have made in office technologies over the years, productivity gains have been hampered by the huge quantity of paper these technologies produce. Now that imaging has arrived to address the paper problem, planning and implementing such systems can provide significant opportunities for re-engineering work processes and streamlining organizations.

Re-engineering, however, is an ongoing process. As such, it does not lend itself to achieving quick gains. It can also be an expensive process, in terms of time and money, and requires an appropriate budget. Although many executives like the idea of re-engineering, few have the mind-set to capitalize on the efficiencies such programs can bring over the long term. Imaging is one manifestation of re-engineering. Its successful implementation has provided many companies with strategic advantages.

With proper planning, the benefits of implementing imaging systems include better document control, faster retrieval, and multi-user access. These benefits can, in turn, improve the quality and timeliness of customer service, which is of strategic importance to most businesses.

Chapter 16

Professional Services for Imaging Implementation

16.1 INTRODUCTION

Businesses are continually seeking new ways to improve internal operations. More often than not, the search for improvement includes looking for ways to streamline workflows to reduce paper and paperwork. Despite their best efforts at control, most businesses experience an increase in paper and paperwork. This, in fact, has led to speculation that the computer revolution failed to increase productivity as much as early visionaries predicted. But this view might simply reflect the difficulty of measuring increased efficiency and underscore the need for new business processes and information management techniques.

Unable to decrease their reliance on paper-based processes, organizations typically look next at how to manage information more effectively. In days past, microfilm and microfiche were the technologies considered for managing paper documents. Today, computerized document imaging systems are becoming the technology of choice.

As noted throughout this book, businesses are considering document imaging systems for a variety of reasons: to shorten processing cycles, to reduce overhead costs, to enhance the quality of work, to expand access to information, or to improve overall customer service. By achieving one or more of these goals, organizations can accrue competitive advantages that, in turn, can enlarge market share. Every increase in market share introduces new resources that organizations must employ to compete in evolving or expanding areas or at a higher level of innovation.

When fundamental business operations are substantially altered, the process is referred to as *re-engineering*. This term refers to a seemingly obvious idea: instead of using computers and information technology to automate inefficient processes, re-engineer the process and then implement the information technology. According to Partners Research, re-engineering can reduce costs by as much as 80%, improve time-to-market by 80%, and even double sales.

These improvements are among the reasons why, increasingly, major Wall Street firms are turning to business and systems re-engineering. Many of the firms are using re-engineering to elevate their services by consolidating the paper trail. For example, Merrill

Lynch implemented imaging technology to reduce the six-day process of opening new retail accounts to 24 hours. Instead of using the old paper-based documentation system, Merrill Lynch restructured the process to run on a workstation. From the workstation, customer information is downloaded to the company's customer account services center, where the type of documentation required by that particular customer is determined and compiled.

Document imaging systems are not only appropriate for businesses, they are also particularly well suited to the public sector, where evidence of a return on investment must be available before the next election. The pressure to improve performance in the public sector is especially acute. Not only is the public sector under continual scrutiny for waste and mismanagement, but budget deficits force cutbacks in staff and spending that often remove opportunities for improvement. The advent of smarter desktops and image-enabled applications can go a long way toward offsetting these disadvantages.

16.2 PRODUCTIVITY ISSUES

Productivity is a measure of work done within a specified time. In the assembly line environment, it is easy to measure productivity in terms of units produced per hour. There, an increase in productivity can be obtained merely by speeding up the assembly line to produce more units per hour. When the assembly line reaches an optimal speed—the point at which an unacceptable number of defective items is produced—productivity can still be increased by adding assembly lines. When the number of assembly lines becomes limited by the available space, productivity can still be increased by adding more factories.

In the office environment, productivity is often viewed in a similar manner—in terms of transactions processed. An insurance company might measure productivity in terms of the number of claims processed per month. A bank might measure productivity by the number of checks processed per day. In the public sector, a court system might measure productivity in terms of the number of cases processed per week. Until recently, it was very difficult to realize the dramatic improvements in transaction processing that are possible in factory assembly lines. Paper-based systems simply did not lend themselves to improvement by automation, even with the advent of microcomputers. The proliferation of microcomputers and other office technologies—photocopiers, laser printers, and facsimile machines—only increased the amount of paper and expanded the requirements for storage. As storage expanded, access to information became a problem because the information took longer to find.

In the re-engineering process, the number of stages involved in completing a transaction must be reduced to a minimum. More stages consume more time and offer greater opportunity for the introduction of errors. The information generated by transaction processing systems can be extremely valuable to a company, but it must first be organized in a manner and format that makes it easily accessible. Successful re-engineering requires a clear picture of how the process currently operates and how it is intended to operate afterward. In essence, systems already in place must be selectively destroyed and replaced with cross-functional systems that allow many departments to share a single "information ware-house."

The correct application of document imaging can open significant opportunities for re-engineering work processes and streamlining the entire organization. A well-managed implementation of imaging can also improve the overall effectiveness of the organization. Document imaging systems provide a level of automation in the transaction processing environment that potentially rivals that found in the factory assembly line environment. But because the implementation of image technology is potentially disruptive, the results must justify the effort. A 1991 study by CSC Index revealed that fundamentally altering a business procedure initiates an average enhancement of 48% in cost, 60% in defects, and 80% in time. The rewards for implementing such re-engineering efforts are often realized within 12 to 24 months.

Document imaging systems are no longer being justified primarily as tactical cost-reduction tools that free expensive floor space, eliminate refiling costs and the costs of searching for filed and misfiled documents, reduce film or paper costs, and the like. The new strategic emphasis is on gaining competitive advantage by having information available to the right person at the right time and by automating the document flow. Because document imaging allows relevant information to be retrieved, distributed, and shared much more rapidly and flexibly, actions can be performed in a timelier and better-informed fashion. These benefits translate into the strategic advantages of providing superior customer service and bringing better products and services to market sooner.

While such justifications sound convincing, the productivity gains of document imaging systems are still often difficult to quantify. However, there have been many widely publicized showcase applications that amply illustrate the benefits of such systems. In 1991, a Unisys customer put a document imaging system to the test with surprising results. Signet Bank, which operates 234 full-service banking offices throughout Virginia, Maryland, and the District of Columbia, implemented the Unisys *InfoImage Item Processing System* (IIPS).

The IIPS system optically scans financial documents, producing a digitized instrument that is processed while the actual paper is stored. The system includes the Expert Balancer, which analyzes out-of-balance work for errors. This technology detects the most common data entry errors, such as normal transpositions, shifted digits, extra or missing digits, double entry items and missing and free items. The Expert Balancer complements the speed of the document processor and effectively balances at the rate of 1,600 documents per minute. When the last check finishes, the work is ready for release.

Imaging allowed Signet to dramatically change its labor-intensive transactions handling by eliminating repetitive physical handling of paper checks, which is currently the industry norm for check processing. As a result of this workflow change, Signet experienced a reduction in manual processing and error exception, an improvement in funds availability, an increase in production and, most importantly, a better working environment for employees. At a single high-resolution data entry workstation, one operator is able to process 18,000 checks a day, versus 7,500 under the old document processing system. This represents a productivity gain of 240%.

The testing system used at Signet and other banks is a self-contained data entry station that captures an image of a check. The station is designed to allow a bank to do a side-by-side comparison of the processing capabilities of image-based and manual check operations. This allows an organization to try an imaging system on for size without incurring a major financial investment. The experience of Signet Bank demonstrates the potential of document imaging systems to dramatically improve an organization's productivity. Without proper planning, however, the promised benefits might prove elusive.

Because document imaging systems can represent a substantial capital investment when implemented enterprisewide, the major computer manufacturers offer a variety of services to assist customers in evaluating the need for document imaging systems before making the commitment to buy. The rest of this chapter focuses on the planning aspects of implementing document imaging systems and, specifically, on how the professional services group at Unisys renders such assistance to potential customers. After that, the offerings of other vendors are summarized.

16.3 PROFESSIONAL SERVICES OVERVIEW

When organizations begin planning for imaging systems they often find themselves between a rock and a hard place: should they first reorganize and redesign their business workflow, or should they begin image-enabling existing processes? The Unisys approach to this dilemma is to promote the concept of workflow analysis as the means for finding the answer to all of a company's problems and as an evaluation tool for justifying the cost of an imaging system.

The Unisys approach entails performing workflow analysis and redesign on a quantifiable piece of the business process—a piece that can gain the most from imaging technology and that can be used for evaluating future improvements or expansion. If the potential for improvement exists, Unisys further defines and evaluates a department's unique requirements and reviews the recommended options for imaging or other appropriate technologies. To help management make confident and informed decisions, Unisys submits an executive report that explains each option and its associated risks and benefits. Should the customer wish to proceed with an imaging solution, Unisys offers its InfoImage Professional Services. These services perform the following tasks:

- Incorporate workflow and business re-engineering techniques;
- Provide line-of-business expertise;
- Reduce risk through comprehensive analysis and reporting procedures;
- Provide the customer with an active role in the imaging project;
- Implement changes with minimal disruption to the company's daily operations;
- Assist the customer in maximizing return on technology investments.

Because implementing an imaging system is a multistep process, Unisys designed a suite of services to help meet users' total requirements. Recognizing the fact that just applying technology to business processes does not produce an adequate return, the company's InfoImage Professional Services methodology is designed to educate and assist users during all phases of an imaging implementation. This methodology follows a logical, step-by-step approach to accomplishing process improvement. In adhering to the modular sequence of services, the customer has the ability to monitor and control the imaging project from start to finish. These services fall into the following categories:

- Predecision
- Preinstallation
- Installation and implementation
- Postinstallation
- Life cycle

The services (Figure 16.1) enable organizations to maximize the return on investment and minimize startup time, while equipping end users with the necessary expertise in imaging system operations. Thus, while the customer's business is being evaluated and possibly re-engineered to allow the imaging system to have its desired result, the Unisys team is working behind the scenes to ensure a smooth transition, in terms of length of the implementation cycle, timely feedback on return on investment, and adequate end-user acceptance.

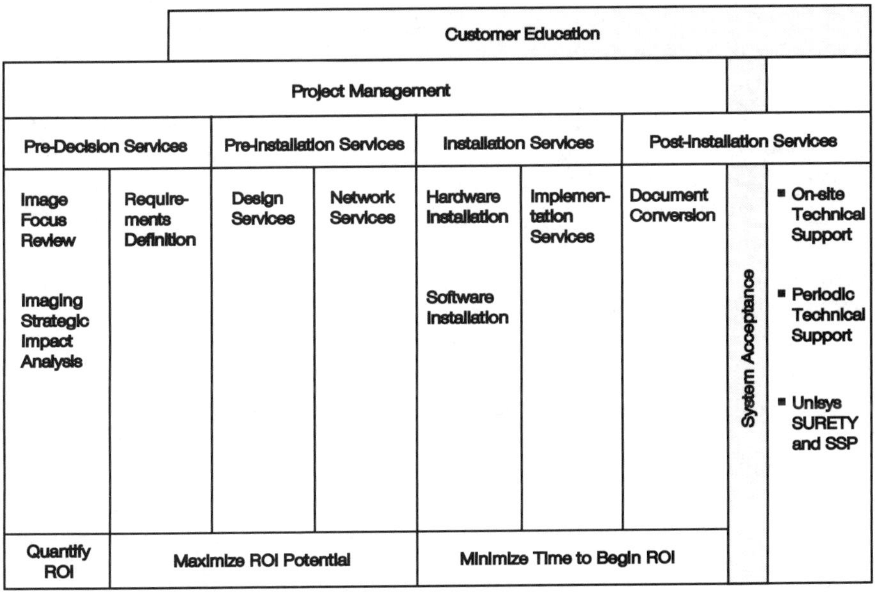

Customer Education								
Project Management								
Pre-Decision Services		Pre-Installation Services		Installation Services		Post-Installation Services		
Image Focus Review Imaging Strategic Impact Analysis	Require-ments Definition	Design Services	Network Services	Hardware Installation Software Installation	Implemen-tation Services	Document Conversion	System Acceptance	■ On-site Technical Support ■ Periodic Technical Support ■ Unisys SURETY and SSP
Quantify ROI	Maximize ROI Potential			Minimize Time to Begin ROI				

Figure 16.1 Summary of InfoImage Professional Services.

While the Unisys project management team is accountable for the project, at the same time the customer is also involved from the beginning, in planning, approval, implementation, and acceptance testing.

16.3.1 Predecision Services

Most departments in a given company have well-defined document management needs. With advances in database management, workstations, optical storage, and networking, today's image processing technology is mature enough to support a distributed, departmental implementation in a cost-effective fashion.

The predecision services determine where image technology should be applied and project potential return on investment, prior to recommending the purchase of a complete system. As part of its predecision services, Unisys provides customers with this documentation: an *image focus review* (IFR), *requirements definition* (RD), and *strategic impact analysis* (SIA).

The IFR is the core service of the program. It addresses an organization's strategic business objectives, identifying potential targets for improvement and providing a high-level cost/benefit analysis. The objective of the review is to outline a preliminary plan for an integrated imaging solution within the existing work environment. The IFR also helps the customer zero in on the department that would gain the most from imaging technology, based on such parameters as volumes of paper processed, user acceptance, and financial considerations. This analysis includes an estimate of the potential return on investment, based on the proposed use of imaging technology.

Once the decision to image-enable a specific business process is made, Unisys provides an RD. The RD builds on the preliminary input from the predecision services to define, analyze, and document the specific needs and scope of the target department's imaging solution. The RD also highlights opportunities for integrating imaging technology with related electronic information already in use.

The RD lays the groundwork for all subsequent design and implementation activities. This service: identifies the proposed project's major inputs, outputs, and volumes; defines the current workflow processes, identifying those that should be automated and those that should not; and defines all hardware, software, and future services that will be required for implementation. Workstation requirements definition takes into account the individual needs of users and the needs of applications that perform such functions as rapid electronic browsing through files, reading and comparing multiple pages, and panning and zooming around large drawings. In addition, database requirements are defined to support various search methodologies in the language employed by the end user.

Once the department's current processing methods are identified and understood, Unisys then incorporates workflow and re-engineering techniques to streamline operations. This analysis ensures that the department's total requirements are explored and understood prior to the company's commitment to purchase an imaging solution. In addition, the RD describes the types of third-party services that are required, such as consultants or document conversion services. These services will be brought in under the direction of the

Unisys project management team. The RD also provides an initial schedule and cost estimates for implementing the solution.

The completion of these services results in a detailed design document, which describes the actual imaging system and how it will be implemented. The document includes information about the system configuration, workflow, and end-user training, and test plans, system acceptance scripts and complete project schedules and timetables.

The SIA takes these processes a step further, evaluating the potential effect of an imaging solution on the entire enterprise. The resulting report recommends an appropriate imaging architecture, a method of enterprise integration, and a specific implementation approach. The SIA is important because even though each department stores, retrieves, distributes, and processes information, the implementation requirements can vary widely across the enterprise. The SIA specifies how the unique needs of each department can be met, while still letting departments share information as needed. The reports explain, for example, how to introduce imaging gradually across the enterprise, with as little peripheral disruption as possible.

The Unisys services are provided by experts—about 200 worldwide—who understand imaging requirements and the issues involved in business re-engineering. They are trained to apply the technology to specific business problems, as opposed to being taught to simply look at the technology in terms of features and functionality. Training includes learning to conduct a detailed workflow analysis that starts with interviews with users in each department in which the technology will reside. Users are questioned about what they do on the job and how information flows in and out of their environment. This gives evaluators a feel for the kinds of supportive information technologies users need to do their jobs.

Sometimes the workflow analysis reveals the need for solutions other than imaging. For example, office automation or *electronic data interchange* (EDI) might be the answer to a particular problem, or a combination of technologies might provide the solution. It is even possible that an analysis done ostensibly to evaluate the need for imaging results in a recommendation for a nontechnical solution. In many cases, it is found that old procedures are still in place that have not been updated to reflect changes in organizational structure or in business practices. Just implementing changes in these areas can streamline internal operations and save companies a lot of money.

Unisys recommends this type of evaluation for any company that is considering an imaging system. It is also recommended as a step companies should perform as part of their business re-engineering effort. Instituting a midcourse correction and hoping that everything will improve is often not enough to achieve productivity increases or cost savings. According to Unisys, companies should continually assess their overall business objectives to determine how new technologies can support them.

16.3.2 Preinstallation Services

Once the customer has accepted the proposal, Unisys uses the information gathered in the predecision evaluation process to provide preinstallation services, which include completion of detailed design and communications plans. The detailed design document defines all hardware and software up front, so that the actual installation can be performed with a minimum of business interruption and in the shortest possible time frame. Included in the detailed design document is a complete description of document routing, the database structure, user forms, process automation, and the configuration of optical and magnetic tape storage. The document also outlines implementation of the system acceptance test plan and scripts, which enables the customer to verify that all requirements are being addressed prior to system installation.

Next, network experts from Unisys evaluate and verify the organization's image communications requirements. They perform LAN requirements analysis and provide planning, design, installation, implementation, and support services. To realize the efficiencies and economies of imaging systems often requires that documents be accessible not only to local users over the LAN, but also to remote users over the WAN. Imaging requires higher transmission speed and throughput, consistent data access, high-speed workstation interfaces, and interoperable communications protocols. Because Unisys defines such requirements at the outset, unnecessary startup delays are eliminated.

In addition, Unisys defines how the organization can address companywide requirements in an expandable, modular fashion that protects existing investments while building for future needs. Such requirements include the need for interconnectivity among operating groups and subsidiary companies.

To ensure the effective implementation of the imaging solution, Unisys stresses an environment that is both structured and flexible. Industry standards provide the structure, while flexibility results from building the solution on standard platforms that can be tailored to specific user needs. In addition to maximizing integration potential, adhering to standards also facilitates the incorporation of technological advances as they occur, regardless of their origin. In other words, as new technologies emerge that better support business strategies, standards permit organizations to take early advantage of the innovations without obsoleting current investments. These new technologies might be refinements to the various imaging components, such as advances in scanner and optical disk technology, or they might be complementary technologies, such as voice annotation and multimedia support. And, with standard communications protocols, true enterprisewide implementations of imaging become practical, rather than merely possible with a lot of patchwork and tweaking.

16.3.3 Installation and Implementation Services

Since imaging systems are new to most companies, Unisys offers "soup-to-nuts" installation services that include all hardware and software. Unisys technical personnel provide site analysis and planning, so equipment and software can be installed at the customer site immediately upon arrival, with minimal impact on the workforce.

During this phase of the project, Unisys customer service engineers install the acquired hardware and software components and bring the system to an operational state. Then the Unisys team initiates a verification process, to confirm that the components are running properly. Next, all the components of the imaging system are documented. This includes the software for OCR, image capture, workflow automation, and various APIs that facilitate development of image applications from standard programming languages.

During the implementation phase of the installation services, the hardware and software elements are bridged. Then, using both the results obtained during the design phase and the system acceptance scripts, the Unisys team tests the imaging system. After receiving customer acceptance, the system is put into service in the production environment.

16.3.4 Postinstallation Services

Typically, imaging systems do not operate in closed environments. The goal of postinstallation is to assist users in integrating imaging technology with mainstream business processes and to address conversion and support issues. Unisys provides technical experts who can integrate imaging systems with nonimaging applications. This allows customers to protect current investments while effectively integrating the various imaging technologies.

Document conversion from paper to digital format can be a mammoth undertaking when an organization makes the transition to image applications. This task is usually farmed out to a third-party service firm which, if contracted through Unisys, is managed as one of the project deliverables.

As part of its postinstallation service, Unisys offers two support programs that provide ongoing maintenance of its InfoImage systems: SURETY and the *Software Support Program* (SSP). SURETY offers on-site hardware repair service, while SSP provides hotline access to Unisys technical staff.

16.3.5 Life Cycle Services

Unisys provides customer education and project management over the entire project life cycle. Specialized courses are conducted at regional Unisys training centers or on location at customer sites. Several training paths are available, including courses for system administrators, managers, workflow analysts, and workstation operators. The training topics range from basic imaging principles to overall system functions.

Ongoing project management ensures success at each step of the planning and implementation process. The Unisys project manager assumes accountability for the entire project from start to finish. This helps minimize startup impact on the customers' operation. Once the imaging system is up and running and has been accepted by the customer, the Unisys project management team is no longer required. However, technical assistance retainer plans are available for customers who wish to make use of the services of the project manager on-site on either an ongoing or periodic basis.

16.3.6 Value-Added Systems Integration

Several factors distinguish InfoImage Professional Services from traditional systems integration services. Whereas the systems integrator typically approaches a problem from the technology perspective, Unisys approaches it from the business perspective. In a traditional systems integration project, the customer often lays down the requirements, while the systems integrator finds the appropriate products and puts them together to meet those requirements. Unisys also gets involved in the "nuts-and-bolts" issues, but does it by first establishing the nature and scope of the business problem.

In the Unisys approach, professional services experts help the customer determine what kind of information needs to be passed to whom and how frequently. That definition determines such things as the number of workstations that will be required on the network and the capacity of the network.

Pricing for InfoImage Professional Services starts at $15,000, with the average cost of $250,000 for a complete departmental implementation. Services for enterprisewide implementations can cost $1 million or more for a Fortune 500 company, depending on the value of the hardware and software. A rule of thumb puts the cost of planning and integrations services at 20 to 50% of the total cost of the system.

16.4 TEAMING ARRANGEMENTS

In addition to the comprehensive support offerings of InfoImage Professional Services, Unisys provides specialized consulting services in conjunction with other management consulting and systems integration firms. To address the unique needs of banks and other financial institutions, for example, Unisys is engaged in a partnership with *Littlewood, Shain & Company* (LSC), a financial services consulting firm in Exton, Pennsylvania, specializing in cash management and check processing. LSC services over 200 banks in the United States, and is known for having developed the banking industry's original float analysis check-clearing management tool, which is currently used by over 75 major banks.

When considering check imaging technology, bank management often needs additional expertise to evaluate and prepare the business case. To assist in this area, LSC works with Unisys to:

- Develop a business case analysis for implementing image processing, which includes identification and assessment of image-based opportunities, workflow modeling, quantification of benefits, and financial analysis;
- Assist in the development of profit-enhancement strategies for float and deposit products;
- Perform operational and clearing analysis to identify cost-improvement opportunities in item processing.

Unisys has a similar teaming arrangement with KPMG Peat Marwick, a management consulting firm with expertise in manufacturing systems. In Europe, Unisys has a teaming arrangement with Coopers & Lybrand Deloitte, the U.K. firm of Coopers & Lybrand, which is also strong in manufacturing systems management. On occasion, Unisys has offered its InfoImage Professional Services in conjunction with Andersen Consulting, based in Chicago.

Through its InfoImage Professional Services, Unisys is positioning itself as a full service, application-oriented imaging systems integrator with a worldwide support network. As an imaging system integrator, Unisys seeks to provide the right mix of products, support, and service.

In addition to banking and manufacturing, Unisys also offers its InfoImage Professional Services to companies in the insurance and pharmaceutical industries and to state and local governments. Approximately 20 organizations have taken advantage of these services since Unisys introduced them in late 1991.

Although document imaging is still an evolving market, it is already becoming indispensable for organizations whose paper storage has reached critical mass. Imaging promises to impact internal operations in a number of ways, reducing not only paperload but also paperwork. In the process, various operations are streamlined, resulting in new efficiencies and economies that improve service delivery and impact competitive position.

Image processing forces the restructuring of work within most organizations, resulting in changes in workflow, job content, and work habits. Imaging might very well entail the consolidation of workgroups or whole departments to achieve optimal work performance. The InfoImage Professional Services provided by Unisys and the similar services of other computer manufacturers are intended to help organizations deal with such consolidations.

16.5 OTHER VENDOR SERVICES

Of course, Unisys is not the only major imaging systems vendor offering professional services.

16.5.1 Wang Laboratories

Wang offers what it calls *life cycle services* to help customers plan, implement, manage, and measure their move to imaging. These services include:

- Feasibility studies
- Strategic planning
- Business-process consulting
- Solution engineering
- Site planning
- Network implementation
- Hardware and software services
- Disaster recovery
- Consulting
- Help desk
- Sociotechnical services
- Training

One of the key life cycle services is business-process consulting, which attempts to understand how the customer currently works and how the customer wants to work in the future. Specifically, this practice looks at what the organization's goals are and how the procedures followed by the organization contribute to achieving those goals.

Wang's business process consulting combines financial analysis, systems design, operational analysis, and industrial engineering to help customers assess their procedures and develop a model for re-engineering them to deliver maximum value. The gains the model provides can be measured by a number of factors, including reduced costs, reduced cycle time, improved customer service, better quality, and higher levels of control.

Wang business process consulting representatives follow these steps to help customers achieve their objectives:

1. Form a study team.
2. Determine organizational goals.
3. Define work processes.
4. Estimate time spent per task.
5. Measure the frequency and volume of tasks.
6. Create a baseline or baselines.
7. Create a process model.
8. Estimate gains from the new model.
9. Modify the design of the model.
10. Prepare cost-benefit analysis.

Wang's sociotechnical services attempt to address image system implementation from the point of view of the people it impacts. Acknowledging that resistance to change can jeopardize the successful implementation of imaging, Wang offers assistance to organizations in understanding the human factors. This assistance is offered in the form of workshops, tools, and consulting.

16.5.2 IBM

IBM offers image consulting that encompasses everything from management services to production operations. Specifically, IBM assists customers by:

- Analyzing organizational processes from the enterprise level to the workgroup level;
- Matching the right applications to imaging solutions;
- Developing more efficient and responsive processes that take advantage of advanced image technology;
- Addressing user and management concerns associated with image technology implementation;
- Designing and implementing image solutions by applying a proven, structured approach;
- Developing customized training and education.

To promote its image consulting services, IBM stresses its wide range of business experience, in both the types and sizes of organizations that it counts among its customers. The company also emphasizes its wealth of technical expertise and its track record for successful implementations.

Based on a customer's specific needs and budget, IBM recommends its own or another vendor's equipment, software, and services. Regardless of where the imaging system components come from, IBM offers customers the benefits of a single-vendor interface.

16.5.3 DEC

DEC's support services, which range from consulting to off-the-shelf support, provide the following assistance:

- Management consulting assists customers in developing business goals and mapping appropriate business technologies to business requirements;
- Architecture development assists customers in developing an information architecture and a solutions approach to meeting business needs;
- Business solution consulting assists customers in preparing the business case for implementing imaging technology by proposing a conceptual solution, then recommending changes to current business processes;
- Integration consulting assists customers in designing a cost-effective imaging solution that is compatible with current applications.

DEC developed a set of preconfigured image systems that can be adapted to become the platform for any business. The integration of a variety of application software packages with the DECimage EXpress software and associated peripherals can be pre-engineered into these systems. DEC also provides customers with support and assistance for integrating third-party devices and software applications with its DECimage EXpress imaging system.

In addition to arranging tours of various reference sites for prospective customers, DEC also maintains image demonstration areas at its Merrimack, New Hampshire and Augusta, Maine facilities.

16.6 VENDOR-PROVIDED SERVICE: PRO AND CON

A relatively new category of systems integrator is the hardware vendor, or, within the context of this book, the computer maker. Hardware vendors leverage their existing software and turnkey systems expertise into integration operations. Recognizing customer concerns about objectivity, these firms usually handle systems integration through a separate division or subsidiary, which is chartered to engage in such activities apart from the firm's product sales and marketing efforts.

Skeptics argue that hardware vendors are merely posing as systems integrators, claiming that such operations are really reconnaissance missions designed to assess new business opportunities, steal accounts from other vendors, and promote their own solutions at the expense of customer needs.

Several factors combine to mitigate this extreme view of the vendors, including: their participation in international standards organizations; their support for OSI, which is demonstrated through membership in the industry consortium Corporation for Open Systems; and their adherence to the various CCITT recommendations on the requirements for communications.

In recent years vendors have come to recognize that they can be more successful if their products can link with the rest of the universe. In fact, their involvement in standards setting and their experience in product design makes some hardware vendors viable candidates for systems integrator. Of course, customers must assess the qualifications and specific areas of expertise claimed by vendors. And vendors who are looking to gain a toehold in the systems integration market must be able to reach outside their own product lines and support open systems architectures.

As for the charge that vendors are using systems integration to steal accounts from other vendors, that is largely the result of one vendor out-performing another, in which case the customer always ends up the winner. There's nothing much to complain about in that regard, unless of course you happen to be the vendor who lost the account.

An alternative to the computer makers are traditional systems integrators, such as TRW and EDS. Such firms are grounded in information systems and, until recently, did most of their business with the federal government. Now that demand for such services is increasingly coming from the commercial sector, these firms are competing aggressively for corporate accounts. Imaging systems integration is viewed by the firms as a highly lucrative opportunity.

Whenever these firms encounter problems they cannot solve alone, they have the strategic relationships already in place and can draw upon the appropriate expertise. This expertise comes from numerous subcontractors and vendors—who are often listed as co-bidders when the integrators pursue large contracts.

Using such firms is not without its share of risks, particularly for non-Fortune 500 companies. The reason is that some of these firms are so big that smaller customers might not be getting the attention they need. Some of these firms are so busy chasing lucrative contracts that support their heavy infrastructures that smaller projects end up being perceived as quite trivial in the overall scheme of things—hardly worth the effort to complete on time and within budget.

16.7 CONCLUSION

Though new imaging and information systems have automated banks, insurance companies, brokerage houses, and financial services firms, the results of these innovations have not significantly altered the economy. Traditionally, productivity has been measured by output per worker, which might no longer be a reliable gauge of productivity. New computer applications, such as imaging, have led to higher standards in the quality of products and the timeliness of responses—innovations that are not usually taken into consideration in output-per-worker studies. Higher levels of graphic design, word processing, and spreadsheet analyses are rarely brought into this equation either. Ultimately, businesses might require a complete re-engineering to allow information technology to automate those processes that can filter down into the economy, and not simply the existing processes within a department that lend themselves to automation.

Appendix

Specialized Imaging Systems

This appendix summarizes some specialized imaging systems, a detailed discussion of which is beyond the scope of this book. These systems include x-ray and computerized tomography for medical applications and holographic and fractal imaging systems for graphics and storage applications. The emerging field of virtual reality is also considered.

Medical Imaging Systems

Some medical applications offer highly sophisticated forms of imaging, including x-ray, computerized tomography, magnetic resonance, and ultrasound. These types of images can be transferred to remote locations to aid patient diagnosis. For example, many hospitals in a large metropolitan area might have magnetic resonance equipment, but not have the expertise to render a proper interpretation of the resulting images. In such cases, the images can be transferred electronically across town via a metropolitan fiber network to a hospital that has qualified staff who can interpret the images and render advice to the patient's physician. This application of imaging can significantly speed up and improve patient diagnoses and help trim medical costs.

Because the density of medical images is quite high, ranging from 1 MB for a magnetic resonance image to 12 MB for an x-ray image, fiber facilities are required for error-free transmission.

Holographic Imaging

Holographic imaging entails the storage and display of images in three dimensions. Most people have become familiar with holograms from seeing the shiny three-dimensional images on their credit cards. These images are used to deter counterfeiting. For more than 30 years, scientists have been searching for ways to make use of the technology in other applications. There has been major progress in developing holographic storage systems. Used in computer memory systems, holograms could potentially store the contents of thousands of books on one piece of material no bigger than a Scrabble tile. Such systems could retrieve in one second the amount of data that existing computer disk drives take five hours to retrieve.

Holographic storage differs from standard disk drive storage in that holographic systems store data in three dimensions, not just two. This gives holographic storage systems the capability to store much more information and retrieve it faster than conventional disk storage systems. Whereas disk drives are electromechanical devices that can retrieve data only a single bit at a time, holographic memory can store and retrieve an entire image at a time, by using one or more small, photorefractive crystals.

Computers with holographic storage systems are able to store at least 10 times as much data as conventional memory systems and retrieve it 1,000 times faster. Bellcore, the research arm of the seven *regional Bell holding companies* (RBHCs), announced in November 1990 that it had demonstrated a holographic system that retrieved a standard page of text in under one nanosecond.

Fractal Imaging Systems

The term *fractal* was coined by IBM scientist Benoit Mandelbrot from the Latin word *fractus*, meaning irregular, and the verb *frangere*, meaning to break. The concept behind fractal imaging is that some images seem to be made of small copies of themselves. The power of fractals lies in the relatively simple mathematical algorithms used to render realistic looking natural objects. These algorithms can also be used to achieve unprecedented data compression ratios.

Using a single fractal equation to map an entire graphics image, a 768-KB 640 by 400 24-bit image can be compressed into a 10 KB file. Fractal image equations also allow select regions of an image to be reconstructed. This provides a greater zoom range than that offered by *discrete cosine transform* (DCT) descriptions, the current standard for image compression and reconstruction. In addition to having compression ratios as high as 2,500 to 1 and faster compression and decompression speeds, *fractal image format* (FIF) compressed images are also resolution-independent, meaning they can be expanded to conform to any future resolution standards.

Virtual Reality

Perhaps the most exotic imaging technology is *virtual reality*. Virtual reality, a concept and term coined by the *Massachusetts Institute of Technology* (MIT) Media Lab, relies on a multimedia computer system and specialized interfaces that allow the user to become totally immersed in a computer-generated world of real-time images—an artificial world in which objects and environments have the illusion of being real. By using helmets that contain stereoscopic viewing systems, data gloves, and other body-mounted devices, the user can see, hear, and touch objects, as well as other people, and can walk, fly, or do anything without physical risk. The multimedia engine provides the computer-generated images, multichannel sound, and motion outputs. Optical disks are used for storage, to enable the use of large databases to hold the simulated virtual worlds.

Games and other leisure activities aside, the practical applications of virtual reality include design and medicine. Using virtual reality, people can explore places that do not exist—architects can walk through the structures they design before building them. Doctors can practice medical procedures and get certified before working with patients.

Another application of virtual reality is product advertising. With virtual reality consumers will one day be able to browse for products in a "virtual showroom." From a remote location, a customer will be able to view and direct a mobile, wide-angle lens camera along rows of product shelves in a warehouse. Such a system is being developed jointly by the Japanese firm Matsushita Electric Industrial Co. and two American firms, Telepresence and Fake Space Laboratories. The virtual showroom could be a reality by 1995.

Another virtual reality application allows aircraft wing designers to use their own hand motions to simulate the flow of air across a wing surface. This "virtual wind tunnel" application is currently in use at the *National Aeronautics and Space Administration* (NASA) Research Center at Moffett Field near Mountain View, California.

Virtual reality is not limited to the display of three-dimensional images. A key component of such systems is sound, specifically, the duplication of the human hearing process in a virtual environment. As users manipulate their way through a simulated environment, sounds change pitch to create the illusion of changes in direction. One application of such acoustic modeling is architectural design. A designer or architect can test how different structural configurations, building materials, or partition positions affect the acoustics of a room or open space.

A potentially large market for virtual reality is the information systems community. According to the concept of *information visualization*, a user can actually go inside a database and select, organize, or manipulate information with hand and body movements. This might give so-called *knowledge workers* an effective way to react to the vast amounts of data that can be endlessly redisplayed during what-if analyses.

A more practical application of information visualization might be in the display of information. The presentation of raw data can easily overwhelm the viewer. But when data is represented in graphical form, it not only becomes more digestible and meaningful, it also leaves a more lasting impression. Graphical forms bring the human sense of vision to bear—and vision is the strongest of all human senses. The objective of information visualization is to allow knowledge workers to quickly detect significant trends or properties by making those properties visible and thus drawing upon the powerful capacity of the human mind for visual correlation.

Virtual reality was actually used in a California court to illustrate the re-enactment of a murder for the jurors. It took only two hours for the jury to reach a verdict of guilty—a possible indication of the technology's effectiveness.

Points of Convergence

Eventually, there will be points of convergence between the conventional document imaging systems used in offices for records management and the graphics-oriented fractal and holographic imaging systems. These points of convergence will come first in the areas of compression and storage, as the amount of stored image documents threatens to overwhelm conventional storage media. Medical imaging technologies also stand to benefit from fractal and holographic imaging systems, not only from the standpoint of compression and storage, but from their image enhancement capabilities as well. Potentially, virtual reality can integrate any other imaging technology, resulting in real-time applications that are barely conceivable today.

About the Author

Nathan J. Muller is an independent consultant in Oxford, Connecticut, specializing in advanced technology marketing and education. In 22 years of industry experience, Muller has written extensively on many aspects of computers and communications and has published 400 articles and six books on such diverse topics as frame relay, the synchronous optical network, LAN interconnection, and network management.

Muller is a regular contributor to *Datapro Research Reports*, *Faulkner Technical Reports*, and Auerbach's *Data Communications Management* and *Information Management* reports. He is contributing editor on networking for *Procomm Magazine* and writes frequently for *Unisphere Magazine*, an independent monthly publication for Unisys computer users. Muller's many editorials on technology and management issues have appeared in *Communications Week* and *Network World*.

Muller has held numerous technical and marketing positions with such companies as Control Data Corporation, Planning Research Corporation, Cable & Wireless Communications, ITT Telecom, and General DataComm. He has an M.A. in Social and Organizational Behavior from George Washington University.

Glossary

Acronym	Definition
2B+D	two B channels plus one D channel
23B+D	twenty-three B channels plus one D channel
30B+D	thirty B channels plus one D channel
4GL	fourth-generation language
AAC	alternative access carrier
ACS	automated cartridge system
ADM	add-drop multiplexer
ADPCM	adaptive differential pulse code modulation
AIIM	Association for Information and Image Management
AIMS	Advanced Image Management System (Hewlett-Packard Co.)
AIP	Advanced Image Processor (Hewlett-Packard Co.)
AIX	Advanced Interactive Executive (IBM)
ANSI	American National Standards Institute
API	application programming interface
APPC	advanced program-to-program communications
ARCnet	Attached Resource Computer Network (Datapoint)
ARDS	Accunet Reserved Digital Service (AT&T)
AS/400	Application System/400 (IBM)
ASCII	American Standard Code for Information Interchange
ASDS	Accunet Spectrum of Digital Services
ASN1	abstract syntax notation 1
AT&T	American Telephone & Telegraph
ATM	asynchronous transfer mode
AWG	American Wire Gauge

BECN	backward explicit congestion notification
BER	bit error rate
BERT	bit error rate tester
BELLCORE	Bell Communications Research
BIOS	basic input/output system
BISDN	broadband ISDN
BLOB	binary large object
BOC	Bell Operating Company
bps	bits per second
BRI	basic rate interface
BSC	binary synchronous communications
CAD	computer-aided design
CAM	computer-aided manufacturing
CAR	character amount recognition
CASE	computer-aided software engineering
CATV	cable television
CCD	charge-coupled device
CCIS	common channel interoffice signaling
CCITT	Consultative Committee for International Telegraph and Telephone
CD-R	compact disk recordable
CD-ROM	compact disk read-only memory
CDA	compound document architecture
CDR	call detail recorder
CEO	chief executive officer
CICS	Customer Information Control System (IBM)
CIR	committed information rate
CLASP	connecting link for applications and source peripherals
CLLM	consolidated link layer management
CO	central office
CO-LAN	central office-based local-area network
COBOL	common business-oriented language
COC	central office connection
CODEC	coder/decoder
COLD	computer output to laser disk
COM	computer output to microfiche
CON	concentrator
COS	Corporation for Open Systems
CPE	customer-premises equipment
CPU	central processing unit

CRC	cyclic redundancy check
CSMA	carrier-sense multiple access
CSMA/CA	carrier-sense multiple access with collision avoidance
CSMA/CD	carrier-sense multiple access with collision detection
CSU	channel service unit
CT	computerized tomography
DACS	digital access and cross-connect system
DADE	DECimage EXpress Application Development Environment
DARPA	Defense Advanced Research Projects Agency
DAS	dual-attached station
DASD	direct-access storage device
DB/2	Data Base/2 (IBM)
DBMS	database management system
dc	direct current
DCA	document content architecture
DCE	data communications equipment
DCRS	DECimage Character Recognition Services
DCS	digital cross-connect system
DCT	discrete cosine transform
DDE	dynamic data exchange
DDS	digital data service
DDS/SC	digital data service with secondary channel
DE	discard eligibility
DEC	Digital Equipment Corporation
DES	data encryption standard
DFP	Data Facility Product (IBM)
DIB	device-independent bit map
DIMMR	Dismountable AIMS Media Manager (Hewlett-Packard Co.)
DIO	Dismountable Input Output (Hewlett-Packard Co.)
DLCI	data link connection identifier
DLL	dynamic link library
DMU	Dismountable Media Utility (Hewlett-Packard Co.)
DOS	disk operating system
DOV	data over voice
DP	data processing
DPI	dots per inch
DQDB	distributed queue dual bus
DS-0	digital signal—level zero
DS-1	digital signal—level one

DS-2	digital signal—level two
DS-3	digital signal—level three
DSU	data service unit
DTE	data terminal equipment
DTIF	Digital document interchange format (Digital Equipment Corp.)
DVI	Digital Video Interactive (Intel Corp.)
E-1	European transmission service at 2.048 Mbps
EBCDIC	extended binary-coded decimal interchange code
ECMA	European Computer Manufacturers Association
ECN	explicit congestion notification
EDI	electronic data interchange
EEROM	electronically erasable read-only memory
EIA	Electronic Industries Association
EISA	extended industry standard architecture
e-MAIL	electronic mail
ECMA	European Computer Manufacturers Association
EMI	electromagnetic interference
EOC	embedded overhead channel
EPS	Encapsulated PostScript
ERO	electronic return originator
ESDI	enhanced small device interface
ESF	extended superframe
ESQL	embedded structured query language
ESQL/C	embedded structured query language and tools for C
ESS	electronic switching system
EXLM	Expert Library Manager (StorageTek)
FAX	facsimile
FCC	Federal Communications Commission
FDA	Food and Drug Administration
FDDI	fiber distributed data interface
FEC	forward error correction
FECN	forward explicit congestion notification
FEP	front-end processor
FFT	final form text
FIF	fractal image format
FM	frequency modulation
FR	frame relay
FRAD	frame relay access device

FRI	frame relay interface
FRS	frame relay switch
FT1	fractional T1
FT3	fractional T3
FTP	file transfer protocol
G	giga—one billion (e.g., Gbps)
GDS	generic digital service
GOSIP	government OSI profile
GUI	graphical user interface
H0	ISDN channel at 384 Kbps
H4X	broadband ISDN channel at 135–155 Mbps
H11	ISDN channel at 1.536 Mbps
H12	ISDN channel at 1.730 Mbps (CCITT)
H21	ISDN channel at 34 Mbps (CCITT)
H22	ISDN channel at 45 Mbps
HDLC	high-level data link control
HDTV	high-density television
HP	Hewlett-Packard
HVTPS	high volume transaction processing system
Hz	hertz
I/O	input/output
IA	integrated access
IAB	Internet Activities Board
IAF	Image Access Facility (FileNet Corp.)
ICB	individual case basis
ID	identification
IDS	Image Display Services (Digital Equipment Corp.)
IEEE	Institute of Electrical and Electronics Engineers
IETF	Internet Engineering Task Force
IFR	Image Focus Review (Unisys Corp.)
IIS	Image Input Services (Digital Equipment Corp.)
IMS/VS	Information Management System/Virtual Storage (IBM)
IN	intelligent network
INMS	integrated network management system
IOC	interoffice channel
IP	Internet protocol
IPC	interprocess communication

IPX	Internet packet exchange
IRS	Internal Revenue Service
IS	information system
ISA	industry standard architecture
ISL	Image Services Library (Digital Equipment Corp.)
ISO	International Organization for Standardization
ISPF	interactive system productivity facility
ISQL	interactive structured query language
IXC	interexchange carrier
JMU	Jukebox Manager Utility (Hewlett-Packard Co.)
JPEG	Joint Photographic Expert Group
K	kilo—one thousand (e.g., Kbps)
KB	kilobyte
KDD	Kokusai Denshin Denwa Co. (Japan)
km	kilometer
LAN	local-area network
LAT	local-area transport
LATA	local-access and transport area
LEC	local exchange carrier
LMI	local management interface
LMSI	Laser Magnetic Storage International
LU	logical unit
M	mega—one million (e.g., Mbps)
mA	milliamp
MAC	media access control
MAN	metropolitan-area network
MAP	manufacturing automation protocol
MAU	multiple access unit
MAU	media access unit
MB	megabyte
MCA	microchannel architecture
MCI	media control interface
MCU	multiport control unit
MES	master earth station
MHS	Message Handling Services (X.400)
MHz	megahertz

MIB	management information base
MIDI	musical instrument digital interface
MIPS	millions of instructions per second
MIS	management information system
MIT	Massachusetts Institute of Technology
mm	millimeter
MMPM	multimedia presentation manager
MPC	multimedia PC
MPEG	Motion Picture Expert Group
MRI	magnetic resonance imaging
ms	millisecond
MUX	multiplexer
NetBIOS	network basic input/output operating system
NI	network interface
NIC	network interface card
NIST	National Institute of Standards and Technology
NMS	network management system
NSA	National Security Agency
NSA	network applications support
NTSC	National Television Standards Committee
NTT	Nippon Telephone & Telegraph
OAM	object access method
OC	optical carrier
OC-1	optical carrier—level 1 (51.84 Mbps)
OC-3	optical carrier—level 3 (155.52 Mbps)
OC-9	optical carrier—level 9 (466.56 Mbps)
OC-12	optical carrier—level 12 (622.08 Mbps)
OC-18	optical carrier—level 18 (933.12 Mbps)
OC-24	optical carrier—level 24 (1.244 Gbps)
OC-36	optical carrier—level 36 (1.866 Gbps)
OC-48	optical carrier—level 48 (2.488 Gbps)
OCR	optical character recognition
ODA	office document architecture
ODIF	office document interchange format
ODSR	Optical Disk Storage and Retrieval (Unisys Corp.)
OEM	original equipment manufacturer
OH	overhead
OLE	object linking and embedding

OLTP	online transaction processing
ONA	open network architecture
OS	operating system
OS/2	Operating System/2 (IBM)
OS/2 EE	Operating System/2 Extended Edition (IBM)
OSA	optical systems architecture
OSAR	Optical Storage and Retrieval Library (FileNet Corp.)
OSF	Open Software Foundation
OSI	open systems interconnection
OSIL	OSI Interoperability Laboratory (Unisys Corp.)
PAD	packet assembler/disassembler
PAL	phase alternative line
PBX	private branch exchange
PC	personal computer
PCM	pulse code modulation
PLV	Production Level Video (Intel Corp.)
POP	point of presence
POSIX	portable operating system interface for computer environments
PPS	packets per second
PPSN	public packet-switched network
PRI	primary rate interface
PSDS	public switched digital service
PSN	packet-switched network
PTT	Post Telephone & Telegraph
PU	physical unit
PVC	permanent virtual connection
PW2	Personal Workstation 2 (Unisys Corp.)
QIC	quarter inch cartridge
RAID	redundant array of inexpensive disks
RAM	random access memory
RBHC	regional Bell holding company
RBOC	regional Bell operating company
RD	Requirements Definition (Unisys Corp.)
RDBMS	relational database management system
RF	radio frequency
RFC	request for comment
RFI	radio frequency interference

RFT	revisable form text
RGB	red green blue
RHC	regional holding company
RI	routing information
RISC	reduced instruction set computing
RJE	remote job entry
ROI	return on investment
ROM	read-only memory
RPC	remote procedure call
RTV	Real Time Video (Intel Corp.)
RTXT	rich text
SAA	systems applications architecture
SAS	single attached station
SCSI	small computer systems interface
SDI	Switched Digital International (AT&T service)
SDDI	shielded twisted-pair distributed data interface
SDH	synchronous digital hierarchy
SDK	software development kit
SDLC	synchronous data link control
SGML	standard generalized markup language
SIA	Strategic Impact Analysis (Unisys Corp.)
SMDS	switched multimegabit data service
SMS	system-managed storage
SMTP	simple mail transfer protocol
SNA	systems network architecture
SNMP	systems network management protocol
SONET	synchronous optical network
SPX	synchronous packet exchange
SQL	structured query language
SR	source routing
SRT	source routing transparent
STA	spanning-tree algorithm
STS-1	synchronous transport signal—level 1 (51.84 Mbps)
STS-3	synchronous transport signal—level 3 (155.52 Mbps)
STS-3c	synchronous transport signal—level 3 concatenated (155.52 Mbps)
SVC	switched virtual circuit
SWC	serving wire center

T	tera—one trillion (e.g., Tbps)
T	transmit
T1	transmission service at the DS—1 rate of 1.544 Mbps
T2	transmission service at the DS—2 rate of 6.312 Mbps
T3	transmission service at the DS—3 rate of 44.736 Mbps
TA	terminal adapter
TAC	Technical Assistance Center (FileNet Corp.)
TCP	transmission control protocol
TDM	time division multiplexing
TIFF	tagged image file format
TLA	three-letter acronym
TPDDI	twisted-pair distributed data interface
TSP	transparent spanning tree
UHF	ultra high frequency
UPS	uninterruptible power supply
UTP	unshielded twisted pair
VAN	value-added network
VCR	video casette recorder
VF	voice frequency
VGA	video graphics array
VGPL	voice-grade private line
VMS	Virtual Machine System (Digital Equipment Corp.)
VPN	virtual private network
VRAM	video random access memory
VSAT	very small aperture terminal
VT	virtual terminal
VTAM	virtual telecommunications access method
WAN	wide-area network
WORM	write once read many
XIE	X Image Extension
XNS	Xerox Network System
XUI	X User Interface

Bibliography

American National Standards Institute, Inc., "Electronic Manuscript Preparation and Markup," ANSI/NISO Z39.59-1988, 1988.

Association for Information and Image Management, "Glossary of Imaging Technology," AIIM TR2-1992, Silver Spring, MD, 1992.

Association for Information and Image Management, "Planning Considerations, Including Preparation of Documents for Image Capture Systems," AIIM TR15-1992, Silver Spring, MD, 1992.

Association for Information and Image Management, "Facsimile and Its Role in Electronic Imaging," AIIM TR17-1989, Silver Spring, MD, 1989.

Association for Information and Image Management, "Electronic Imaging Display Devices, Current Technologies in the Office Document Management Environment," AIIM TR19-1992, Silver Spring, MD, 1992.

Association for Information and Image Management, "The Use of Optical Disks for Public Records," AIIM TR25-1990, Silver Spring, MD, 1990.

Association for Information and Image Management, "Electronic Imaging RFP Guidelines," AIIM TR27-1991, Silver Spring, MD, 1991.

Bertsekas, Dimitri and Robert Gallager, *Data Networks*, Englewood Cliffs, NJ: Prentice-Hall, Inc., 1987.

Courtot, Marilyn, "Imaging Standards," Association for Information and Image Management, Resource Report L001, Silver Spring, MD, 1992.

Fortier, Paul J., *Handbook of LAN Technology*, New York, NY: McGraw-Hill, Inc., 1989.

Goldfarb, Charles F., *The SGML Handbook,* New York, NY: Oxford University Press, 1991.

International Organization for Standardization, "Information Processing Text and Office Systems—Standard Generalized Markup Language (SGML)," ISO 8879-1986 and Amendment 1-1988, 1988.

International Organization for Standardization, "Volume and File Structure of CD-ROM for Information Interchange," ISO 9660-1988, 1988.

Martin, James, *Local-Area Networks: Architectures and Implementations*, Englewood Cliffs, NJ: Prentice-Hall, Inc., 1989.

McConnell, Kenneth R., Richard Schaphorst, and Dennis Bodson, *FAX: Digital Facsimile Technology and Applications*, Dedham, MA: Artech House, Inc., 1989.

Muller, Nathan J., "Bridges, Routers, and Gateways: What Is the Difference?" *Data Communications Management,* 1990.

Muller, Nathan J., "Data Communications Innovations in the Public Network," *Data Communications Management,* 1992.

Muller, Nathan J., "Frame Relay: The Next Generation of X.25 Networks," *Data Communications Management,* 1991.

Muller, Nathan J., "A Guide to Conferencing Technologies," *Information Management,* 1992.

Muller, Nathan J., "How to Choose a Systems Integrator," *Data Communications Management,* 1989.

Muller, Nathan J., "A Management Briefing on the Emerging Synchronous Optical Network," *Data Communications Management,* 1991.

Muller, Nathan J., "The Migration from Narrowband to Broadband Networks," *Data Communications Management,* 1991.

Muller, Nathan J., "Planning and Implementing Electronic Data Interchange," *Information Management,* 1991.

Stallings, William, *ISDN: An Introduction*, New York, NY: MacMillan Publishing Company, 1989.

Townsend, Carl, "Networking with the IBM Token Ring," Blue Ridge Summit, PA: TAB Books, Inc., 1987.

Van Herwijnen, Eric, *Practical SGML*, Norwell, MA: Kluwer Academic Publishers, 1990.

Virando, Jacqueline A., "Educational Courses in the Image Processing Industry," Association for Information and Image Management, Silver Spring, MD, 1991.

Index

The Artech House Telecommunications Library

Vinton G. Cerf, Series Editor

For further information on these and other Artech House titles, contact:

Artech House
685 Canton Street
Norwood, MA 01602
(617) 769-9750
Fax:(617) 762-9230
Telex: 951-659

Artech House
6 Buckingham Gate
London SW1E6JP England
+44(0)71 630-0166
+44(0)71 630-0166
Telex-951-659